D1643201

MST210

Mathematical methods, models and modelling

Book B

Cover image: This shows arrows representing a vector field and a corresponding contour map. The vector field shows the direction of change for a model of two competing populations of animals. You will meet this model in Unit 12.

This publication forms part of an Open University module. Details of this and other Open University modules can be obtained from the Student Registration and Enquiry Service, The Open University, PO Box 197, Milton Keynes MK7 6BJ, United Kingdom (tel. +44 (0)845 300 6090; email general-enquiries@open.ac.uk).

Alternatively, you may visit the Open University website at www.open.ac.uk where you can learn more about the wide range of modules and packs offered at all levels by The Open University.

To purchase a selection of Open University materials visit www.ouw.co.uk, or contact Open University Worldwide, Walton Hall, Milton Keynes MK7 6AA, United Kingdom for a brochure (tel. +44 (0)1908 858779; fax +44 (0)1908 858787; email ouw-customer-services@open.ac.uk).

The Open University, Walton Hall, Milton Keynes, MK7 6AA.

First published 2014.

Edited, designed and typeset by The Open University, using the Open University TeX System.

Printed in the United Kingdom by Hobbs the Printers Ltd, Totton, Hampshire.

ISBN 978 1 7800 7868 7

1.1

Contents

Contents

Unit 4

Matrices and determinants

Introduction

In this unit we examine some of the properties and applications of matrices, where an $m \times n$ **matrix** is a rectangular array of *elements* with m rows and n columns. For example, $\begin{pmatrix} 1 & 2 & 3 \\ 4 & 5 & 6 \end{pmatrix}$ is a 2×3 matrix.

In this module the elements of matrices are real numbers. Other words for *element* are *component* and *entry*.

Among their many applications, matrices are useful in describing electrical circuits, in the analysis of forces, and in writing down the equations of motion for a system of particles; and they form an essential component of an engineer's or scientist's toolkit. Matrices have a role to play whenever we need to manipulate arrays of numbers; in applications, m and n may be very large, so do not be misled by the fact that the discussion concentrates on small matrices.

In applied mathematics, one common problem is to solve a system of equations involving unknown constants, that is, to determine values of the constants that satisfy the equations. Matrices can be used to store details of such a problem. For example, a system of equations such as

$$\begin{cases} 2x + 3y = 8, \\ 4x - 5y = -6, \end{cases} \tag{1}$$

contains three relevant pieces of information:

We sometimes use a curly bracket as shown here to emphasise that we are dealing with a *system* of equations.

- the numbers on the left-hand sides of the equations, which can be stored in the 2×2 matrix

$$\begin{pmatrix} 2 & 3 \\ 4 & -5 \end{pmatrix}$$

- the constants to be determined, which can be stored in the 2×1 matrix

$$\begin{pmatrix} x \\ y \end{pmatrix}$$

A matrix with one column is often referred to as a *vector*, or sometimes as a *column vector*. You met vectors in Unit 2.

- the numbers on the right-hand sides of the equations, which can be stored in the 2×1 matrix

$$\begin{pmatrix} 8 \\ -6 \end{pmatrix}.$$

With this notation, the essential information in these equations can be written in the form

$$\begin{pmatrix} 2 & 3 \\ 4 & -5 \end{pmatrix} \begin{pmatrix} x \\ y \end{pmatrix} = \begin{pmatrix} 8 \\ -6 \end{pmatrix}. \tag{2}$$

If we put

$$\mathbf{A} = \begin{pmatrix} 2 & 3 \\ 4 & -5 \end{pmatrix}, \quad \mathbf{x} = \begin{pmatrix} x \\ y \end{pmatrix}, \quad \mathbf{b} = \begin{pmatrix} 8 \\ -6 \end{pmatrix},$$

then equation (2) can be written as

As with vectors, in handwritten work, matrices are denoted with a straight or wavy underline, e.g. $\underline{A}$ or $\underset{\sim}{A}$.

$$\mathbf{A}\mathbf{x} = \mathbf{b}. \tag{3}$$

For the moment you may regard equation (2) as merely a convenient shorthand for the original system of equations, but later we will see that it is compatible with matrix multiplication. Generally, the matrix $\mathbf{A}$ will be an $n \times n$ matrix, while $\mathbf{x}$ and $\mathbf{b}$ are vectors containing n elements, where n may be large. In this unit we will be concerned with the solutions of such systems, which are known as systems of *linear* equations, and the problem of finding a solution can be expressed as one of finding the vector $\mathbf{x}$ that satisfies equation (3).

The term *linear* comes from the fact that each of the equations can be represented graphically by a straight line.

There is a graphical interpretation of the system of equations (1). Each equation represents a straight line, as you can see by rearranging the equations as $y = -\frac{2}{3}x + \frac{8}{3}$ and $y = \frac{4}{5}x + \frac{6}{5}$. The solution of this system of equations thus lies at the point of intersection of the graphs of the straight lines, as illustrated in Figure 1. For this pair of equations, there is just one solution, namely $x = 1$, $y = 2$.

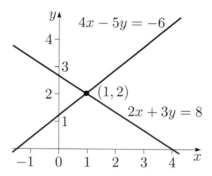

Figure 1   The intersection of two straight lines

For two equations in two unknowns it is easy to draw graphs or to manipulate the equations to determine the solution. It would be much more difficult if we were faced with a problem involving 100 equations in 100 unknowns. Then we would need a systematic method for working with matrices to obtain the solution, because this would enable us to program a computer to solve systems of linear equations.

Matrices and matrix operations are revised in Section 2.

You may already have met a matrix method for solving a system of two linear equations in two unknowns using the inverse of a matrix. Although this method works well for 2×2 matrices, it is not very efficient for large systems of equations compared with other methods.

In Section 1 you will be introduced to a matrix method for solving large systems of linear equations – the Gaussian elimination method – and you will see the conditions required for the method to work. In Section 2 we review some of the properties of matrices that make them so useful, and introduce the determinant of a matrix (a concept that is important for the discussion of eigenvalues in the next unit). In Section 3 we investigate the problem of determining a polynomial of degree n that passes through $n + 1$ data points. Section 4 shows that in certain situations, numerical errors can accumulate and render a solution unreliable.

1 Simultaneous linear equations

The purpose of this section is to outline an efficient systematic method for obtaining the solution of a system of linear equations, known as *Gaussian elimination*. In Subsection 1.1 we introduce the method by manipulating equations, then in Subsection 1.2 we do the same calculations using matrices. To complete this section we look at the types of solution that can arise when solving such systems of linear equations. We illustrate the method by solving systems of three equations in three unknowns.

Gaussian elimination is named after the great mathematician Carl Friedrich Gauss (1777–1855).

1.1 Manipulating equations

We begin with an example where the solution of a system of three equations in three unknowns can be found fairly easily.

Example 1

Find the solution of the system of equations

$$\begin{aligned} x_1 - 4x_2 + 2x_3 &= -9, & E_1 \\ 10x_2 - 3x_3 &= 34, & E_2 \\ 2x_3 &= 4. & E_3 \end{aligned}$$

For ease of reference, we label the equations E_1, E_2 and E_3. The unknowns in our equations will always be written in the order x_1, x_2, x_3.

Solution

Starting with E_3, we obtain $x_3 = 2$. Substituting this value into E_2, we obtain $10x_2 - (3 \times 2) = 34$, so $x_2 = 4$. Substituting the values for x_2 and x_3 into E_1, we obtain $x_1 - (4 \times 4) + (2 \times 2) = -9$, so $x_1 = 3$. Hence the solution is

$$x_1 = 3, \quad x_2 = 4, \quad x_3 = 2.$$

The system of equations in the above example is easy to solve because the equations are in **upper triangular form**, that is, the first non-zero coefficient in E_i is the coefficient of x_i. For a system of equations of the form

$$\begin{aligned} x_1 - 4x_2 + 2x_3 &= -9, & E_1 \\ 3x_1 - 2x_2 + 3x_3 &= 7, & E_2 \\ 8x_1 - 2x_2 + 9x_3 &= 34, & E_3 \end{aligned}$$

the objective of the first stage of the Gaussian elimination process is to manipulate the equations so that they are in upper triangular form. The second stage of the process is to solve the system of equations in upper triangular form using **back substitution**: starting with the last equation, we work *back* to the first equation, *substituting* the known values in order to determine the next value, as demonstrated in Example 1.

Stage 1: elimination

Stage 2: back substitution

The key property that we will use is that we may add and subtract multiples of the equations without affecting the desired solution. For example, $x_1 = 3$, $x_2 = 4$, $x_3 = 2$ satisfies both of the equations

$$x_1 - 4x_2 + 2x_3 = -9, \qquad E_1$$
$$3x_1 - 2x_2 + 3x_3 = 7. \qquad E_2$$

Suppose that we form E_{2a} by subtracting 3 times E_1 from E_2 $(E_{2a} = E_2 - 3E_1)$:

$$3x_1 - 2x_2 + 3x_3 - 3(x_1 - 4x_2 + 2x_3) = 7 - 3(-9),$$

giving

$$10x_2 - 3x_3 = 34 \qquad E_{2a}.$$

Then $x_1 = 3$, $x_2 = 4$, $x_3 = 2$ also satisfies E_{2a}.

More generally, we could form an equation E_{2a} by writing $E_{2a} = pE_1 + qE_2$ for any numbers p and q. Then E_{2a} is said to be a *linear combination* of E_1 and E_2, and again $x_1 = 3$, $x_2 = 4$, $x_3 = 2$ satisfies E_{2a}.

An *algorithm* is a procedure or set of rules to be used in a calculation.

Our strategy in the elimination stage is to form linear combinations of equations to reduce the system to upper triangular form. The Gaussian elimination method uses a particular algorithm in which linear combinations of the form $E_{2a} = E_2 - mE_1$ are used, as you will see in the following discussion and examples.

Example 2

Use the Gaussian elimination method to reduce the following simultaneous equations (introduced above) to upper triangular form, and hence deduce their solution:

$$x_1 - 4x_2 + 2x_3 = -9, \qquad E_1$$
$$3x_1 - 2x_2 + 3x_3 = 7, \qquad E_2$$
$$8x_1 - 2x_2 + 9x_3 = 34. \qquad E_3$$

Solution

Stage 1: elimination.

Each step of the Gaussian elimination algorithm is indicated in the margin below.

We begin with the elimination stage, where we eliminate x_1 (in Stage 1(a)) and then x_2 (in Stage 1(b)).

Stage 1(a)   To eliminate x_1, first we subtract a multiple of E_1 from E_2 to obtain a new equation with no term in x_1. Subtracting 3 times E_1 from E_2 gives

$E_{2a} = E_2 - 3E_1$

$$10x_2 - 3x_3 = 34. \qquad E_{2a}$$

Now we subtract a multiple of E_1 from E_3 to obtain a new equation with no term in x_1. Subtracting 8 times E_1 from E_3 gives

$E_{3a} = E_3 - 8E_1$

$$30x_2 - 7x_3 = 106. \qquad E_{3a}$$

So on completion of Stage 1(a), the equations have been reduced to

$$x_1 - 4x_2 + 2x_3 = -9, \qquad E_1$$
$$10x_2 - 3x_3 = 34, \qquad E_{2a}$$
$$30x_2 - 7x_3 = 106. \qquad E_{3a}$$

Stage 1(b) Next we eliminate x_2. We see that E_{2a} and E_{3a} are two equations in two unknowns. So we subtract a multiple of E_{2a} from E_{3a} to obtain an equation E_{3b} with no term in x_2. Subtracting 3 times E_{2a} from E_{3a} gives

$$2x_3 = 4. \qquad E_{3b}$$

$E_{3b} = E_{3a} - 3E_{2a}$

At this point, the elimination process is finished. We have brought our equations into upper triangular form as

$$x_1 - 4x_2 + 2x_3 = -9, \qquad E_1$$
$$10x_2 - 3x_3 = 34, \qquad E_{2a}$$
$$2x_3 = 4. \qquad E_{3b}$$

Stage 2: back substitution.

This system was solved in Example 1, using back substitution, to give the solution

$$x_1 = 3, \quad x_2 = 4, \quad x_3 = 2.$$

Checking that the solution satisfies the original system of equations, we have

LHS of $E_1 = x_1 - 4x_2 + 2x_3 = (1 \times 3) - (4 \times 4) + (2 \times 2) = -9 = \text{RHS}$,
LHS of $E_2 = 3x_1 - 2x_2 + 3x_3 = (3 \times 3) - (2 \times 4) + (3 \times 2) = 7 = \text{RHS}$,
LHS of $E_3 = 8x_1 - 2x_2 + 9x_3 = (8 \times 3) - (2 \times 4) + (9 \times 2) = 34 = \text{RHS}$.

The process of solving simultaneous equations described in Examples 1 and 2 is called the **Gaussian elimination method**. The method provides a systematic approach to the problem of solving simultaneous equations that should cope with the rather larger sets of equations that can occur in real-life applications. In practice, hand calculation will almost certainly involve fractions, and computer calculations will involve numeric approximations to these fractions and so will introduce rounding errors. We have avoided such problems in Example 2 and in the next exercise.

We do not give a formal procedure for the Gaussian elimination method at this point, since we give a matrix formulation shortly.

Exercise 1

Solve the following simultaneous equations using the Gaussian elimination method:

$$x_1 + x_2 - x_3 = 2, \qquad E_1$$
$$5x_1 + 2x_2 + 2x_3 = 20, \qquad E_2$$
$$4x_1 - 2x_2 - 3x_3 = 15. \qquad E_3$$

1.2   Manipulating matrices

The Gaussian elimination method relies on manipulating equations. In this subsection you will see that it can be formulated efficiently in terms of matrices.

When we use the Gaussian elimination method to solve the equations in Example 2, the new equation E_{2a} is obtained by subtracting a multiple of E_1 from E_2. The actions are performed on the numbers multiplying x_1, x_2 and x_3 (the coefficients of x_1, x_2 and x_3). For instance, the operation on the coefficients of x_2 in the equation $E_{2a} = E_2 - 3E_1$, namely $-2x_2 - 3 \times (-4x_2) = 10x_2$, could be recorded as $-2 - 3 \times (-4) = 10$, provided that we remember that the operation is associated with x_2.

Thus during the elimination stage, we need to record just the coefficients of x_1, x_2 and x_3, and the right-hand side of each equation, rather than the whole system of equations each time. We record the coefficients in E_1, E_2 and E_3 in a **coefficient matrix A**, the unknown constants in a vector **x**, and the right-hand sides in a **right-hand-side vector b** as

$$\mathbf{A} = \begin{pmatrix} 1 & -4 & 2 \\ 3 & -2 & 3 \\ 8 & -2 & 9 \end{pmatrix}, \quad \mathbf{x} = \begin{pmatrix} x_1 \\ x_2 \\ x_3 \end{pmatrix}, \quad \mathbf{b} = \begin{pmatrix} -9 \\ 7 \\ 34 \end{pmatrix}.$$

The problem, in terms of matrices, is to determine the vector **x** that satisfies the equation $\mathbf{Ax} = \mathbf{b}$, which can be written as

$$\underbrace{\begin{pmatrix} 1 & -4 & 2 \\ 3 & -2 & 3 \\ 8 & -2 & 9 \end{pmatrix}}_{\mathbf{A}} \underbrace{\begin{pmatrix} x_1 \\ x_2 \\ x_3 \end{pmatrix}}_{\mathbf{x}} = \underbrace{\begin{pmatrix} -9 \\ 7 \\ 34 \end{pmatrix}}_{\mathbf{b}}.$$

For computing purposes it is sufficient just to record the information in the **augmented matrix**

$$\mathbf{A} | \mathbf{b} = \begin{pmatrix} 1 & -4 & 2 & | & -9 \\ 3 & -2 & 3 & | & 7 \\ 8 & -2 & 9 & | & 34 \end{pmatrix}.$$

Alternatively, we could say that the first three columns of $\mathbf{A}|\mathbf{b}$ represent, respectively, the coefficients of x_1, x_2 and x_3, and the column after the bar represents the right-hand sides of the equations.

The first row of $\mathbf{A}|\mathbf{b}$ contains the coefficients of x_1, x_2 and x_3, and the right-hand side of E_1; the second row contains similar information about E_2; and the third row contains similar information about E_3.

Exercise 2

Write the following systems of equations in augmented matrix form.

(a) $\begin{cases} 3x_1 - 5x_2 = 8 \\ 4x_1 + 7x_2 = 11 \end{cases}$ (b) $\begin{cases} x_1 + 2x_2 = 3 \\ 2x_1 - x_2 + x_3 = 1 \\ x_2 - x_3 = -1 \end{cases}$

Once the information has been written in augmented matrix form, the stages in the Gaussian elimination process are equivalent to manipulating the rows of the matrix, as we demonstrate in the next example.

Example 3

Solve the simultaneous equations of Example 2 using the matrix form of the Gaussian elimination method, that is,

$$\mathbf{A}|\mathbf{b} = \begin{pmatrix} 1 & -4 & 2 & | & -9 \\ 3 & -2 & 3 & | & 7 \\ 8 & -2 & 9 & | & 34 \end{pmatrix}.$$

Solution

We use the matrix representing these equations throughout the elimination procedure. For brevity, we denote the first row of the matrix, namely $\begin{pmatrix} 1 & -4 & 2 & | & -9 \end{pmatrix}$, by $\mathbf{R}_1$, and so on.

$$\mathbf{A}|\mathbf{b} = \begin{pmatrix} 1 & -4 & 2 & | & -9 \\ 3 & -2 & 3 & | & 7 \\ 8 & -2 & 9 & | & 34 \end{pmatrix} \begin{matrix} \mathbf{R}_1 \\ \mathbf{R}_2 \\ \mathbf{R}_3 \end{matrix}$$

Notice that $\mathbf{R}_i$ encapsulates all the information about the equation E_i.

Stage 1: elimination.

Each part of the elimination stage in Example 2 has an equivalent part in matrix form.

Stage 1(a)   First we eliminate x_1, as before. Equation E_{2a} in Example 2 was found by subtracting $3E_1$ from E_2. Arithmetically, this is the same operation as subtracting $3\mathbf{R}_1$ from $\mathbf{R}_2$, and it is useful to record this operation. The way in which the new rows are formed is recorded on the left of the matrix.

Adding or subtracting a multiple of one row to/from another is called a **row operation**.

$$\begin{matrix} \\ \mathbf{R}_2 - 3\mathbf{R}_1 \\ \mathbf{R}_3 - 8\mathbf{R}_1 \end{matrix} \begin{pmatrix} 1 & -4 & 2 & | & -9 \\ 0 & 10 & -3 & | & 34 \\ 0 & 30 & -7 & | & 106 \end{pmatrix} \begin{matrix} \mathbf{R}_1 \\ \mathbf{R}_{2a} \\ \mathbf{R}_{3a} \end{matrix}$$

It is essential to keep a written record of the derivation of each row if you wish to check your working, as illustrated in the example.

Stage 1(b)   Now we eliminate x_2, as before.

$$\begin{matrix} \\ \\ \mathbf{R}_{3a} - 3\mathbf{R}_{2a} \end{matrix} \begin{pmatrix} 1 & -4 & 2 & | & -9 \\ 0 & 10 & -3 & | & 34 \\ 0 & 0 & 2 & | & 4 \end{pmatrix} \begin{matrix} \mathbf{R}_1 \\ \mathbf{R}_{2a} \\ \mathbf{R}_{3b} \end{matrix}$$

A triangle of zeros appears in the matrix at the end of the elimination stage. This shows us that each equation has one fewer unknown than the previous one, which is what we need in order to do the back substitution.

The final coefficient matrix is known as an **upper triangular matrix** because the only non-zero elements that it contains are on or above the **leading diagonal**, that is, the diagonal from top left to bottom right, here containing the numbers 1, 10 and 2.

The leading diagonal is sometimes called the *main diagonal*.

Stage 2: back substitution.

Before carrying out the back substitution stage, we write the final matrix as a system of equations:

$$\begin{aligned} x_1 - 4x_2 + 2x_3 &= -9, & E_1 \\ 10x_2 - 3x_3 &= 34, & E_{2a} \\ 2x_3 &= 4. & E_{3b} \end{aligned}$$

This is exactly the same as in Example 2. The solution $x_1 = 3$, $x_2 = 4$, $x_3 = 2$ is then found using back substitution as before.

The objective of Stage 1 of the Gaussian elimination method is to reduce the matrix $\mathbf{A}$ to an upper triangular matrix, $\mathbf{U}$ say. At the same time, the right-hand-side vector $\mathbf{b}$ is transformed into a new right-hand-side vector, $\mathbf{c}$ say, where in this example,

$$\mathbf{U} = \begin{pmatrix} 1 & -4 & 2 \\ 0 & 10 & -3 \\ 0 & 0 & 2 \end{pmatrix}, \quad \mathbf{c} = \begin{pmatrix} -9 \\ 34 \\ 4 \end{pmatrix}.$$

The Gaussian elimination method in Procedure 1 underpins the algorithm used by many computer algebra packages.

This procedure does not always work. We examine cases where it breaks down in the next subsection.

Stage 1: elimination

Stage 1(a)

Stage 1(b)

Stage 1(c), ...

Stage 2: back substitution

> **Procedure 1   Gaussian elimination method**
>
> To solve a system of n linear equations in n unknowns, with coefficient matrix $\mathbf{A}$ and right-hand-side vector $\mathbf{b}$, carry out the following steps.
>
> 1. Write down the augmented matrix $\mathbf{A}|\mathbf{b}$ with rows $\mathbf{R}_1, \ldots, \mathbf{R}_n$.
> 2. Subtract multiples of $\mathbf{R}_1$ from $\mathbf{R}_2, \mathbf{R}_3, \ldots, \mathbf{R}_n$ to reduce the elements below the leading diagonal in the first column to zero.
>
>   In the new matrix obtained, subtract multiples of $\mathbf{R}_2$ from $\mathbf{R}_3, \mathbf{R}_4, \ldots, \mathbf{R}_n$ to reduce the elements below the leading diagonal in the second column to zero.
>
>   Continue this process until $\mathbf{A}|\mathbf{b}$ is reduced to $\mathbf{U}|\mathbf{c}$, where $\mathbf{U}$ is an upper triangular matrix.
> 3. Solve the system of equations with coefficient matrix $\mathbf{U}$ and right-hand-side vector $\mathbf{c}$ by back substitution.

The steps of the elimination stage of Example 3 are

$$\mathbf{R}_{2a} = \mathbf{R}_2 - 3\mathbf{R}_1,$$
$$\mathbf{R}_{3a} = \mathbf{R}_3 - 8\mathbf{R}_1,$$
$$\mathbf{R}_{3b} = \mathbf{R}_{3a} - 3\mathbf{R}_{2a}.$$

The numbers 3, 8 and 3 are called *multipliers*. In general, to obtain, for example, an equation E_{2a} without a term in x_1 from

$$a_{11}x_1 + a_{12}x_2 + \cdots = d_1, \qquad E_1$$
$$a_{21}x_1 + a_{22}x_2 + \cdots = d_2, \qquad E_2$$
$$a_{31}x_1 + a_{32}x_2 + \cdots = d_3, \qquad E_3$$

where $a_{11} \neq 0$, we subtract $(a_{21}/a_{11})E_1$ from E_2. The number a_{21}/a_{11} is the **multiplier**.

In forming a multiplier, we divide by a number, a_{11} in the above generalisation. The number by which we divide is referred to as a **pivot** or **pivot element**, and the row in which it lies is the **pivot row**.

Looking again at Example 3: in Stage 1(a) the multipliers are $3 = 3/1 = a_{21}/a_{11}$ and $8 = 8/1 = a_{31}/a_{11}$, and the pivot is $a_{11} = 1$; in Stage 1(b) the multiplier is $3 = 30/10 = a_{32}/a_{22}$, and the pivot is $a_{22} = 10$. In general, the kth pivot is the number in the denominator of the multipliers in Stage 1(k) of the elimination stage. At the end of the elimination stage, the pivots comprise the elements of the leading diagonal of $\mathbf{U}$.

Example 4

Use the matrix form of the Gaussian elimination method to solve the following simultaneous equations:

$$
\begin{aligned}
3x_1 + x_2 - x_3 &= 1, & E_1 \\
5x_1 + x_2 + 2x_3 &= 6, & E_2 \\
4x_1 - 2x_2 - 3x_3 &= 3. & E_3
\end{aligned}
$$

Solution

The augmented matrix representing these equations is as follows.

$$
\left(\begin{array}{ccc|c}
3 & 1 & -1 & 1 \\
5 & 1 & 2 & 6 \\
4 & -2 & -3 & 3
\end{array}\right)
\begin{array}{l}
\mathbf{R}_1 \\
\mathbf{R}_2 \\
\mathbf{R}_3
\end{array}
$$

The row operations used to solve this example are highlighted in the margin below.

Stage 1(a)   We reduce the elements below the leading diagonal in column 1 to zero.

The pivot is a_{11}.

$$
\begin{array}{l}
\\
\mathbf{R}_2 - \frac{5}{3}\mathbf{R}_1 \\
\mathbf{R}_3 - \frac{4}{3}\mathbf{R}_1
\end{array}
\left(\begin{array}{ccc|c}
3 & 1 & -1 & 1 \\
0 & -\frac{2}{3} & \frac{11}{3} & \frac{13}{3} \\
0 & -\frac{10}{3} & -\frac{5}{3} & \frac{5}{3}
\end{array}\right)
\begin{array}{l}
\mathbf{R}_1 \\
\mathbf{R}_{2a} \\
\mathbf{R}_{3a}
\end{array}
$$

$\mathbf{R}_{2a} = \mathbf{R}_2 - (a_{21}/a_{11})\mathbf{R}_1$

$\mathbf{R}_{3a} = \mathbf{R}_3 - (a_{31}/a_{11})\mathbf{R}_1$

Stage 1(b)   We reduce the element below the leading diagonal in column 2 to zero.

The pivot is a_{22}.

$$
\begin{array}{l}
\\
\\
\mathbf{R}_{3a} - \frac{(-10/3)}{(-2/3)}\mathbf{R}_{2a}
\end{array}
\left(\begin{array}{ccc|c}
3 & 1 & -1 & 1 \\
0 & -\frac{2}{3} & \frac{11}{3} & \frac{13}{3} \\
0 & 0 & -20 & -20
\end{array}\right)
\begin{array}{l}
\mathbf{R}_1 \\
\mathbf{R}_{2a} \\
\mathbf{R}_{3b}
\end{array}
$$

$\mathbf{R}_{3b} = \mathbf{R}_{3a} - (a_{32}/a_{22})\mathbf{R}_{2a}$, so here $\mathbf{R}_{3b} = \mathbf{R}_{3a} - 5\mathbf{R}_{2a}$.

Stage 2   The equations represented by the new matrix are

$$
\begin{aligned}
3x_1 + x_2 - x_3 &= 1, & E_1 \\
-\tfrac{2}{3}x_2 + \tfrac{11}{3}x_3 &= \tfrac{13}{3}, & E_{2a} \\
-20x_3 &= -20. & E_{3b}
\end{aligned}
$$

From E_{3b}, we have $x_3 = 1$. From E_{2a}, we have $-\frac{2}{3}x_2 + \frac{11}{3} = \frac{13}{3}$, so $x_2 = -1$. From E_1, we have $3x_1 - 1 - 1 = 1$, so $x_1 = 1$. Hence the solution is

$$
x_1 = 1, \quad x_2 = -1, \quad x_3 = 1.
$$

You can test the validity of this solution by showing that E_2 and E_3 are satisfied by these values. Such a final step is always a worthwhile check on your working.

Exercise 3

Use the matrix form of the Gaussian elimination method to solve the following simultaneous equations:

$$\begin{aligned} x_1 + 2x_2 &= 4, & E_1 \\ 3x_1 - x_2 &= 5. & E_2 \end{aligned}$$

Exercise 4

Use the matrix form of the Gaussian elimination method to solve the following simultaneous equations:

$$\begin{aligned} x_1 + x_2 - x_3 &= 2, & E_1 \\ 5x_1 + 2x_2 + 2x_3 &= 20, & E_2 \\ 4x_1 - 2x_2 - 3x_3 &= 15. & E_3 \end{aligned}$$

1.3   Special cases

The previous examples and exercises may have led you to believe that Procedure 1 will always be successful, but this is not the case. The procedure will fail if at any stage of the calculation a pivot is zero. We will see that sometimes it is possible to overcome this difficulty, but this is not so in every case. In the following example we point out some difficulties, and indicate whether they can be overcome.

Example 5

Consider the following four systems of linear equations. Try to solve them using the matrix form of the Gaussian elimination method as given in Procedure 1. In each case the method breaks down. Suggest, if possible, a method of overcoming the difficulty, and hence determine the solution if one exists.

(a) $$\begin{cases} 10x_2 - 3x_3 = 34 \\ x_1 - 4x_2 + 2x_3 = -9 \\ 2x_3 = 4 \end{cases}$$

(b) $$\begin{cases} x_1 + 10x_2 - 3x_3 = 8 \\ x_1 + 10x_2 + 2x_3 = 13 \\ x_1 + 4x_2 + 2x_3 = 7 \end{cases}$$

(c) $$\begin{cases} x_1 + 4x_2 - 3x_3 = 2 \\ x_1 + 2x_2 + 2x_3 = 5 \\ 2x_1 + 2x_2 + 9x_3 = 7 \end{cases}$$

(d) $$\begin{cases} x_1 + 4x_2 - 3x_3 = 2 \\ x_1 + 2x_2 + 2x_3 = 5 \\ 2x_1 + 2x_2 + 9x_3 = 13 \end{cases}$$

Solution

(a) Since the first pivot a_{11} is zero, there is no multiple of the first row that we can subtract from the second row to eliminate the term in x_1. However, interchanging two equations does not change the solution of a system of equations. Hence interchanging the first two equations gives a system of equations in upper triangular form, from which we can determine the solution

$$x_1 = 3, \quad x_2 = 4, \quad x_3 = 2.$$

This may appear to be a trivial difficulty, but if we hope to devise a procedure that could be implemented on a computer, the process must allow for every contingency.

(b) We begin by writing down the augmented matrix.

$$\begin{pmatrix} 1 & 10 & -3 & | & 8 \\ 1 & 10 & 2 & | & 13 \\ 1 & 4 & 2 & | & 7 \end{pmatrix} \begin{matrix} \mathbf{R}_1 \\ \mathbf{R}_2 \\ \mathbf{R}_3 \end{matrix}$$

Stage 1(a)   We reduce the elements below the leading diagonal in column 1 to zero.

$$\begin{matrix} \\ \mathbf{R}_2 - \mathbf{R}_1 \\ \mathbf{R}_3 - \mathbf{R}_1 \end{matrix} \begin{pmatrix} 1 & 10 & -3 & | & 8 \\ 0 & 0 & 5 & | & 5 \\ 0 & -6 & 5 & | & -1 \end{pmatrix} \begin{matrix} \mathbf{R}_1 \\ \mathbf{R}_{2a} \\ \mathbf{R}_{3a} \end{matrix}$$

Stage 1(b)   We now want to reduce the element in column 2 that is below the leading diagonal to zero. The difficulty here is that we cannot subtract a multiple of $\mathbf{R}_{2a}$ from $\mathbf{R}_{3a}$ to eliminate the coefficient of x_2, since the pivot a_{22} is zero.

We can overcome this difficulty by interchanging $\mathbf{R}_{2a}$ and $\mathbf{R}_{3a}$.

$$\begin{matrix} \\ \\ \mathbf{R}_{2a} \leftrightarrow \mathbf{R}_{3a} \end{matrix} \begin{pmatrix} 1 & 10 & -3 & | & 8 \\ 0 & -6 & 5 & | & -1 \\ 0 & 0 & 5 & | & 5 \end{pmatrix} \begin{matrix} \mathbf{R}_1 \\ \mathbf{R}_{2b} \\ \mathbf{R}_{3b} \end{matrix}$$

This is now in upper triangular form, and we can proceed to Stage 2 to determine the solution using back substitution. We find that the solution is

$$x_1 = x_2 = x_3 = 1.$$

The notation $\mathbf{R}_{2a} \leftrightarrow \mathbf{R}_{3a}$ indicates that we have interchanged $\mathbf{R}_{2a}$ with $\mathbf{R}_{3a}$. Such interchanges are also called row operations.

(c) We begin by writing down the augmented matrix.

$$\begin{pmatrix} 1 & 4 & -3 & | & 2 \\ 1 & 2 & 2 & | & 5 \\ 2 & 2 & 9 & | & 7 \end{pmatrix} \begin{matrix} \mathbf{R}_1 \\ \mathbf{R}_2 \\ \mathbf{R}_3 \end{matrix}$$

Stage 1(a)   We reduce the elements below the leading diagonal in column 1 to zero.

$$\begin{matrix} \\ \mathbf{R}_2 - \mathbf{R}_1 \\ \mathbf{R}_3 - 2\mathbf{R}_1 \end{matrix} \begin{pmatrix} 1 & 4 & -3 & | & 2 \\ 0 & -2 & 5 & | & 3 \\ 0 & -6 & 15 & | & 3 \end{pmatrix} \begin{matrix} \mathbf{R}_1 \\ \mathbf{R}_{2a} \\ \mathbf{R}_{3a} \end{matrix}$$

Stage 1(b) We reduce the element below the leading diagonal in column 2 to zero.

$$\mathbf{R}_{3a} - 3\mathbf{R}_{2a} \begin{pmatrix} 1 & 4 & -3 & | & 2 \\ 0 & -2 & 5 & | & 3 \\ 0 & 0 & 0 & | & -6 \end{pmatrix} \begin{matrix} \mathbf{R}_1 \\ \mathbf{R}_{2a} \\ \mathbf{R}_{3b} \end{matrix}$$

Stage 2 We now try to solve the system of equations represented by the above matrix by back substitution. The coefficient matrix is in upper triangular form, but if we write out the system of equations as

$$\begin{aligned} x_1 + 4x_2 - 3x_3 &= 2, \\ -2x_2 + 5x_3 &= 3, \\ 0x_3 &= -6, \end{aligned}$$

we see that the last equation has no solution since no value of x_3 can give $0x_3 = -6$. Hence the system of equations has no solution.

(d) We begin by writing down the augmented matrix.

$$\begin{pmatrix} 1 & 4 & -3 & | & 2 \\ 1 & 2 & 2 & | & 5 \\ 2 & 2 & 9 & | & 13 \end{pmatrix} \begin{matrix} \mathbf{R}_1 \\ \mathbf{R}_2 \\ \mathbf{R}_3 \end{matrix}$$

We will refer back to these steps in Example 6.

Stage 1(a) We reduce the elements below the leading diagonal in column 1 to zero.

$$\begin{matrix} \\ \mathbf{R}_2 - \mathbf{R}_1 \\ \mathbf{R}_3 - 2\mathbf{R}_1 \end{matrix} \begin{pmatrix} 1 & 4 & -3 & | & 2 \\ 0 & -2 & 5 & | & 3 \\ 0 & -6 & 15 & | & 9 \end{pmatrix} \begin{matrix} \mathbf{R}_1 \\ \mathbf{R}_{2a} \\ \mathbf{R}_{3a} \end{matrix}$$

Stage 1(b) We reduce the element below the leading diagonal in column 2 to zero.

$$\mathbf{R}_{3a} - 3\mathbf{R}_{2a} \begin{pmatrix} 1 & 4 & -3 & | & 2 \\ 0 & -2 & 5 & | & 3 \\ 0 & 0 & 0 & | & 0 \end{pmatrix} \begin{matrix} \mathbf{R}_1 \\ \mathbf{R}_{2a} \\ \mathbf{R}_{3b} \end{matrix}$$

Systems of equations of this kind occur in Unit 5, so you should take careful note of the method of solution used in this example.

Stage 2 We now try to solve the system of equations represented by the above matrix by back substitution. The coefficient matrix is in upper triangular form, but if we write out the system of equations as

$$\begin{aligned} x_1 + 4x_2 - 3x_3 &= 2, \\ -2x_2 + 5x_3 &= 3, \\ 0x_3 &= 0, \end{aligned}$$

we see that *any* value of x_3 gives $0x_3 = 0$. If we let $x_3 = k$, where k is an arbitrary number, then proceeding with the back substitution gives $-2x_2 + 5k = 3$, so $x_2 = -\frac{3}{2} + \frac{5}{2}k$. The first equation gives $x_1 + (-6 + 10k) - 3k = 2$, so $x_1 = 8 - 7k$. So there is an infinite number of solutions of the form

$$x_1 = 8 - 7k, \quad x_2 = -\frac{3}{2} + \frac{5}{2}k, \quad x_3 = k.$$

Here we have used the *transpose* notation, which you met in Unit 2. More will be said about transposes of matrices in Subsection 2.1.

The *general solution* can be written as $(8 - 7k \quad -\frac{3}{2} + \frac{5}{2}k \quad k)^T$, where k is an arbitrary number. You should verify that this solution satisfies the original equations.

In Example 5 parts (a) and (b), we were able to overcome the difficulty of a zero pivot by making an **essential row interchange**. In general, whenever one of the pivots is zero, we interchange that row of the augmented matrix with the first available row below it that would lead to a non-zero pivot, effectively reordering the original system of equations. The difficulties in (a) and (b) are thus easily overcome, but those occurring in (c) and (d) are more fundamental. In (c) there was a zero pivot that could not be avoided by interchanging rows, and we were left with an **inconsistent system of equations** for which there is no solution. The final example (d) illustrates the case where a pivot is zero and the system of equations has an **infinite number of solutions**. It is these last two cases in particular that we explore in the next subsection.

1.4   No solutions and an infinite number of solutions

We begin by looking at the general system of two linear equations in two unknowns, given by

$$ax + by = e, \qquad E_1$$
$$cx + dy = f. \qquad E_2$$

All the points satisfying E_1 lie on one straight line, while all the points satisfying E_2 lie on another. The solution of the system of linear equations can be described graphically as the coordinates of the point of intersection of these two lines. However, if we draw two lines at random in a plane, there are three situations that can arise, as illustrated in Figure 2.

- Figure 2(a) illustrates the typical case, where the two lines are not parallel and there is a *unique solution* of the system of linear equations, corresponding to the point of intersection of the two lines.

- Figure 2(b) illustrates the special case where the two lines are parallel (thus do not intersect) and the corresponding system of linear equations has *no solution.*

- Figure 2(c) illustrates the very special case where the two lines coincide, so any point on the line satisfies both equations and we have an *infinite number of solutions.*

Figure 2   Points of intersection of two straight lines

Exercise 5

For each of the following pairs of linear equations, sketch their graphs and hence determine the number of solutions.

(a) $\begin{cases} x + y = 4 \\ 2x + 2y = 5 \end{cases}$ (b) $\begin{cases} x + y = 4 \\ 2x - 3y = 8 \end{cases}$

(c) $\begin{cases} x + y = 4 \\ 2x + 2y = 8 \end{cases}$ (d) $\begin{cases} y = 4 \\ 2x + 2y = 5 \end{cases}$

Exercise 6

For the system of equations

$$ax + by = e,$$
$$cx + dy = f,$$

what conditions ensure that the two lines are parallel or coincident?

A linear equation involving three unknowns x, y and z of the form

$$ax + by + cz = d,$$

where a, b, c and d are constants, can be represented graphically as a plane in three-dimensional space. (Further explanation of this graphical representation will be given in Unit 7.) For a system of three equations in three unknowns, a graphical interpretation gives rise to three types of solution, as illustrated in Figure 3 where none of the planes are parallel or coincident. (Two non-parallel or non-coincident planes intersect along a line called the *line of intersection*.)

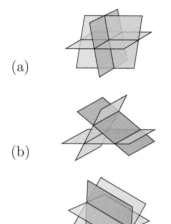

- Figure 3(a) illustrates the situation when the three planes intersect at a single point, so there is a *unique solution* at the point of intersection.

- Figure 3(b) illustrates the situation when the three planes form a tent shape, having no point of intersection and hence *no solution* (the three lines where a pair of planes meet are parallel). A variant of this case occurs when two (or even all three) of the planes are parallel, thus cannot meet at all.

- Figure 3(c) illustrates the situation when the three planes have (at least) a common line of intersection and hence an *infinite number of solutions*. A variant of this case occurs when at least two of the planes are coincident.

(a)

(b)

(c)

Figure 3 Points of intersection of three planes

The next example gives an algebraic interpretation of one of these three types of solution. For this example, the following definition is required.

Linear combination

A **linear combination** of rows $\mathbf{R}_1, \mathbf{R}_2, \ldots, \mathbf{R}_n$ is a row $\mathbf{R}$ such that $\mathbf{R} = q_1\mathbf{R}_1 + q_2\mathbf{R}_2 + \cdots + q_n\mathbf{R}_n$, where the q_i $(i = 1, 2, \ldots, n)$ are numbers.

A **non-trivial linear combination** is one where at least one q_i is non-zero.

Example 6

Consider the system of linear equations in Example 5(d), where the corresponding augmented matrix is as follows.

$$\mathbf{A}|\mathbf{b} = \begin{pmatrix} 1 & 4 & -3 & | & 2 \\ 1 & 2 & 2 & | & 5 \\ 2 & 2 & 9 & | & 13 \end{pmatrix} \begin{matrix} \mathbf{R}_1 \\ \mathbf{R}_2 \\ \mathbf{R}_3 \end{matrix}$$

Show that there is a non-trivial linear combination of the rows of this matrix that is equal to a row of zeros.

Solution

We use the results of the elimination process in Example 5(d), noting that $\mathbf{R}_{3b}$ is equal to a row of zeros, that is, $\mathbf{R}_{3b} = \mathbf{0}$. From this, we see that

$$\begin{aligned} \mathbf{R}_{3b} &= \mathbf{R}_{3a} - 3\mathbf{R}_{2a} \\ &= (\mathbf{R}_3 - 2\mathbf{R}_1) - 3(\mathbf{R}_2 - \mathbf{R}_1) = \mathbf{R}_1 - 3\mathbf{R}_2 + \mathbf{R}_3 = \mathbf{0}. \end{aligned}$$

We use $\mathbf{0}$ to denote a row of zeros (or 'zero row').

Hence there is a non-trivial linear combination of the rows that is equal to the zero row.

In Example 6 we saw that $\mathbf{R}_{3b} = \mathbf{R}_1 - 3\mathbf{R}_2 + \mathbf{R}_3$, which means that $\mathbf{R}_{3b}$ is a linear combination of the rows of $\mathbf{A}|\mathbf{b}$. However, in this example, we have something more: such a linear combination produces a row of zeros (and the corresponding equations have an infinite number of solutions, as we found in Example 5(d)). When such a relationship exists between the rows of a matrix, we say that the rows are *linearly dependent*.

This is the case where the three planes, corresponding to the three equations, meet in a line (see Figure 3(c)).

> ### Linear dependence and linear independence
>
> The rows $\mathbf{R}_1, \mathbf{R}_2, \ldots, \mathbf{R}_n$ of a matrix are **linearly dependent** if a non-trivial linear combination of these rows is equal to the zero row, that is,
>
> $$q_1\mathbf{R}_1 + q_2\mathbf{R}_2 + \cdots + q_n\mathbf{R}_n = \mathbf{0}, \tag{4}$$
>
> where the numbers $q_1, q_2, \ldots, q_n$ are not all zero.
>
> Rows that are not linearly dependent are **linearly independent**.

If the rows of the matrix $\mathbf{A}$ are linearly independent, then the Gaussian elimination method works and produces a unique solution of the system of equations $\mathbf{A}\mathbf{x} = \mathbf{b}$. However, if the rows of $\mathbf{A}$ are linearly dependent, then the corresponding system of linear equations may have an infinite number of solutions, or no solution. The elimination process will reveal which is the case.

Exercise 7

In the following systems of linear equations, determine which has a single solution, which has an infinite number of solutions, and which has no solution. Where the equations have a unique solution, find it. Where the equations have an infinite number of solutions, find the general solution and a non-trivial linear combination of the rows of $\mathbf{A}|\mathbf{b}$ that gives a row of zeros.

(a) $\begin{cases} x_1 - \ 2x_2 + \ 5x_3 = \ \ 7 \\ x_1 + \ 3x_2 - \ 4x_3 = 20 \\ x_1 + 18x_2 - 31x_3 = 40 \end{cases}$
    (b) $\begin{cases} x_1 - 2x_2 + \ 5x_3 = \ \ 6 \\ x_1 + 3x_2 - \ \ 4x_3 = \ \ 7 \\ 2x_1 + 6x_2 - 12x_3 = 12 \end{cases}$

(c) $\begin{cases} x_1 - \ 4x_2 + \ \ x_3 = \ \ 14 \\ 5x_1 - \ \ x_2 - \ \ x_3 = \ \ \ \ 2 \\ 6x_1 + 14x_2 - 6x_3 = -52 \end{cases}$

2 Properties of matrices

Matrices were first used in 1858 by the English mathematician Arthur Cayley.

In this section we review the algebraic properties of matrices, and show how solving the matrix equation $\mathbf{Ax} = \mathbf{b}$ can be interpreted as finding the vector $\mathbf{x}$ that is mapped to the vector $\mathbf{b}$ by the transformation defined by $\mathbf{A}$. Then we investigate a related number, called the *determinant* of the matrix, that can be used to decide whether a given system of linear equations has a unique solution. Finally, we look at some applications of determinants.

2.1 Algebra of matrices

A matrix of **order** or **size** $m \times n$ is a rectangular array of elements (usually real numbers) with m rows and n columns. If $m = n$, the matrix is a **square matrix**, an example of which is the 2×2 matrix $\begin{pmatrix} 3 & 4 \\ 5 & 6 \end{pmatrix}$. If $m = 1$, the matrix can be regarded as a **row vector**, an example of which is the 1×3 matrix $\begin{pmatrix} 2 & 3 & 4 \end{pmatrix}$. If $n = 1$, the matrix can be regarded as a

You met these notations for column vectors in Unit 2.

The element a_{ij} is in the ith row and the jth column.

column vector, an example of which is the 2×1 matrix $\begin{pmatrix} 5 \\ 7 \end{pmatrix}$, which we often write in text as $\begin{pmatrix} 5 & 7 \end{pmatrix}^T$. The general $m \times n$ matrix $\mathbf{A}$ can be written as (a_{ij}) to denote the matrix

$$\mathbf{A} = \begin{pmatrix} a_{11} & a_{12} & \cdots & a_{1n} \\ a_{21} & a_{22} & \cdots & a_{2n} \\ \vdots & \vdots & \vdots & \vdots \\ a_{m1} & a_{m2} & \cdots & a_{mn} \end{pmatrix}.$$

Two matrices $\mathbf{A} = (a_{ij})$ and $\mathbf{B} = (b_{ij})$ are **equal** if they have the same order and $a_{ij} = b_{ij}$ for all $i = 1, 2, \ldots, m$ and $j = 1, 2, \ldots, n$. If all the elements of a matrix are zero, the matrix is the **zero matrix**, denoted by $\mathbf{0}$. (Strictly speaking, we should write the $m \times n$ zero matrix as $\mathbf{0}_{mn}$, but the size of the zero matrix will always be clear from the context.)

Addition and scalar multiplication of $m \times n$ matrices

If $\mathbf{A} = (a_{ij})$ and $\mathbf{B} = (b_{ij})$ are matrices of the same order, we can form the **sum**

$$\mathbf{A} + \mathbf{B} = (a_{ij} + b_{ij}) \quad \text{(componentwise addition)}. \tag{5}$$

Note that matrix addition is commutative, $\mathbf{A} + \mathbf{B} = \mathbf{B} + \mathbf{A}$, and associative, $(\mathbf{A} + \mathbf{B}) + \mathbf{C} = \mathbf{A} + (\mathbf{B} + \mathbf{C})$.

For any matrix $\mathbf{A}$, and $\mathbf{0}$ of the same order,

$$\mathbf{A} + \mathbf{0} = \mathbf{0} + \mathbf{A} = \mathbf{A} \quad \text{(the components are unaltered)}. \tag{6}$$

The **scalar multiple** of a matrix $\mathbf{A} = (a_{ij})$ by a number k is given by

$$k\mathbf{A} = (ka_{ij}) \quad \text{(multiply each component by } k\text{)}. \tag{7}$$

The **negative** of the matrix $\mathbf{A} = (a_{ij})$ is $-\mathbf{A} = (-a_{ij})$, so

$$\mathbf{A} + (-\mathbf{A}) = -\mathbf{A} + \mathbf{A} = \mathbf{0}. \tag{8}$$

For two matrices $\mathbf{A}$ and $\mathbf{B}$ of the same order, $\mathbf{A} - \mathbf{B}$ is given by

$$\mathbf{A} + (-\mathbf{B}). \tag{9}$$

In this context, the number k is sometimes referred to as a *scalar* in order to distinguish it from a matrix. The same idea was used in Unit 2 in the context of vectors.

Exercise 8

Let $\mathbf{A} = \begin{pmatrix} 1 & 2 & 3 \\ 4 & 5 & 6 \end{pmatrix}$, $\mathbf{B} = \begin{pmatrix} 1 & 3 & 7 \\ 4 & -5 & 0 \end{pmatrix}$ and $\mathbf{C} = \begin{pmatrix} -2 & 1 & -6 \\ -5 & 3 & 3 \end{pmatrix}$.

(a) Calculate $3\mathbf{A}$ and $-\mathbf{A}$.

(b) Calculate $\mathbf{A} + \mathbf{B}$ and $\mathbf{B} + \mathbf{C}$.

(c) Use the results of part (b) to verify that $(\mathbf{A} + \mathbf{B}) + \mathbf{C} = \mathbf{A} + (\mathbf{B} + \mathbf{C})$.

Exercise 9

Let $\mathbf{A} = \begin{pmatrix} 1 & -2 \\ 7 & -3 \end{pmatrix}$ and $\mathbf{B} = \begin{pmatrix} -3 & 0 \\ 4 & -5 \end{pmatrix}$.

(a) Calculate $\mathbf{A} - \mathbf{B}$ and $\mathbf{B} - \mathbf{A}$.

(b) Verify that $\mathbf{B} - \mathbf{A} = -(\mathbf{A} - \mathbf{B})$.

Exercise 10

Let $\mathbf{A} = \begin{pmatrix} 1 & 2 & 3 \\ 4 & 5 & 6 \end{pmatrix}$ and $\mathbf{B} = \begin{pmatrix} 1 & 3 & 7 \\ 4 & -5 & 0 \end{pmatrix}$.

(a) Calculate $2\mathbf{A} - 5\mathbf{B}$.

(b) Verify that $3(\mathbf{A} + \mathbf{B}) = 3\mathbf{A} + 3\mathbf{B}$.

The multiplication of matrices is more complicated. We illustrate the method by forming the product of two 2×2 matrices.

Let $\mathbf{A} = \begin{pmatrix} 1 & 2 \\ 3 & 4 \end{pmatrix}$ and $\mathbf{B} = \begin{pmatrix} 5 & 6 \\ 7 & 8 \end{pmatrix}$. To form the product $\mathbf{AB} = \mathbf{C}$, we define c_{ij} using the ith row of $\mathbf{A}$ and the jth column of $\mathbf{B}$, so that

$$c_{11} = a_{11}b_{11} + a_{12}b_{21} = (1 \times 5) + (2 \times 7) = 19,$$
$$c_{12} = a_{11}b_{12} + a_{12}b_{22} = (1 \times 6) + (2 \times 8) = 22,$$
$$c_{21} = a_{21}b_{11} + a_{22}b_{21} = (3 \times 5) + (4 \times 7) = 43,$$
$$c_{22} = a_{21}b_{12} + a_{22}b_{22} = (3 \times 6) + (4 \times 8) = 50.$$

Thus

$$\mathbf{C} = \mathbf{AB} = \begin{pmatrix} 1 & 2 \\ 3 & 4 \end{pmatrix} \begin{pmatrix} 5 & 6 \\ 7 & 8 \end{pmatrix} = \begin{pmatrix} 19 & 22 \\ 43 & 50 \end{pmatrix}.$$

Similarly, if $\mathbf{A} = \begin{pmatrix} 1 & 2 & 3 \\ 4 & 5 & 6 \end{pmatrix}$ and $\mathbf{B} = \begin{pmatrix} 2 & 4 \\ -1 & -2 \\ 5 & 3 \end{pmatrix}$, then

$$\mathbf{AB} = \begin{pmatrix} (1 \times 2) + (2 \times (-1)) + (3 \times 5) & (1 \times 4) + (2 \times (-2)) + (3 \times 3) \\ (4 \times 2) + (5 \times (-1)) + (6 \times 5) & (4 \times 4) + (5 \times (-2)) + (6 \times 3) \end{pmatrix}$$
$$= \begin{pmatrix} 15 & 9 \\ 33 & 24 \end{pmatrix}.$$

The above procedure can be carried out only when the number of columns of $\mathbf{A}$ is equal to the number of rows of $\mathbf{B}$.

Matrix multiplication

The **product** of an $m \times p$ matrix $\mathbf{A}$ and a $p \times n$ matrix $\mathbf{B}$ is the $m \times n$ matrix $\mathbf{C} = \mathbf{AB}$, where c_{ij} is formed using the ith row of $\mathbf{A}$ and the jth column of $\mathbf{B}$, so that

$$c_{ij} = a_{i1}b_{1j} + a_{i2}b_{2j} + \cdots + a_{ip}b_{pj} = \sum_{k=1}^{p} a_{ik}b_{kj}. \tag{10}$$

Exercise 11

Calculate the following matrix products, where they exist.

(a) $\begin{pmatrix} 1 & 2 \\ 2 & -3 \end{pmatrix} \begin{pmatrix} 1 & 3 \\ 2 & -1 \end{pmatrix}$

(b) $\begin{pmatrix} 2 & 1 \end{pmatrix} \begin{pmatrix} 1 & 6 \\ 0 & 2 \end{pmatrix}$

(c) $\begin{pmatrix} 1 \\ 2 \end{pmatrix} \begin{pmatrix} 3 & 0 & -4 \end{pmatrix}$

(d) $\begin{pmatrix} 3 & 1 & 2 \\ 0 & 5 & 1 \end{pmatrix} \begin{pmatrix} -2 & 0 & 1 \\ 1 & 3 & 0 \\ 4 & 1 & -1 \end{pmatrix}$

(e) $\begin{pmatrix} 2 \\ 4 \\ -1 \end{pmatrix} \begin{pmatrix} 3 & 2 \\ 4 & -1 \end{pmatrix}$

Exercise 12

Calculate $\mathbf{Ax}$ when

$$\mathbf{A} = \begin{pmatrix} 3 & -1 & 5 \\ 6 & 4 & 7 \\ 2 & -3 & 0 \end{pmatrix} \quad \text{and} \quad \mathbf{x} = \begin{pmatrix} x_1 \\ x_2 \\ x_3 \end{pmatrix},$$

and hence show that the equation $\mathbf{Ax} = \mathbf{b}$, where $\mathbf{b} = (2 \quad 5 \quad 6)^T$, is equivalent to the system of equations

$$3x_1 - x_2 + 5x_3 = 2,$$
$$6x_1 + 4x_2 + 7x_3 = 5,$$
$$2x_1 - 3x_2 \qquad = 6.$$

In Section 1 we referred to $\mathbf{Ax} = \mathbf{b}$ as a convenient representation of a system of equations. This is consistent with the interpretation of $\mathbf{Ax}$ as the matrix product of $\mathbf{A}$ with $\mathbf{x}$, as we show here.

Earlier, you saw that addition of matrices is commutative and associative. We now give the rules of matrix multiplication.

Rules of matrix multiplication

For any matrices $\mathbf{A}$, $\mathbf{B}$ and $\mathbf{C}$ of appropriate sizes, matrix multiplication is **associative**, that is,

$$(\mathbf{AB})\mathbf{C} = \mathbf{A}(\mathbf{BC}), \tag{11}$$

and **distributive** over matrix addition, that is,

$$\mathbf{A}(\mathbf{B} + \mathbf{C}) = \mathbf{AB} + \mathbf{AC}. \tag{12}$$

The phrase 'of appropriate sizes' means that all the matrix sums and products can be formed.

In general, matrix multiplication is *not commutative*, so $\mathbf{AB}$ may not be equal to $\mathbf{BA}$. But multiplication of numbers *is* commutative: $ab = ba$ for any numbers a and b. So this is a significant difference between the algebra of matrices and the algebra of numbers.

Exercise 13

Let $\mathbf{A} = \begin{pmatrix} 1 & 1 \\ 3 & 2 \end{pmatrix}$, $\mathbf{B} = \begin{pmatrix} 1 & 4 \\ 2 & 1 \end{pmatrix}$ and $\mathbf{C} = \begin{pmatrix} 2 & 0 \\ 1 & 5 \end{pmatrix}$.

Verify each of the following statements.

(a) $\mathbf{AB} \neq \mathbf{BA}$ (b) $(\mathbf{AB})\mathbf{C} = \mathbf{A}(\mathbf{BC})$ (c) $\mathbf{A}(\mathbf{B} + \mathbf{C}) = \mathbf{AB} + \mathbf{AC}$

For a square matrix $\mathbf{A}$, we define **powers** of the matrix in the obvious way: $\mathbf{A}^2 = \mathbf{AA}$, $\mathbf{A}^3 = \mathbf{AAA}$, and so on.

$\mathbf{A}^T$ is read as 'A transpose'.

If we denote $\mathbf{A}$ by (a_{ij}) and $\mathbf{A}^T$ by (a_{ij}^T), then $a_{ij}^T = a_{ji}$.

An operation that we can apply to any matrix $\mathbf{A}$ is to form its **transpose** $\mathbf{A}^T$ by interchanging its rows and columns. Thus the rows of $\mathbf{A}^T$ are the columns of $\mathbf{A}$, and the columns of $\mathbf{A}^T$ are the rows of $\mathbf{A}$, taken in the same order. If $\mathbf{A}$ is an $m \times n$ matrix, then $\mathbf{A}^T$ is an $n \times m$ matrix. Examples of transposes are

$$\begin{pmatrix} 1 & 2 & 3 \\ 4 & 5 & 6 \\ 7 & 8 & 9 \end{pmatrix}^T = \begin{pmatrix} 1 & 4 & 7 \\ 2 & 5 & 8 \\ 3 & 6 & 9 \end{pmatrix}, \quad \begin{pmatrix} 2 & 7 \\ -6 & 1 \\ 0 & 4 \end{pmatrix}^T = \begin{pmatrix} 2 & -6 & 0 \\ 7 & 1 & 4 \end{pmatrix}.$$

Rules for transposes of matrices

For any matrix $\mathbf{A}$,

$$(\mathbf{A}^T)^T = \mathbf{A}. \tag{13}$$

For any matrices $\mathbf{A}$ and $\mathbf{B}$ of the same size,

$$(\mathbf{A} + \mathbf{B})^T = \mathbf{A}^T + \mathbf{B}^T. \tag{14}$$

If $\mathbf{A}$ is an $m \times p$ matrix and $\mathbf{B}$ is a $p \times n$ matrix, then

Notice the change in order of the terms involving $\mathbf{A}$ and $\mathbf{B}$.

$$(\mathbf{AB})^T = \mathbf{B}^T \mathbf{A}^T. \tag{15}$$

Remember that a vector is simply a matrix with one column.

Notice in passing that the dot product of two vectors can be written using matrix multiplication: if $\mathbf{a} = (a_1 \quad a_2 \quad a_3)^T$ and $\mathbf{b} = (b_1 \quad b_2 \quad b_3)^T$, then

$$\mathbf{a} \cdot \mathbf{b} = a_1 b_1 + a_2 b_2 + a_3 b_3 = (a_1 \quad a_2 \quad a_3) \begin{pmatrix} b_1 \\ b_2 \\ b_3 \end{pmatrix} = \mathbf{a}^T \mathbf{b}.$$

This fact will turn out to be extremely useful when we come to discuss vector calculus later in the module.

A square matrix $\mathbf{A}$ is **symmetric** if $\mathbf{A} = \mathbf{A}^T$. Symmetric here refers to symmetry about the leading diagonal. The matrices

$$\begin{pmatrix} 1 & 2 \\ 2 & 3 \end{pmatrix} \quad \text{and} \quad \begin{pmatrix} 1 & 2 & 3 \\ 2 & 3 & 4 \\ 3 & 4 & 5 \end{pmatrix}$$

are examples of symmetric matrices.

Exercise 14

Let $\mathbf{A} = \begin{pmatrix} 1 & 2 \\ 3 & 4 \\ 5 & 6 \end{pmatrix}$, $\mathbf{B} = \begin{pmatrix} 2 & 5 \\ -1 & -4 \\ 3 & 1 \end{pmatrix}$ and $\mathbf{C} = \begin{pmatrix} 1 & 0 \\ 2 & 3 \end{pmatrix}$.

(a) Write down $\mathbf{A}^T$, $\mathbf{B}^T$ and $\mathbf{C}^T$.

(b) Verify that $(\mathbf{A} + \mathbf{B})^T = \mathbf{A}^T + \mathbf{B}^T$.

(c) Verify that $(\mathbf{AC})^T = \mathbf{C}^T \mathbf{A}^T$.

(d) Explain why $\mathbf{C}$ is not a symmetric matrix.

(e) Is $\mathbf{CC}^T$ a symmetric matrix?

Exercise 15

Given the symmetric matrices

$$\mathbf{A} = \begin{pmatrix} 1 & 2 & 1 \\ 2 & 3 & -1 \\ 1 & -1 & 0 \end{pmatrix} \quad \text{and} \quad \mathbf{B} = \begin{pmatrix} 1 & 1 & 0 \\ 1 & 0 & 1 \\ 0 & 1 & 1 \end{pmatrix},$$

show that $\mathbf{AB}$ is not symmetric. Verify that $(\mathbf{AB})^T = \mathbf{B}^T \mathbf{A}^T$.

Of particular importance in the solution of simultaneous linear equations are the triangular matrices. An **upper triangular matrix** is a square matrix in which each element below the leading diagonal is 0. A **lower triangular matrix** is a square matrix in which each element above the leading diagonal is 0. A **diagonal matrix** is a square matrix where all the elements off the leading diagonal are 0. A matrix that is upper triangular, lower triangular or both (i.e. diagonal) is sometimes referred to simply as a **triangular matrix**. For example, the matrix on the left below is upper triangular, the one in the middle is lower triangular, and the one on the right is diagonal:

$$\begin{pmatrix} 1 & 2 & 3 \\ 0 & 4 & 5 \\ 0 & 0 & 6 \end{pmatrix}, \quad \begin{pmatrix} 1 & 0 & 0 \\ 2 & 4 & 0 \\ 0 & 5 & 6 \end{pmatrix}, \quad \begin{pmatrix} 1 & 0 & 0 \\ 0 & 4 & 0 \\ 0 & 0 & 6 \end{pmatrix}.$$

You met examples of an upper triangular matrix $\mathbf{U}$ in Section 1.

Note that the transpose of an upper triangular matrix is a lower triangular matrix, and vice versa.

Exercise 16

For each of the following matrices, state whether it is upper triangular, lower triangular, diagonal, or none of these.

(a) $\begin{pmatrix} 1 & 1 & 0 \\ 0 & 0 & 3 \\ 0 & 0 & 3 \end{pmatrix}$ (b) $\begin{pmatrix} 0 & 0 & 1 \\ 0 & 1 & 2 \\ 1 & 2 & 3 \end{pmatrix}$ (c) $\begin{pmatrix} 6 & 0 & 0 \\ 0 & 5 & 0 \\ 0 & 0 & 4 \end{pmatrix}$

Strictly speaking, we should write the $n \times n$ identity matrix as $\mathbf{I}_n$, but the size of any identity matrix will be clear from the context.

Earlier, you met the $m \times n$ zero matrix $\mathbf{0}$, which has the property that $\mathbf{A} + \mathbf{0} = \mathbf{A}$ for each $m \times n$ matrix $\mathbf{A}$. The analogue for matrix multiplication is the $n \times n$ **identity matrix I**, which is a diagonal matrix where each diagonal element is 1. For example, the 3×3 identity matrix is

$$\mathbf{I} = \begin{pmatrix} 1 & 0 & 0 \\ 0 & 1 & 0 \\ 0 & 0 & 1 \end{pmatrix}.$$

If $\mathbf{A}$ is an $n \times n$ matrix and $\mathbf{I}$ is the $n \times n$ identity matrix, then

$$\mathbf{IA} = \mathbf{AI} = \mathbf{A}.$$

$\mathbf{A}^{-1}$ is read as 'A inverse'.

An invertible matrix is sometimes called *non-singular*, while a non-invertible matrix is called *singular*.

If there exists a matrix $\mathbf{B}$ such that $\mathbf{AB} = \mathbf{BA} = \mathbf{I}$, then $\mathbf{B}$ is called the **inverse** of $\mathbf{A}$, and we write $\mathbf{B} = \mathbf{A}^{-1}$. Only square matrices can have inverses. A matrix that has an inverse is called **invertible** (and a matrix that does not have an inverse is called **non-invertible!**).

Exercise 17

For each of the following pairs of matrices $\mathbf{A}$ and $\mathbf{B}$, calculate $\mathbf{AB}$ and deduce that $\mathbf{B} = \mathbf{A}^{-1}$.

(a) $\mathbf{A} = \begin{pmatrix} 2 & 1 \\ 7 & 8 \end{pmatrix}$ and $\mathbf{B} = \begin{pmatrix} \frac{8}{9} & -\frac{1}{9} \\ -\frac{7}{9} & \frac{2}{9} \end{pmatrix}$

(b) $\mathbf{A} = \begin{pmatrix} 1 & 3 & -1 \\ -2 & -5 & 1 \\ 4 & 11 & -2 \end{pmatrix}$ and $\mathbf{B} = \begin{pmatrix} -1 & -5 & -2 \\ 0 & 2 & 1 \\ -2 & 1 & 1 \end{pmatrix}$

Finding the inverse of an invertible matrix

There is a way to compute the inverse of an invertible square matrix using row operations similar to those used for Gaussian elimination. An example will make the method clear.

Example 7

Find the inverse of the invertible matrix

$$\mathbf{A} = \begin{pmatrix} 2 & 2 & -1 \\ 3 & 5 & 1 \\ 1 & 2 & 1 \end{pmatrix}.$$

Solution

We form the augmented 3×6 matrix

$$\begin{pmatrix} 2 & 2 & -1 & | & 1 & 0 & 0 \\ 3 & 5 & 1 & | & 0 & 1 & 0 \\ 1 & 2 & 1 & | & 0 & 0 & 1 \end{pmatrix} \begin{matrix} \mathbf{R}_1 \\ \mathbf{R}_2 \\ \mathbf{R}_3 \end{matrix}$$

consisting of $\mathbf{A}$ together with the identity matrix. Then we perform row operations in order to reduce the left-hand matrix to the identity, as follows.

Stage 1(a)   We reduce the elements below the leading diagonal in column 1 to zero.

$$\begin{matrix} \\ \mathbf{R}_2 - \frac{3}{2}\mathbf{R}_1 \\ \mathbf{R}_3 - \frac{1}{2}\mathbf{R}_1 \end{matrix} \left(\begin{array}{ccc|ccc} 2 & 2 & -1 & 1 & 0 & 0 \\ 0 & 2 & \frac{5}{2} & -\frac{3}{2} & 1 & 0 \\ 0 & 1 & \frac{3}{2} & -\frac{1}{2} & 0 & 1 \end{array} \right) \begin{matrix} \mathbf{R}_1 \\ \mathbf{R}_{2a} \\ \mathbf{R}_{3a} \end{matrix}$$

Stage 1(b)   We reduce the element below the leading diagonal in column 2 to zero.

$$\begin{matrix} \\ \\ \mathbf{R}_{3a} - \frac{1}{2}\mathbf{R}_{2a} \end{matrix} \left(\begin{array}{ccc|ccc} 2 & 2 & -1 & 1 & 0 & 0 \\ 0 & 2 & \frac{5}{2} & -\frac{3}{2} & 1 & 0 \\ 0 & 0 & \frac{1}{4} & \frac{1}{4} & -\frac{1}{2} & 1 \end{array} \right) \begin{matrix} \mathbf{R}_1 \\ \mathbf{R}_{2a} \\ \mathbf{R}_{3b} \end{matrix}$$

Note that the left-hand matrix is now in upper triangular form.

Stage 2(a)   We adjust the element at the bottom of column 3 to one.

$$\begin{matrix} \\ \\ 4\mathbf{R}_{3b} \end{matrix} \left(\begin{array}{ccc|ccc} 2 & 2 & -1 & 1 & 0 & 0 \\ 0 & 2 & \frac{5}{2} & -\frac{3}{2} & 1 & 0 \\ 0 & 0 & 1 & 1 & -2 & 4 \end{array} \right) \begin{matrix} \mathbf{R}_1 \\ \mathbf{R}_{2a} \\ \mathbf{R}_{3c} \end{matrix}$$

Stage 2(b)   We reduce the elements above the leading diagonal in column 3 to zero.

$$\begin{matrix} \mathbf{R}_1 + \mathbf{R}_{3c} \\ \mathbf{R}_{2a} - \frac{5}{2}\mathbf{R}_{3c} \\ \end{matrix} \left(\begin{array}{ccc|ccc} 2 & 2 & 0 & 2 & -2 & 4 \\ 0 & 2 & 0 & -4 & 6 & -10 \\ 0 & 0 & 1 & 1 & -2 & 4 \end{array} \right) \begin{matrix} \mathbf{R}_{1a} \\ \mathbf{R}_{2b} \\ \mathbf{R}_{3c} \end{matrix}$$

Stage 2(c)   We adjust the element on the leading diagonal in column 2 to one.

$$\begin{matrix} \\ \frac{1}{2}\mathbf{R}_{2b} \\ \end{matrix} \left(\begin{array}{ccc|ccc} 2 & 2 & 0 & 2 & -2 & 4 \\ 0 & 1 & 0 & -2 & 3 & -5 \\ 0 & 0 & 1 & 1 & -2 & 4 \end{array} \right) \begin{matrix} \mathbf{R}_{1a} \\ \mathbf{R}_{2c} \\ \mathbf{R}_{3c} \end{matrix}$$

Stage 2(d)   We reduce the element at the top of column 2 to zero.

$$\begin{matrix} \mathbf{R}_{1a} - 2\mathbf{R}_{2c} \\ \\ \end{matrix} \left(\begin{array}{ccc|ccc} 2 & 0 & 0 & 6 & -8 & 14 \\ 0 & 1 & 0 & -2 & 3 & -5 \\ 0 & 0 & 1 & 1 & -2 & 4 \end{array} \right) \begin{matrix} \mathbf{R}_{1b} \\ \mathbf{R}_{2c} \\ \mathbf{R}_{3c} \end{matrix}$$

Stage 2(e)   We adjust the element at the top of column 1 to one.

$$\begin{matrix} \frac{1}{2}\mathbf{R}_{1b} \\ \\ \end{matrix} \left(\begin{array}{ccc|ccc} 1 & 0 & 0 & 3 & -4 & 7 \\ 0 & 1 & 0 & -2 & 3 & -5 \\ 0 & 0 & 1 & 1 & -2 & 4 \end{array} \right) \begin{matrix} \mathbf{R}_{1c} \\ \mathbf{R}_{2c} \\ \mathbf{R}_{3c} \end{matrix}$$

The resulting matrix on the right-hand side is the required inverse,

$$\mathbf{A}^{-1} = \left(\begin{array}{ccc} 3 & -4 & 7 \\ -2 & 3 & -5 \\ 1 & -2 & 4 \end{array} \right),$$

as you can readily check by showing that $\mathbf{A}\mathbf{A}^{-1} = \mathbf{A}^{-1}\mathbf{A} = \mathbf{I}$.

This technique extends to larger square matrices, but because it is rather inefficient, it is not widely used.

Procedure 2   Finding the inverse of an invertible square matrix

To find the inverse of an invertible square matrix **A**, carry out the following steps.

1.   Form the augmented matrix **A|I**, where **I** is the identity matrix of the same size as **A**.

2.   Use row operations to reduce the left-hand side to the identity matrix **I**.

3.   The matrix on the right-hand side is the inverse of **A**.

Row interchanges will be necessary if one or more of the pivots is zero.

Exercise 18

Use Procedure 2 to find the inverse of a general 2×2 matrix

$$\mathbf{A} = \begin{pmatrix} a & b \\ c & d \end{pmatrix} \quad \text{(where } ad - bc \neq 0\text{).}$$

Note that you will have to treat $a = 0$ as a special case.

The existence (or otherwise) of the inverse of a given square matrix **A** depends solely on the value of a single number called the *determinant* of **A**, written $\det \mathbf{A}$. For a 2×2 matrix, Exercise 18 yields the following result (which saves us working through Procedure 2).

It is sometimes convenient to write $\det(\mathbf{A})$ rather than $\det \mathbf{A}$. We study determinants in Subsection 2.3.

Inverse of an invertible 2×2 matrix

If $\mathbf{A} = \begin{pmatrix} a & b \\ c & d \end{pmatrix}$, then the **determinant** of **A** is $\det \mathbf{A} = ad - bc$.

If $\det \mathbf{A} \neq 0$, then **A** is invertible and

$$\mathbf{A}^{-1} = \frac{1}{ad - bc} \begin{pmatrix} d & -b \\ -c & a \end{pmatrix}. \tag{16}$$

So to find the inverse of a 2×2 matrix, interchange the diagonal elements, take the negatives of the other two elements, and divide each resulting element by the determinant. You may like to check that $\mathbf{A}\mathbf{A}^{-1} = \mathbf{I}$.

You will see shortly that it is possible to define $\det \mathbf{A}$ for all square matrices, and the following result holds (although we do not prove it).

Condition for invertibility of a matrix A

A matrix $\mathbf{A}$ is invertible if and only if $\det \mathbf{A} \neq 0$.

This is equivalent to saying that a matrix $\mathbf{A}$ is non-invertible if and only if $\det \mathbf{A} = 0$.

Exercise 19

For each of the following 2×2 matrices $\mathbf{A}$, calculate $\det \mathbf{A}$ and determine $\mathbf{A}^{-1}$, if it exists.

(a) $\mathbf{A} = \begin{pmatrix} 7 & 4 \\ 5 & 3 \end{pmatrix}$ (b) $\mathbf{A} = \begin{pmatrix} 6 & 2 \\ 9 & 3 \end{pmatrix}$ (c) $\mathbf{A} = \begin{pmatrix} 4 & 2 \\ 5 & 3 \end{pmatrix}$

Properties of invertible matrices

- The inverse of an invertible matrix $\mathbf{A}$ is unique (i.e. if $\mathbf{AB} = \mathbf{I}$ and $\mathbf{AC} = \mathbf{I}$, then $\mathbf{B} = \mathbf{C} = \mathbf{A}^{-1}$).

- If $\mathbf{AB} = \mathbf{I}$, then $\mathbf{BA} = \mathbf{I}$, so $\mathbf{AA}^{-1} = \mathbf{A}^{-1}\mathbf{A} = \mathbf{I}$, and hence the inverse of $\mathbf{A}^{-1}$ is $\mathbf{A}$.

- The rows of a square matrix are linearly independent if and only if the matrix is invertible.

- If $\mathbf{A}$ and $\mathbf{B}$ are invertible matrices of the same size, then $\mathbf{AB}$ is invertible and $(\mathbf{AB})^{-1} = \mathbf{B}^{-1}\mathbf{A}^{-1}$.

We do not prove these properties here.

Notice the change in order of the terms involving $\mathbf{A}$ and $\mathbf{B}$.

Exercise 20

(a) Show that if $\mathbf{A}$ and $\mathbf{B}$ are any two square matrices of the same size, then $(\mathbf{AB})^{-1} = \mathbf{B}^{-1}\mathbf{A}^{-1}$.

(b) Now let $\mathbf{A} = \begin{pmatrix} 2 & 2 \\ 4 & 5 \end{pmatrix}$ and $\mathbf{B} = \begin{pmatrix} 3 & 4 \\ -1 & -2 \end{pmatrix}$.

   Find $\mathbf{A}^{-1}$ and $\mathbf{B}^{-1}$.

(c) For $\mathbf{A}, \mathbf{B}$ as in part (b), verify that $(\mathbf{A} + \mathbf{B})^{-1} \neq \mathbf{A}^{-1} + \mathbf{B}^{-1}$.

(d) For $\mathbf{A}, \mathbf{B}$ as in part (b), verify that $(\mathbf{AB})^{-1} = \mathbf{B}^{-1}\mathbf{A}^{-1}$.

2.2 Linear transformations of the plane

Linear transformations of the plane provide examples of a use of matrices.

You will see further examples in Unit 5.

The transformation is called *linear* because straight lines are mapped to straight lines.

A **linear transformation** of the plane is a function that maps a two-dimensional vector $(x \quad y)^T$ to the image vector $(ax + by \quad cx + dy)^T$, where a, b, c and d are real numbers.

We can represent any such linear transformation by the matrix $\mathbf{A} = \begin{pmatrix} a & b \\ c & d \end{pmatrix}$, since $\mathbf{A}\begin{pmatrix} x \\ y \end{pmatrix} = \begin{pmatrix} a & b \\ c & d \end{pmatrix}\begin{pmatrix} x \\ y \end{pmatrix} = \begin{pmatrix} ax + by \\ cx + dy \end{pmatrix}$. The image of any given vector can then be calculated. For example, the matrix $\mathbf{A} = \begin{pmatrix} 3 & 2 \\ 1 & 4 \end{pmatrix}$ maps $\begin{pmatrix} 2 \\ 1 \end{pmatrix}$ to $\mathbf{A}\begin{pmatrix} 2 \\ 1 \end{pmatrix} = \begin{pmatrix} 3 & 2 \\ 1 & 4 \end{pmatrix}\begin{pmatrix} 2 \\ 1 \end{pmatrix} = \begin{pmatrix} 8 \\ 6 \end{pmatrix}$.

Exercise 21

Consider the linear transformation that maps a vector $(x \quad y)^T$ to the image vector $(x + 2y \quad 3x + 4y)^T$.

(a) Write down the matrix $\mathbf{A}$ for this linear transformation.

(b) Use the matrix $\mathbf{A}$ to find the image of each of the following vectors.

$\quad$ (i) $\begin{pmatrix} 3 \\ 1 \end{pmatrix}$ $\qquad$ (ii) $\begin{pmatrix} -1 \\ 1 \end{pmatrix}$ $\qquad$ (iii) $\begin{pmatrix} 0 \\ 0 \end{pmatrix}$

For any linear transformation with matrix $\mathbf{A}$, the images of the Cartesian unit vectors $\mathbf{i} = (1 \quad 0)^T$ and $\mathbf{j} = (0 \quad 1)^T$ are the columns of $\mathbf{A}$. To see this, consider the general linear transformation that maps each vector $(x \quad y)^T$ to the image vector $(a_{11}x + a_{12}y \quad a_{21}x + a_{22}y)^T$. Then

$$\text{the image of } \begin{pmatrix} 1 \\ 0 \end{pmatrix} \text{ is } \begin{pmatrix} a_{11} \times 1 + a_{12} \times 0 \\ a_{21} \times 1 + a_{22} \times 0 \end{pmatrix} = \begin{pmatrix} a_{11} \\ a_{21} \end{pmatrix},$$

and

$$\text{the image of } \begin{pmatrix} 0 \\ 1 \end{pmatrix} \text{ is } \begin{pmatrix} a_{11} \times 0 + a_{12} \times 1 \\ a_{21} \times 0 + a_{22} \times 1 \end{pmatrix} = \begin{pmatrix} a_{12} \\ a_{22} \end{pmatrix}.$$

These images are the columns of the matrix $\mathbf{A} = \begin{pmatrix} a_{11} & a_{12} \\ a_{21} & a_{22} \end{pmatrix}$.

An interesting offshoot of these ideas concerns the *determinant* of the matrix of a linear transformation.

Consider the general linear transformation with matrix

$$\mathbf{A} = \begin{pmatrix} a & b \\ c & d \end{pmatrix}.$$

The image of $(1 \quad 0)^T$ is $(a \quad c)^T$, and the image of $(0 \quad 1)^T$ is $(b \quad d)^T$. It can be shown that the unit square (with vertices at the points $(0,0)$, $(1,0)$, $(1,1)$ and $(0,1)$) is mapped to the parallelogram defined by these image vectors, as shown in Figure 4.

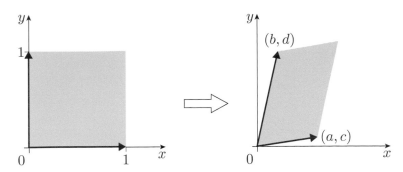

Figure 4   The unit square maps to a parallelogram

From Unit 2, we know that the area of this parallelogram is the magnitude of the cross product of the two position vectors $(a \quad c)^T$ and $(b \quad d)^T$, which is $|(a\mathbf{i} + c\mathbf{j}) \times (b\mathbf{i} + d\mathbf{j})| = |ad - bc|$. The determinant of $\mathbf{A}$ is $\det \mathbf{A} = ad - bc$. So the area of the parallelogram is the magnitude of $\det \mathbf{A}$, denoted $|\det \mathbf{A}|$. But the parallelogram is the image of the unit square defined by the two vectors $(1 \quad 0)^T$ and $(0 \quad 1)^T$, so $|\det \mathbf{A}|$ is the area of the image of the unit square. Accordingly, the larger $|\det \mathbf{A}|$, the larger the images of shapes under the transformation.

Exercise 22

For each of the following matrices, calculate $\det \mathbf{A}$ and compare your answer with the area of the parallelogram defined by the images of the Cartesian unit vectors $\mathbf{i}$ and $\mathbf{j}$.

(a) $\mathbf{A} = \begin{pmatrix} 1 & 1 \\ -1 & 1 \end{pmatrix}$ (b) $\mathbf{A} = \begin{pmatrix} 3 & 2 \\ 1 & -6 \end{pmatrix}$ (c) $\mathbf{A} = \begin{pmatrix} 4 & 6 \\ 2 & 3 \end{pmatrix}$

We can also link these ideas with systems of linear equations. For example, the system of linear equations

$$\begin{cases} x_1 + x_2 = 0, \\ x_1 + 2x_2 = 1, \end{cases} \tag{17}$$

can be written in matrix form as $\mathbf{Ax} = \mathbf{b}$, given by

$$\begin{pmatrix} 1 & 1 \\ 1 & 2 \end{pmatrix} \begin{pmatrix} x_1 \\ x_2 \end{pmatrix} = \begin{pmatrix} 0 \\ 1 \end{pmatrix}. \tag{18}$$

Solving equations (17) is equivalent to finding the vector $\mathbf{x}$ that is mapped to the vector $\mathbf{b}$ by the linear transformation with matrix $\mathbf{A}$ as shown in equation (18). This is the 'inverse process' of our earlier work (e.g. in Exercise 21), where we were given $\mathbf{x}$ and asked to find the image vector $\mathbf{b} = \mathbf{Ax}$. This suggests that we might consider using the inverse matrix as a way of solving such systems of linear equations.

For the matrix $\mathbf{A}$ in equation (18),

$$\mathbf{A}^{-1} = \begin{pmatrix} 1 & 1 \\ 1 & 2 \end{pmatrix}^{-1} = \begin{pmatrix} 2 & -1 \\ -1 & 1 \end{pmatrix}.$$

Here $\det \mathbf{A} = 1$.

We wish to multiply the equation $\mathbf{Ax} = \mathbf{b}$ by $\mathbf{A}^{-1}$, but we must be careful with the order of the multiplication. Multiplying both sides of the equation *on the left* by $\mathbf{A}^{-1}$, we obtain

$$\mathbf{A}^{-1}\mathbf{Ax} = \mathbf{A}^{-1}\mathbf{b}.$$

Since $\mathbf{A}^{-1}\mathbf{A} = \mathbf{I}$, we have

$$\mathbf{x} = \mathbf{A}^{-1}\mathbf{b},$$

Here we use associativity:
$\mathbf{A}^{-1}(\mathbf{Ax}) = (\mathbf{A}^{-1}\mathbf{A})\mathbf{x}.$

so $\mathbf{x}$ is the image of $\mathbf{b}$ under transformation by the inverse matrix $\mathbf{A}^{-1}$. Therefore

$$\begin{pmatrix} x_1 \\ x_2 \end{pmatrix} = \begin{pmatrix} 2 & -1 \\ -1 & 1 \end{pmatrix} \begin{pmatrix} 0 \\ 1 \end{pmatrix}$$
$$= \begin{pmatrix} -1 \\ 1 \end{pmatrix}.$$

Thus $x_1 = -1$, $x_2 = 1$ is the solution of this system of linear equations.

Exercise 23

Given $\mathbf{A} = \begin{pmatrix} 1 & 2 \\ -1 & 1 \end{pmatrix}$, calculate $\det \mathbf{A}$ and $\mathbf{A}^{-1}$. Hence write down the solution of the system of equations

$$\begin{aligned} x + 2y &= 1, \\ -x + y &= -1. \end{aligned}$$

This matrix approach to solving a system of linear equations can be used whenever the matrix $\mathbf{A}^{-1}$ exists, that is, whenever $\mathbf{A}$ is invertible. However, except for 2×2 matrices, the inverse matrix is usually tedious to calculate, and it is more efficient to use the Gaussian elimination method to solve the system of equations.

We come now to a result that is important with respect to the material in the next unit. Suppose that $\mathbf{b} = \mathbf{0}$, so that we are looking for a solution to $\mathbf{Ax} = \mathbf{0}$. What can we say about $\mathbf{x}$? If $\mathbf{A}$ has an inverse, then multiplying both sides of $\mathbf{Ax} = \mathbf{0}$ on the left by $\mathbf{A}^{-1}$ gives $\mathbf{A}^{-1}\mathbf{Ax} = \mathbf{A}^{-1}\mathbf{0}$, so $\mathbf{x} = \mathbf{0}$. Therefore, if $\mathbf{Ax} = \mathbf{0}$ is to have a non-zero solution $\mathbf{x}$, then $\mathbf{A}$ cannot have an inverse, that is, it must be non-invertible. So we have the following result.

Non-invertible square matrix

If $\mathbf{A}$ is a square matrix and $\mathbf{Ax} = \mathbf{0}$ with $\mathbf{x} \neq \mathbf{0}$, then $\mathbf{A}$ is non-invertible and therefore $\det \mathbf{A} = 0$.

2.3 Determinants

In this subsection we summarise the main properties of determinants of 2×2 matrices and extend the ideas to $n \times n$ matrices.

Properties of 2×2 determinants

We frequently use the 'vertical line' notation for determinants:

$$\text{if } \mathbf{A} = \begin{pmatrix} a & b \\ c & d \end{pmatrix}, \text{ then } \det \mathbf{A} = \begin{vmatrix} a & b \\ c & d \end{vmatrix} = ad - bc.$$

Earlier in this section you saw that if $\det \mathbf{A} \neq 0$, then $\mathbf{A}$ is invertible. In the following exercise we investigate some further properties of 2×2 determinants.

Exercise 24

Calculate the determinants of the following matrices, which are related to the matrix $\mathbf{A} = \begin{pmatrix} a & b \\ c & d \end{pmatrix}$. In parts (b), (c), (e), (f), (g) and (h), compare your answer with $\det \mathbf{A}$.

We will refer back to the results of this exercise later.

(a) $\begin{pmatrix} a & 0 \\ c & d \end{pmatrix}$, $\begin{pmatrix} a & b \\ 0 & d \end{pmatrix}$ and $\begin{pmatrix} a & 0 \\ 0 & d \end{pmatrix}$ (lower triangular, upper triangular and diagonal matrices)

(b) $\begin{pmatrix} c & d \\ a & b \end{pmatrix}$ and $\begin{pmatrix} b & a \\ d & c \end{pmatrix}$ (formed by interchanging rows or columns of $\mathbf{A}$)

(c) $\mathbf{A}^T = \begin{pmatrix} a & c \\ b & d \end{pmatrix}$

(d) $\begin{pmatrix} a & b \\ a & b \end{pmatrix}$ and $\begin{pmatrix} a & a \\ c & c \end{pmatrix}$ (matrices with linearly dependent rows or columns)

(e) $\begin{pmatrix} ka & kb \\ c & d \end{pmatrix}$ and $\begin{pmatrix} ka & b \\ kc & d \end{pmatrix}$ (formed by multiplying a row or column of $\mathbf{A}$ by a scalar k)

(f) $k\mathbf{A} = \begin{pmatrix} ka & kb \\ kc & kd \end{pmatrix}$

(g) $\begin{pmatrix} a & b \\ c - ma & d - mb \end{pmatrix}$ and $\begin{pmatrix} a - mc & b - md \\ c & d \end{pmatrix}$ (formed by subtracting a multiple of one row of $\mathbf{A}$ from the other row)

(h) $\mathbf{A}^{-1} = \begin{pmatrix} \dfrac{d}{ad - bc} & -\dfrac{b}{ad - bc} \\ -\dfrac{c}{ad - bc} & \dfrac{a}{ad - bc} \end{pmatrix}$

Introducing 3×3 and $n \times n$ determinants

Just as the magnitude of the 2×2 determinant

$$\begin{vmatrix} a_1 & a_2 \\ b_1 & b_2 \end{vmatrix}$$

represents the area of the parallelogram defined by the vectors $(a_1 \quad a_2)^T$ and $(b_1 \quad b_2)^T$, so we can define a 3×3 determinant

$$\begin{vmatrix} a_1 & a_2 & a_3 \\ b_1 & b_2 & b_3 \\ c_1 & c_2 & c_3 \end{vmatrix}$$

whose magnitude represents the volume of the parallelepiped defined by the vectors $\mathbf{a} = (a_1 \quad a_2 \quad a_3)^T$, $\mathbf{b} = (b_1 \quad b_2 \quad b_3)^T$ and $\mathbf{c} = (c_1 \quad c_2 \quad c_3)^T$, as shown in Figure 5. (We will look at this further in Subsection 2.4.)

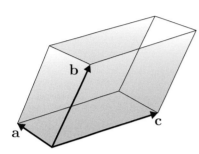

Figure 5 A parallelepiped defined by the vectors $\mathbf{a}$, $\mathbf{b}$ and $\mathbf{c}$

This is sometimes known as 'expanding the determinant by the top row'. Notice the minus sign before the second term.

> The **determinant** of the 3×3 matrix
>
> $$\mathbf{A} = \begin{pmatrix} a_1 & a_2 & a_3 \\ b_1 & b_2 & b_3 \\ c_1 & c_2 & c_3 \end{pmatrix}$$
>
> is given by
>
> $$\det \mathbf{A} = a_1 \begin{vmatrix} b_2 & b_3 \\ c_2 & c_3 \end{vmatrix} - a_2 \begin{vmatrix} b_1 & b_3 \\ c_1 & c_3 \end{vmatrix} + a_3 \begin{vmatrix} b_1 & b_2 \\ c_1 & c_2 \end{vmatrix}, \tag{19}$$
>
> or equivalently,
>
> $$\det \mathbf{A} = a_1 b_2 c_3 - a_1 b_3 c_2 - a_2 b_1 c_3 + a_2 b_3 c_1 + a_3 b_1 c_2 - a_3 b_2 c_1. \tag{20}$$

As before, we frequently use 'vertical line' notation. For example,

$$\begin{vmatrix} 1 & 2 & 4 \\ 3 & 1 & -1 \\ 2 & 5 & 6 \end{vmatrix} = 1 \begin{vmatrix} 1 & -1 \\ 5 & 6 \end{vmatrix} - 2 \begin{vmatrix} 3 & -1 \\ 2 & 6 \end{vmatrix} + 4 \begin{vmatrix} 3 & 1 \\ 2 & 5 \end{vmatrix} = 11 - 40 + 52 = 23.$$

Exercise 25

Evaluate the following determinants.

(a) $\begin{vmatrix} 4 & 1 & 0 \\ 0 & 2 & -1 \\ 2 & 3 & 1 \end{vmatrix}$ (b) $\begin{vmatrix} 1 & 2 & 3 \\ 4 & 5 & 6 \\ 7 & 8 & 9 \end{vmatrix}$ (c) $\begin{vmatrix} 1 & 2 & 3 \\ 0 & 4 & 5 \\ 0 & 0 & 6 \end{vmatrix}$

As a way to understand how to expand 3×3 determinants, first consider the matrix of signs

$$\begin{pmatrix} + & - & + \\ - & + & - \\ + & - & + \end{pmatrix},$$

which we will call the **sign matrix**. To evaluate the determinant of the 3×3 matrix $\mathbf{A}$ in the above definition, select a row or column. The determinant is then given by a sum of three terms, one for each element in the selected row or column. Each term consists of the element itself multiplied by the determinant of the 2×2 matrix formed by removing the row and column passing through the element, and this is then multiplied by the corresponding sign in the above sign matrix.

Note that in the definition of the determinant in equation (19), this procedure was carried out by selecting the top row. If the middle row is chosen for the expansion, then det $\mathbf{A}$ is given by

$$\det \mathbf{A} = -b_1 \begin{vmatrix} a_2 & a_3 \\ c_2 & c_3 \end{vmatrix} + b_2 \begin{vmatrix} a_1 & a_3 \\ c_1 & c_3 \end{vmatrix} - b_3 \begin{vmatrix} a_1 & a_2 \\ c_1 & c_2 \end{vmatrix},$$

and if the third column is selected, then det $\mathbf{A}$ is given by

$$\det \mathbf{A} = a_3 \begin{vmatrix} b_1 & b_2 \\ c_1 & c_2 \end{vmatrix} - b_3 \begin{vmatrix} a_1 & a_2 \\ c_1 & c_2 \end{vmatrix} + c_3 \begin{vmatrix} a_1 & a_2 \\ b_1 & b_2 \end{vmatrix},$$

Note how the signs of the terms correspond to those of the middle row of the sign matrix.

Note how the signs of the terms correspond to those of the third column of the sign matrix.

and so on. Any row or column could be selected for the expansion.

You can see from this procedure that the sign of the determinant will change if two adjacent rows or two adjacent columns are interchanged.

You can also see that

$$\det(\mathbf{A}^T) = \det \mathbf{A},$$

a result that extends to $n \times n$ matrices (though we do not prove this). This is a consequence of the fact that to evaluate det $\mathbf{A}$ using the above procedure, we can expand using columns in place of rows, as illustrated in Example 8 below.

In fact, the procedure makes it easy to evaluate any 3×3 determinant in which one row or column is particularly simple, such as when a row or column contains mainly zeros.

Example 8

Evaluate the determinant of each of the following matrices.

(a) $\mathbf{A} = \begin{pmatrix} 8 & 9 & -6 \\ 1 & 0 & 0 \\ 32 & -7 & 14 \end{pmatrix}$ (b) $\mathbf{B} = \begin{pmatrix} 8 & 9 & 0 \\ 13 & -4 & 2 \\ -6 & 2 & 0 \end{pmatrix}$

Solution

(a) We choose to expand det $\mathbf{A}$ by the second row, as this contains two zeros:

$$\begin{vmatrix} 8 & 9 & -6 \\ 1 & 0 & 0 \\ 32 & -7 & 14 \end{vmatrix} = -1 \begin{vmatrix} 9 & -6 \\ -7 & 14 \end{vmatrix} + 0 \begin{vmatrix} 8 & -6 \\ 32 & 14 \end{vmatrix} - 0 \begin{vmatrix} 8 & 9 \\ 32 & -7 \end{vmatrix}$$

$$= -1(126 - 42)$$

$$= -84.$$

(b) We choose to expand $\det \mathbf{B}$ by the third column, as this contains two zeros:

$$\begin{vmatrix} 8 & 9 & 0 \\ 13 & -4 & 2 \\ -6 & 2 & 0 \end{vmatrix} = 0\begin{vmatrix} 13 & -4 \\ -6 & 2 \end{vmatrix} - 2\begin{vmatrix} 8 & 9 \\ -6 & 2 \end{vmatrix} + 0\begin{vmatrix} 8 & 9 \\ 13 & -4 \end{vmatrix}$$
$$= -2(16 + 54)$$
$$= -140.$$

The armoury of techniques for evaluating determinants can be expanded by noting some general rules.

The general $n \times n$ determinant is defined below.

You may find it helpful to compare these general rules with the results for 2×2 matrices in Exercise 24. The letters (a) to (h) here relate to the relevant parts of that exercise.

Rules for $n \times n$ determinants

(a) If $\mathbf{A}$ is a diagonal, upper triangular or lower triangular matrix, then $\det \mathbf{A}$ is the product of the diagonal elements.

(b) Interchanging any two rows or any two columns of $\mathbf{A}$ changes the sign of $\det \mathbf{A}$.

(c) $\det(\mathbf{A}^T) = \det \mathbf{A}$.

(d) If the rows or columns of $\mathbf{A}$ are linearly dependent, then $\det \mathbf{A} = 0$; otherwise, $\det \mathbf{A} \neq 0$.

(e) Multiplying any row or any column of $\mathbf{A}$ by a scalar k multiplies $\det \mathbf{A}$ by k.

(f) For any number k, $\det(k\mathbf{A}) = k^n \det \mathbf{A}$.

The multiple can be negative or positive, so rule (g) covers subtracting a multiple of one row from another row.

(g) Adding a multiple of one row of $\mathbf{A}$ to another row does not change $\det \mathbf{A}$.

(h) The matrix $\mathbf{A}$ is non-invertible if and only if $\det \mathbf{A} = 0$. If $\det \mathbf{A} \neq 0$, then $\det(\mathbf{A}^{-1}) = 1/\det \mathbf{A}$.

(i) For any two $n \times n$ matrices $\mathbf{A}$ and $\mathbf{B}$, we have

$$\det(\mathbf{AB}) = \det \mathbf{A} \det \mathbf{B}.$$

Note that since $\det(\mathbf{A}^T) = \det \mathbf{A}$, we can also deduce that $\det \mathbf{A} = 0$ if and only if the *columns* of $\mathbf{A}$ are linearly dependent.

Rule (d) tells us that $\det \mathbf{A} = 0$ if and only if the rows of $\mathbf{A}$ are linearly dependent. Hence any system of linear equations with coefficient matrix $\mathbf{A}$ has a *unique* solution if and only if $\det \mathbf{A} \neq 0$. If $\det \mathbf{A} = 0$, then the system has an infinite number of solutions or no solution.

Exercise 26

(a) Calculate $\begin{vmatrix} 2 & 1 & 3 \\ 0 & 2 & 1 \\ 3 & 1 & 6 \end{vmatrix}$.

(b) Use the result of part (a) and the above rules to *write down* the values of the following determinants.

(i) $\begin{vmatrix} 2 & 1 & 3 \\ 3 & 1 & 6 \\ 0 & 2 & 1 \end{vmatrix}$
(ii) $\begin{vmatrix} 2 & 0 & 3 \\ 1 & 2 & 1 \\ 3 & 1 & 6 \end{vmatrix}$
(iii) $\begin{vmatrix} 2 & 3 & 3 \\ 3 & 3 & 6 \\ 0 & 6 & 1 \end{vmatrix}$

(c) Let $\mathbf{A} = \begin{pmatrix} 1 & 3 & 2 \\ 0 & 1 & -1 \\ 0 & 2 & 3 \end{pmatrix}$. Calculate $\det \mathbf{A}$.

Subtract twice the second row of $\mathbf{A}$ from the third row to obtain an upper triangular matrix $\mathbf{U}$. Calculate $\det \mathbf{U}$ using the definition of a 3×3 determinant, and compare this with the product of the diagonal elements of $\mathbf{U}$.

It is also possible to define larger determinants. To do this, we proceed one step at a time, defining an $n \times n$ determinant in terms of $(n-1) \times (n-1)$ determinants in a way analogous to the definition of a 3×3 determinant. For example, to define a 4×4 determinant, we have the sign matrix

$$\begin{pmatrix} + & - & + & - \\ - & + & - & + \\ + & - & + & - \\ - & + & - & + \end{pmatrix},$$

and proceed by selecting a row or column. The determinant is now given as a sum of four terms, one for each element in the selected row or column. Again, each term consists of the element itself but now multiplied by the determinant of the 3×3 matrix formed by removing the row and column passing through the element, and this is then multiplied by the corresponding sign in the 4×4 sign matrix. So, for example, by selecting the top row, we have

Note how the signs of the terms correspond to those of the top row of the sign matrix.

$$\begin{vmatrix} a_1 & a_2 & a_3 & a_4 \\ b_1 & b_2 & b_3 & b_4 \\ c_1 & c_2 & c_3 & c_4 \\ d_1 & d_2 & d_3 & d_4 \end{vmatrix} = a_1 \begin{vmatrix} b_2 & b_3 & b_4 \\ c_2 & c_3 & c_4 \\ d_2 & d_3 & d_4 \end{vmatrix} - a_2 \begin{vmatrix} b_1 & b_3 & b_4 \\ c_1 & c_3 & c_4 \\ d_1 & d_3 & d_4 \end{vmatrix}$$

$$+ a_3 \begin{vmatrix} b_1 & b_2 & b_4 \\ c_1 & c_2 & c_4 \\ d_1 & d_2 & d_4 \end{vmatrix} - a_4 \begin{vmatrix} b_1 & b_2 & b_3 \\ c_1 & c_2 & c_3 \\ d_1 & d_2 & d_3 \end{vmatrix}.$$

Except in special cases, the calculation of large determinants like this can be very tedious. However, rule (g) for determinants provides the clue to a simpler method. Procedure 1 (Gaussian elimination) applied to a matrix $\mathbf{A}$ consists of a sequence of row operations where a multiple of one row is subtracted from another. Each such operation does not change the value of the determinant. Thus we can deduce that $\det \mathbf{A} = \det \mathbf{U}$, where $\mathbf{U}$ is the upper triangular matrix obtained at the end of the elimination stage. Since the determinant of an upper triangular matrix is the product of the diagonal elements, Procedure 1 also provides an efficient way of calculating determinants of any size.

If we need to make essential row interchanges to avoid a zero pivot, we note that each row interchange will change the sign of the determinant (see rule (b)).

Exercise 27

In Example 3 we applied the Gaussian elimination method to the matrix
$$\mathbf{A} = \begin{pmatrix} 1 & -4 & 2 \\ 3 & -2 & 3 \\ 8 & -2 & 9 \end{pmatrix} \text{ to obtain } \mathbf{U} = \begin{pmatrix} 1 & -4 & 2 \\ 0 & 10 & -3 \\ 0 & 0 & 2 \end{pmatrix}.$$

Calculate $\det \mathbf{A}$ and $\det \mathbf{U}$, and hence show that $\det \mathbf{A} = \det \mathbf{U}$.

Exercise 28

Evaluate
$$\begin{vmatrix} 1 & -2 & 0 & 3 \\ 4 & -5 & 0 & 6 \\ -2 & -1 & 10 & 4 \\ 5 & -7 & 0 & 9 \end{vmatrix}.$$

2.4 Some applications

We conclude this section by illustrating how 3×3 determinants can be used to represent areas and volumes, and products of vectors. We start by revisiting the scalar triple product.

Scalar triple products and the other topics in this subsection were mentioned in Unit 2.

Scalar triple product

Let $\mathbf{a} = a_1\mathbf{i} + a_2\mathbf{j} + a_3\mathbf{k}$, $\mathbf{b} = b_1\mathbf{i} + b_2\mathbf{j} + b_3\mathbf{k}$ and $\mathbf{c} = c_1\mathbf{i} + c_2\mathbf{j} + c_3\mathbf{k}$. The volume of the parallelepiped with sides defined by the vectors $\mathbf{a}$, $\mathbf{b}$ and $\mathbf{c}$ (see Figure 5) is given by the magnitude of the scalar triple product $(\mathbf{b} \times \mathbf{c}) \cdot \mathbf{a}$, which can also be written as $\mathbf{a} \cdot (\mathbf{b} \times \mathbf{c})$. The cross product of vectors $\mathbf{b}$ and $\mathbf{c}$ is

In Unit 2, the scalar triple product was written as $(\mathbf{a} \times \mathbf{b}) \cdot \mathbf{c}$. But because any of the faces of the parallelepiped can be thought of as the base, we can begin this expression with the cross product of *any two* of the defining vectors and not alter the *magnitude* of the scalar triple product.

$$\begin{aligned} \mathbf{b} \times \mathbf{c} &= (b_2c_3 - b_3c_2)\mathbf{i} + (b_3c_1 - b_1c_3)\mathbf{j} + (b_1c_2 - b_2c_1)\mathbf{k} \\ &= \begin{vmatrix} b_2 & b_3 \\ c_2 & c_3 \end{vmatrix}\mathbf{i} - \begin{vmatrix} b_1 & b_3 \\ c_1 & c_3 \end{vmatrix}\mathbf{j} + \begin{vmatrix} b_1 & b_2 \\ c_1 & c_2 \end{vmatrix}\mathbf{k}, \end{aligned} \qquad (21)$$

hence

$$
\mathbf{a} \cdot (\mathbf{b} \times \mathbf{c}) = a_1 \begin{vmatrix} b_2 & b_3 \\ c_2 & c_3 \end{vmatrix} - a_2 \begin{vmatrix} b_1 & b_3 \\ c_1 & c_3 \end{vmatrix} + a_3 \begin{vmatrix} b_1 & b_2 \\ c_1 & c_2 \end{vmatrix}
$$

$$
= \begin{vmatrix} a_1 & a_2 & a_3 \\ b_1 & b_2 & b_3 \\ c_1 & c_2 & c_3 \end{vmatrix}. \tag{22}
$$

Exercise 29

Use equation (22) and the result of Exercise 26(a) to find the scalar triple product $\mathbf{a} \cdot (\mathbf{b} \times \mathbf{c})$ when

$$
\mathbf{a} = 2\mathbf{i} + \mathbf{j} + 3\mathbf{k}, \quad \mathbf{b} = 2\mathbf{j} + \mathbf{k} \quad \text{and} \quad \mathbf{c} = 3\mathbf{i} + \mathbf{j} + 6\mathbf{k}.
$$

Exercise 30

Use equation (22) to find the volume of the parallelepiped defined by the vectors

$$
\mathbf{a} = \mathbf{i} + \mathbf{k}, \quad \mathbf{b} = \mathbf{i} + 2\mathbf{j} \quad \text{and} \quad \mathbf{c} = \mathbf{j} + 3\mathbf{k}.
$$

Cross product

The similarity between formula (20) for a 3×3 determinant and the component form of the cross product of two vectors in equation (21) gives another way of remembering the formula for the cross product. We have seen above that if $\mathbf{b} = (b_1 \quad b_2 \quad b_3)^T$ and $\mathbf{c} = (c_1 \quad c_2 \quad c_3)^T$, then

$$
\mathbf{b} \times \mathbf{c} = \begin{vmatrix} b_2 & b_3 \\ c_2 & c_3 \end{vmatrix} \mathbf{i} - \begin{vmatrix} b_1 & b_3 \\ c_1 & c_3 \end{vmatrix} \mathbf{j} + \begin{vmatrix} b_1 & b_2 \\ c_1 & c_2 \end{vmatrix} \mathbf{k}.
$$

This expression can be remembered more easily if we write it as a 3×3 determinant:

$$
\mathbf{b} \times \mathbf{c} = \begin{vmatrix} \mathbf{i} & \mathbf{j} & \mathbf{k} \\ b_1 & b_2 & b_3 \\ c_1 & c_2 & c_3 \end{vmatrix}.
$$

Exercise 31

Express $\mathbf{b} \times \mathbf{c}$ as a determinant, and calculate its value, in the following cases.

(a) $\mathbf{b} = 3\mathbf{i} + 2\mathbf{j} - 4\mathbf{k}$ and $\mathbf{c} = \mathbf{i} - \mathbf{j} + 3\mathbf{k}$

(b) $\mathbf{b} = (1 \quad 2 \quad 3)^T$ and $\mathbf{c} = (6 \quad 5 \quad 4)^T$

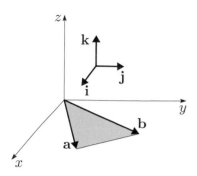

Figure 6 Triangle in the plane defined by the vectors **a** and **b**

As in the solution to Exercise 30, we use det for determinant here, rather than | |, to avoid confusion with the modulus function, which is also present.

Recall that $\mathbf{c} \times \mathbf{c} = \mathbf{0}$ and $-\mathbf{c} \times \mathbf{b} = \mathbf{b} \times \mathbf{c}$ (see Unit 2).

Area of a triangle in the plane

Consider the triangle defined by the origin and the points with position vectors $\mathbf{a} = (a_1 \quad a_2 \quad 0)^T$ and $\mathbf{b} = (b_1 \quad b_2 \quad 0)^T$, as shown in Figure 6. Its area A is given by

$$A = \tfrac{1}{2} |\mathbf{a} \times \mathbf{b}|$$

$$= \tfrac{1}{2} \left| \det \begin{pmatrix} \mathbf{i} & \mathbf{j} & \mathbf{k} \\ a_1 & a_2 & 0 \\ b_1 & b_2 & 0 \end{pmatrix} \right|$$

$$= \tfrac{1}{2} \left| \det \begin{pmatrix} a_1 & a_2 \\ b_1 & b_2 \end{pmatrix} \mathbf{k} \right|$$

$$= \tfrac{1}{2} \left| \det \begin{pmatrix} a_1 & a_2 \\ b_1 & b_2 \end{pmatrix} \right|.$$

This formula agrees with our earlier interpretation of the magnitude of the determinant as the area of the parallelogram defined by **a** and **b**.

We can extend this result to give a formula containing determinants for the area of a triangle whose vertices have position vectors $\mathbf{a} = (a_1 \quad a_2 \quad 0)^T$, $\mathbf{b} = (b_1 \quad b_2 \quad 0)^T$ and $\mathbf{c} = (c_1 \quad c_2 \quad 0)^T$. Two sides of the triangle are given by the vectors $\mathbf{a} - \mathbf{c}$ and $\mathbf{b} - \mathbf{c}$, so we can find the area as

$$A = \tfrac{1}{2} |(\mathbf{a} - \mathbf{c}) \times (\mathbf{b} - \mathbf{c})|$$

$$= \tfrac{1}{2} |(\mathbf{a} \times \mathbf{b}) - (\mathbf{a} \times \mathbf{c}) + (\mathbf{b} \times \mathbf{c})|$$

$$= \tfrac{1}{2} \left| \det \begin{pmatrix} \mathbf{i} & \mathbf{j} & \mathbf{k} \\ a_1 & a_2 & 0 \\ b_1 & b_2 & 0 \end{pmatrix} - \det \begin{pmatrix} \mathbf{i} & \mathbf{j} & \mathbf{k} \\ a_1 & a_2 & 0 \\ c_1 & c_2 & 0 \end{pmatrix} + \det \begin{pmatrix} \mathbf{i} & \mathbf{j} & \mathbf{k} \\ b_1 & b_2 & 0 \\ c_1 & c_2 & 0 \end{pmatrix} \right|$$

$$= \tfrac{1}{2} |(a_1 b_2 - a_2 b_1)\mathbf{k} - (a_1 c_2 - a_2 c_1)\mathbf{k} + (b_1 c_2 - b_2 c_1)\mathbf{k}|$$

$$= \tfrac{1}{2} |(a_1 b_2 - a_2 b_1) - (a_1 c_2 - a_2 c_1) + (b_1 c_2 - b_2 c_1)|$$

$$= \tfrac{1}{2} \left| \det \begin{pmatrix} 1 & 1 & 1 \\ a_1 & b_1 & c_1 \\ a_2 & b_2 & c_2 \end{pmatrix} \right|. \tag{23}$$

Exercise 32

Use equation (23) to find the area of the triangle whose vertices are

$$\mathbf{a} = 3\mathbf{i} + \mathbf{j}, \quad \mathbf{b} = \mathbf{i} + 2\mathbf{j} \quad \text{and} \quad \mathbf{c} = 2\mathbf{i} - \mathbf{j}$$

(see Figure 7).

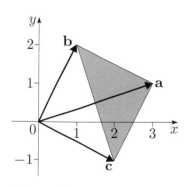

Figure 7

3 Polynomial interpolation

In Section 1 we used matrix notation to describe the solution of systems of linear equations by the Gaussian elimination method. The ubiquitous nature of matrices is partially explained by the fact that such systems of equations arise in many areas of applied mathematics, numerical analysis and statistics. In this section we look at an application that involves solving systems of linear equations: *polynomial interpolation.*

In this application, we are given a set of $n+1$ data points (x_i, y_i), $i = 0, 1, \ldots, n$, where $x_0 < x_1 < \ldots < x_n$, as shown in Figure 8. We determine the polynomial $y(x) = a_0 + a_1 x + \cdots + a_n x^n$ such that $y(x_i) = y_i$, $i = 0, 1, \ldots, n$. This polynomial, defined on the interval $x_0 \le x \le x_n$, is called the **interpolating polynomial**. The graph of such a function passes through each data point.

Figure 8 A set of data points

We are often given a table of values showing the variation of one variable with another. For example, in Example 5 of Unit 1 we met the initial-value problem

$$\frac{dy}{dx} = x + y, \quad y(0) = 1. \tag{24}$$

Using Euler's method with step size $h = 0.2$, we obtained the approximate values for the solution shown in Table 1.

Table 1

i	x_i	Y_i
0	0	1
1	0.2	1.2
2	0.4	1.48
3	0.6	1.856
4	0.8	2.347 2
5	1.0	2.976 64

Suppose that we wish to approximate the solution at $x = 0.47$. One way of doing this is to construct a polynomial through some or all of the data values and then use this interpolating polynomial to approximate the solution at $x = 0.47$. There are many ways of constructing interpolating polynomials, but we present just one method here. We start with a straight-line approximation through the two data points closest to $x = 0.47$.

Example 9

Find the equation of the straight line through $(0.4, 1.48)$ and $(0.6, 1.856)$, and use it to approximate the solution of system (24) at $x = 0.47$.

Solution

Suppose that the line is $y = a_0 + a_1 x$. Since, from Table 1, $y = 1.48$ when $x = 0.4$, and $y = 1.856$ when $x = 0.6$, we obtain the system of equations

$$a_0 + 0.4a_1 = 1.48,$$
$$a_0 + 0.6a_1 = 1.856.$$

The solution of these equations is $a_0 = 0.728$, $a_1 = 1.88$. Hence the equation of the straight line is

$$y = 0.728 + 1.88x.$$

When $x = 0.47$, we have $y = 0.728 + 1.88 \times 0.47 = 1.6116$.

In general, if we require the line through (x_0, y_0) and (x_1, y_1), we have (as in Example 9)

$$a_0 + a_1 x_0 = y_0,$$
$$a_0 + a_1 x_1 = y_1,$$

which can be written in matrix form as

$$\begin{pmatrix} 1 & x_0 \\ 1 & x_1 \end{pmatrix} \begin{pmatrix} a_0 \\ a_1 \end{pmatrix} = \begin{pmatrix} y_0 \\ y_1 \end{pmatrix};$$

that is,

$$\mathbf{Xa} = \mathbf{y},$$

where the matrix $\mathbf{X}$ contains the given values x_i, and the vector $\mathbf{y}$ contains the given values y_i $(i = 1, 2)$. We wish to determine the vector $\mathbf{a}$, and this could be done, for example, by using Gaussian elimination.

Exercise 33

Consider the data in Table 1. Find the straight line through the points $(0.6, 1.856)$ and $(0.8, 2.3472)$, and use it to find an approximation to the value of y at $x = 0.65$ and at $x = 0.47$.

We now have two approximations for $y(0.47)$, which do not agree, even to one decimal place. However, in Example 9 the value of $x = 0.47$ lies within the domain $0.4 \leq x \leq 0.6$ of the interpolating polynomial, and we have *interpolated* a straight line to obtain the approximation. In Exercise 33 the value of $x = 0.47$ lies outside the domain $0.6 \leq x \leq 0.8$ of the interpolating polynomial, and we have *extrapolated* a straight line to obtain the approximation. **Extrapolation** is, in general, less accurate than interpolation, and we should use the result for the approximate value of $y(0.47)$ from Example 9 rather than that from Exercise 33.

In general, given $n + 1$ data points, we can determine the interpolating polynomial of degree n of the form

$$y = a_0 + a_1 x + a_2 x^2 + \cdots + a_n x^n$$

in a similar way, so we can fit a straight line through two points, a quadratic through three points, a cubic through four points, and so on.

Example 10

Find the interpolating quadratic polynomial for the three data points $(0.4, 1.48)$, $(0.6, 1.856)$ and $(0.8, 2.3472)$, and use it to find an approximation to the value of y at $x = 0.47$.

Solution

The three data points give rise to the system of linear equations

$$a_0 + 0.4a_1 + (0.4)^2 a_2 = 1.48,$$
$$a_0 + 0.6a_1 + (0.6)^2 a_2 = 1.856,$$
$$a_0 + 0.8a_1 + (0.8)^2 a_2 = 2.3472,$$

that is,

$$\underbrace{\begin{pmatrix} 1 & 0.4 & 0.16 \\ 1 & 0.6 & 0.36 \\ 1 & 0.8 & 0.64 \end{pmatrix}}_{\mathbf{X}} \underbrace{\begin{pmatrix} a_0 \\ a_1 \\ a_2 \end{pmatrix}}_{\mathbf{a}} = \underbrace{\begin{pmatrix} 1.48 \\ 1.856 \\ 2.3472 \end{pmatrix}}_{\mathbf{y}}.$$

Using the Gaussian elimination method to solve these equations, we find $a_0 = 1.0736$, $a_1 = 0.44$, $a_2 = 1.44$. Hence the interpolating quadratic polynomial is

$$y = 1.0736 + 0.44x + 1.44x^2.$$

So $y(0.47) = 1.598\,496$.

This value for $y(0.47)$ is fairly close to the solution found in Example 9.

Procedure 3 Polynomial interpolation

To determine the interpolating polynomial of degree n

$$y = a_0 + a_1 x + a_2 x^2 + \cdots + a_n x^n, \tag{25}$$

through $n + 1$ data points (x_i, y_i), $i = 0, 1, \ldots, n$, proceed as follows.

Solve, for the coefficients $a_0, a_1, \ldots, a_n$, the system of equations $\mathbf{Xa} = \mathbf{y}$ given by

$$\begin{pmatrix} 1 & x_0 & x_0^2 & \cdots & x_0^n \\ 1 & x_1 & x_1^2 & \cdots & x_1^n \\ \vdots & \vdots & \vdots & \vdots & \vdots \\ 1 & x_n & x_n^2 & \cdots & x_n^n \end{pmatrix} \begin{pmatrix} a_0 \\ a_1 \\ \vdots \\ a_n \end{pmatrix} = \begin{pmatrix} y_0 \\ y_1 \\ \vdots \\ y_n \end{pmatrix}. \tag{26}$$

There are a number of questions that should be asked at this stage.

- *Will we always obtain a unique polynomial?*
  The answer is yes, provided that all the x_i values are different.

Table 1 provides only an approximate solution to the differential equation at the specified values of x, and this illustrates a case where the initial data do not represent values of the 'true' function. The accuracy of the interpolated values is then limited by the accuracy of the values of y.

- *How accurate is any estimate obtained from an interpolating polynomial?*

  This depends on the accuracy of the data. For accurate data, it is often sufficient to obtain interpolating polynomials of increasing degree and then to look for consistency in the estimates. Estimates for values of x close to the data points are likely to be more accurate than those that are further away from the data points. Interpolation is, in general, more accurate than extrapolation.

- *What degree polynomial should we use?*

  This again depends on the accuracy of the data. In theory, if the data are very accurate, then we can use polynomials of high degree. In practice, high-degree interpolating polynomials often oscillate rapidly, which may cause difficulties. A sensible strategy is to start with a low-degree polynomial and increase the degree while looking for an appropriate level of consistency in the estimates.

- *Which points should we use?*

  The best strategy, when using an interpolating polynomial of degree n, is to select the $n + 1$ points that are closest to the value of x for which you want to estimate the value of the underlying function. Unfortunately, if you need estimates at several different points, this might involve calculating several different interpolating polynomials of degree n, each based on a different subset of $n + 1$ points selected from the data points. A sensible compromise might be to use a different interpolating polynomial of degree n for each subinterval $x_i \leq x \leq x_{i+1}$, based on the $n + 1$ data points closest to this subinterval.

Exercise 34

Determine the quadratic polynomial that passes through the data points $(0.2, 1.2)$, $(0.4, 1.48)$ and $(0.6, 1.856)$ from Table 1. Use it to estimate the solution of the initial-value problem $dy/dx = x + y$, $y(0) = 1$ at $x = 0.47$. Is this estimate likely to be more accurate than that found in Example 10?

---

4 Ill-conditioning

Such changes 'perturb' the data.

Problems that are not ill-conditioned are said to be **well-conditioned**.

In this section we briefly examine a difficulty that may occur when we attempt to find the numerical solution to a given problem. This arises because some problems are inherently unstable in the sense that very small changes to the input data (due perhaps to experimental errors or rounding errors) may dramatically alter the output numerical values. Such problems are said to be **ill-conditioned**.

We use examples to help us to define what we mean by ill-conditioning for a system of linear equations $\mathbf{Ax} = \mathbf{b}$. A proper analysis of ill-conditioning for such a system would include a discussion of the effect of small changes to the coefficient matrix $\mathbf{A}$, but to simplify the theory, we discuss only the effect of small changes to the right-hand-side vector $\mathbf{b}$, and we assume that $\mathbf{A}$ is exact.

In earlier modules, we introduced the idea of *absolute error*: for real numbers, the error in an estimate $\overline{x}$ of the exact value x is $\overline{x} - x$, and the absolute error is $|\overline{x} - x|$. We need to extend this idea to vectors. There are a number of ways of doing this; we do it by defining the **norm of a vector** $\mathbf{x} = (x_1 \quad x_2 \quad \ldots \quad x_n)^T$ as the magnitude of the element of largest magnitude in $\mathbf{x}$. Thus the norm of $\mathbf{x}$, using the notation $\|\mathbf{x}\|$, is

$$\|\mathbf{x}\| = \max_{i=1,\ldots,n} |x_i|.$$

For example, if $\mathbf{x} = (2 \quad -3 \quad 1)^T$, then $\|\mathbf{x}\| = \max\{2, 3, 1\} = 3$.

Suppose that we have two vectors, $\mathbf{x}$ and $\overline{\mathbf{x}}$, where $\overline{\mathbf{x}}$ is an estimate of the exact vector $\mathbf{x}$. The **change** in $\mathbf{x}$ is $\delta\mathbf{x} = \overline{\mathbf{x}} - \mathbf{x}$, and the **absolute change** is $\|\delta\mathbf{x}\| = \|\overline{\mathbf{x}} - \mathbf{x}\|$.

> See the Handbook.
>
> Note that $\overline{x}$ here denotes the estimate of x, *not* the complex conjugate.

> We prefer to discuss changes here rather than errors, since we are making small changes to the data to see the effect on the solution.

Example 11

Suppose that $\mathbf{x} = (2 \quad -3 \quad 1)^T$ and that $\overline{\mathbf{x}} = (2.02 \quad -3.11 \quad 1.03)^T$ is an approximation to $\mathbf{x}$. Compute the change and the absolute change in $\mathbf{x}$.

Solution

The change is $\delta\mathbf{x} = \overline{\mathbf{x}} - \mathbf{x} = (0.02 \quad -0.11 \quad 0.03)^T$.

The absolute change is $\|\delta\mathbf{x}\| = \max\{0.02, 0.11, 0.03\} = 0.11$.

Exercise 35

Determine the absolute change in the approximation $\overline{\mathbf{x}} = (3.04 \quad 2.03 \quad 0.95)^T$ to the exact vector $\mathbf{x} = (3 \quad 2 \quad 1)^T$.

In discussing ill-conditioning, we are interested in the solution $\mathbf{x}$ of the equation

$$\mathbf{Ax} = \mathbf{b},$$

and, in particular, in how small changes in $\mathbf{b}$ give rise to changes in $\mathbf{x}$. The solution may be written as $\mathbf{x} = \mathbf{A}^{-1}\mathbf{b}$, which we can regard as a linear transformation of $\mathbf{b}$ to $\mathbf{x}$. If we allow each element of $\mathbf{b}$ to change by the small amount $\pm\varepsilon$, forming the vector $\overline{\mathbf{b}} = \mathbf{b} + \delta\mathbf{b}$, then the solution that we obtain will be $\overline{\mathbf{x}} = \mathbf{A}^{-1}(\mathbf{b} + \delta\mathbf{b})$, where the change is

> We assume that $\mathbf{A}$ is invertible.

$$\delta\mathbf{x} = \overline{\mathbf{x}} - \mathbf{x} = \mathbf{A}^{-1}(\mathbf{b} + \delta\mathbf{b}) - \mathbf{A}^{-1}\mathbf{b} = \mathbf{A}^{-1}\delta\mathbf{b}. \tag{27}$$

If $\|\delta\mathbf{x}\|$ is large compared to $\|\delta\mathbf{b}\|$, then we know that the system of equations is ill-conditioned.

Example 12

Consider the equation

$$\begin{pmatrix} 1 & -2 \\ 1 & -1.9 \end{pmatrix} \mathbf{x} = \begin{pmatrix} -1 \\ -0.8 \end{pmatrix}. \tag{28}$$

If the values on the right-hand side are changed by ± 0.1, how big a change in the solution might arise?

Solution

We have

$$\mathbf{A} = \begin{pmatrix} 1 & -2 \\ 1 & -1.9 \end{pmatrix} \quad \text{and} \quad \mathbf{b} = \begin{pmatrix} -1 \\ -0.8 \end{pmatrix}, \quad \text{so} \quad \mathbf{A}^{-1} = \begin{pmatrix} -19 & 20 \\ -10 & 10 \end{pmatrix}.$$

Thus the solution of equation (28) is

$$\mathbf{x} = \begin{pmatrix} -19 & 20 \\ -10 & 10 \end{pmatrix} \begin{pmatrix} -1 \\ -0.8 \end{pmatrix} = \begin{pmatrix} 3 \\ 2 \end{pmatrix}.$$

Now taking $\varepsilon = 0.1$, the possible values for $\overline{\mathbf{b}}$ are

$$\begin{pmatrix} -1.1 \\ -0.9 \end{pmatrix}, \quad \begin{pmatrix} -1.1 \\ -0.7 \end{pmatrix}, \quad \begin{pmatrix} -0.9 \\ -0.9 \end{pmatrix}, \quad \begin{pmatrix} -0.9 \\ -0.7 \end{pmatrix},$$

with corresponding values for $\delta \mathbf{b}$

$$\begin{pmatrix} -0.1 \\ -0.1 \end{pmatrix}, \quad \begin{pmatrix} -0.1 \\ 0.1 \end{pmatrix}, \quad \begin{pmatrix} 0.1 \\ -0.1 \end{pmatrix}, \quad \begin{pmatrix} 0.1 \\ 0.1 \end{pmatrix}.$$

Note that $\|\delta \mathbf{b}\| = 0.1$ for each of these vectors.

Applying $\mathbf{A}^{-1}$ to each $\delta \mathbf{b}$ yields, respectively, the following values of $\delta \mathbf{x}$:

$$\begin{pmatrix} -0.1 \\ 0 \end{pmatrix}, \quad \begin{pmatrix} 3.9 \\ 2 \end{pmatrix}, \quad \begin{pmatrix} -3.9 \\ -2 \end{pmatrix}, \quad \begin{pmatrix} 0.1 \\ 0 \end{pmatrix}.$$

Looking at the norm of $\delta \mathbf{x}$ in each case, we see that the middle two vectors have

$$\|\delta \mathbf{x}\| = 3.9,$$

which is 39 times bigger than the norm of $\delta \mathbf{b}$. Thus a change of magnitude 0.1 in the elements of $\mathbf{b}$ may cause a change of magnitude 3.9 in the elements of the solution.

A geometric interpretation will help to make this clearer. If, in Example 12, we change the elements of $\mathbf{b}$ by ± 0.1, then the changed vector $\overline{\mathbf{b}}$ lies at a corner of the square with centre $\mathbf{b} = (-1 \quad -0.8)^T$ shown in Figure 9.

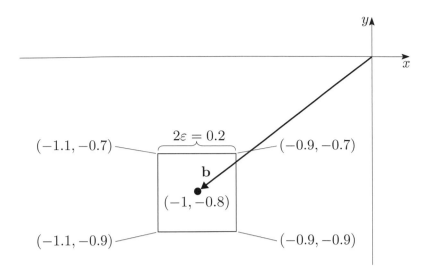

Figure 9   Changing elements of vector **b** to $\overline{\mathbf{b}}$, which lies at a corner of the square (not to scale)

Such a point $\overline{\mathbf{b}}$ is mapped to a point $\overline{\mathbf{x}}$ under the linear transformation represented by $\mathbf{A}^{-1}$, that is, $\overline{\mathbf{x}} = \mathbf{A}^{-1}\overline{\mathbf{b}}$, so the point $\overline{\mathbf{x}}$ must lie at a vertex of the parallelogram shown in Figure 10. (You saw in Subsection 2.2 how linear transformations map squares to parallelograms.)

Vector positions for the vertices of the parallelogram are $\mathbf{b} + \delta\mathbf{b}$, namely $\begin{pmatrix} 3 \\ 2 \end{pmatrix} \pm \begin{pmatrix} 3.9 \\ 2 \end{pmatrix}$ and $\begin{pmatrix} 3 \\ 2 \end{pmatrix} \pm \begin{pmatrix} 0.1 \\ 0 \end{pmatrix}$.

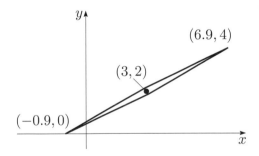

Figure 10   Transformation of the square in Figure 9

The greatest change in $\mathbf{x}$ occurs when $\overline{\mathbf{x}}$ is at a vertex furthest from (the exact solution) $\mathbf{x} = (3 \quad 2)^T$ in Figure 10, in other words either at $\overline{\mathbf{x}} = (6.9 \quad 4)^T$ or at $\overline{\mathbf{x}} = (-0.9 \quad 0)^T$.

The vertex $\overline{\mathbf{x}} = (6.9 \quad 4)^T$ arises from choosing $\overline{\mathbf{b}} = (-1.1 \quad -0.7)^T$, and $\overline{\mathbf{x}} = (-0.9 \quad 0)^T$ arises from choosing $\overline{\mathbf{b}} = (-0.9 \quad -0.9)^T$.

In either case, $\|\delta\mathbf{x}\| = \|\overline{\mathbf{x}} - \mathbf{x}\| = 3.9$, as we have seen. So here we have a situation in which a numerical change of 0.1 in the elements of **b** has caused a change of 3.9 in an element of the solution. We would certainly regard such a system of equations as ill-conditioned. It is the ratio of $\|\delta\mathbf{x}\|$ to $\|\delta\mathbf{b}\|$ that is relevant here. In this instance, we have found a point $\overline{\mathbf{b}}$ and its image $\overline{\mathbf{x}}$ for which this ratio is $3.9/0.1 = 39$ (a rather large number). Once we have found one instance of $\overline{\mathbf{b}}$ for which the ratio is large, we say that the system of equations is ill-conditioned.

We define the **absolute condition number** k_a for the problem of solving $\mathbf{Ax} = \mathbf{b}$, when $\mathbf{b}$ is subject to small changes of up to ε in magnitude, to be the largest possible value of the ratio of $\|\delta\mathbf{x}\|$ to $\|\delta\mathbf{b}\|$, that is,

$$k_a = \max_{\|\delta\mathbf{b}\| \leq \varepsilon} \frac{\|\delta\mathbf{x}\|}{\|\delta\mathbf{b}\|}.$$

We do not prove this here.

Because $\mathbf{A}^{-1}$ represents a linear transformation, this largest value occurs when the perturbed vector $\overline{\mathbf{b}}$ lies at a corner of the square of side 2ε centred on $\mathbf{b}$. In the example above, we have shown that $k_a = 39$, which tells us that the system of equations is *absolutely ill-conditioned*.

We will discuss methods of determining k_a and specific criteria for absolute ill-conditioning shortly.

The cause of the ill-conditioning can be deduced by a re-examination of equation (28). Solving this equation corresponds to finding the point of intersection of the two lines $x - 2y = -1$ and $x - 1.9y = -0.8$. These lines are almost parallel, so a small change in $\mathbf{b}$ can give rise to a large change in the solution.

These ideas can be applied to many problems other than those involving systems of linear equations.

Criteria for absolute ill-conditioning

Alternatively, we can think of small errors or uncertainties in the data giving rise to significantly larger errors or uncertainties in the solution.

Suppose that small changes are made in the data for a problem. The problem is **absolutely ill-conditioned** if it is possible for the absolute change in the solution to be significantly larger than the absolute change in the data.

Usually, the interpretation of *significantly larger* is dependent on the context. However, for the sake of clarity and certainty, we adopt the following module convention. A problem is judged to be:

- absolutely well-conditioned if the absolute condition number k_a for the problem is less than 5

Different numbers might be more appropriate for large systems of equations, but 5 and 10 are suitable choices for systems of two or three linear equations.

- neither absolutely well-conditioned nor absolutely ill-conditioned if k_a is greater than 5 but less than 10

- absolutely ill-conditioned if k_a is greater than 10.

Changes that we have not tried might cause significantly larger changes in the solution.

For very large systems of equations, we may try to detect ill-conditioning by making small changes in the data. If, for the changes that we try, the changes in the solution remain small, then we can say only that we have found *no evidence of ill-conditioning* and that the problem *may* be well-conditioned. For small systems of equations, however, where it is feasible to compute the inverse matrix $\mathbf{A}^{-1}$, we can give a much better way of detecting ill-conditioning or well-conditioning.

From equation (27) we have

$$\delta\mathbf{x} = \mathbf{A}^{-1}\delta\mathbf{b}.$$

Hence any change in the right-hand-side vector $\mathbf{b}$ will be multiplied by $\mathbf{A}^{-1}$ to give the change in the solution.

To see how this works, we return to the linear problem in Example 12:

$$\begin{pmatrix} 1 & -2 \\ 1 & -1.9 \end{pmatrix} \mathbf{x} = \begin{pmatrix} -1 \\ -0.8 \end{pmatrix},$$

where

$$\mathbf{A}^{-1} = \begin{pmatrix} -19 & 20 \\ -10 & 10 \end{pmatrix}.$$

The argument will be clearer if we let $\delta\mathbf{b} = (\varepsilon_1 \quad \varepsilon_2)^T$, where $\varepsilon_1 = \pm\varepsilon$ and $\varepsilon_2 = \pm\varepsilon$. Then we have

$$\delta\mathbf{x} = \mathbf{A}^{-1}\delta\mathbf{b} = \begin{pmatrix} -19 & 20 \\ -10 & 10 \end{pmatrix} \begin{pmatrix} \varepsilon_1 \\ \varepsilon_2 \end{pmatrix} = \begin{pmatrix} -19\varepsilon_1 + 20\varepsilon_2 \\ -10\varepsilon_1 + 10\varepsilon_2 \end{pmatrix}.$$

We can see that the largest element of $\delta\mathbf{x}$ takes its maximum value when $\varepsilon_1 = -\varepsilon$ and $\varepsilon_2 = \varepsilon$, giving $\delta\mathbf{x} = (39\varepsilon \quad 20\varepsilon)^T$ and $\|\delta\mathbf{x}\| = 39\varepsilon$.

Now $\|\delta\mathbf{b}\| = \varepsilon$, therefore $k_a = 39$, as we observed above. It is no coincidence that this is also the maximum row sum (i.e. the sum of the elements in a row) of the magnitudes of the elements of $\mathbf{A}^{-1}$.

Notice that the sign of ε_i is taken to be the same as that of the element of $\mathbf{A}$ that multiplies it so as to give the largest possible result for $\|\delta\mathbf{x}\|$.

This example illustrates the following result (which we do not prove here).

> **Absolute condition number of an invertible $n \times n$ matrix**
>
> The absolute condition number for small changes to the right-hand-side vector $\mathbf{b}$ in the solution of $\mathbf{Ax} = \mathbf{b}$ is given by the maximum row sum of the magnitudes of the elements of $\mathbf{A}^{-1}$, that is,
>
> $$k_a = \max_i \{|c_{i1}| + |c_{i2}| + \cdots + |c_{in}|\}, \tag{29}$$
>
> where the c_{ij} are the elements of the matrix $\mathbf{C} = \mathbf{A}^{-1}$.

Exercise 36

(a) Determine the absolute condition number for small changes to the right-hand-side vector $\mathbf{b}$ in the solution of $\mathbf{Ax} = \mathbf{b}$ when $\mathbf{A}$ and its inverse are given by

$$\mathbf{A} = \begin{pmatrix} 6 & 4 & 3 \\ 7.5 & 6 & 5 \\ 10 & 7.5 & 6 \end{pmatrix}, \quad \mathbf{A}^{-1} = \begin{pmatrix} 6 & 6 & -8 \\ -20 & -24 & 30 \\ 15 & 20 & -24 \end{pmatrix}.$$

(b) What form does $\delta\mathbf{b} = (\varepsilon_1 \quad \varepsilon_2 \quad \varepsilon_3)^T$ take, where $\varepsilon_1 = \pm\varepsilon$, $\varepsilon_2 = \pm\varepsilon$ and $\varepsilon_3 = \pm\varepsilon$, so that $\|\delta\mathbf{x}\|$ takes its maximum value? Confirm that the largest value of $\|\delta\mathbf{x}\|/\|\delta\mathbf{b}\|$ equals the absolute condition number.

In order to determine the conditioning of a problem, we have had to do what we had hoped to avoid: calculate the inverse of the matrix $\mathbf{A}$. However, this may be the price that we have to pay if we are worried that our problem may be sensitive to small changes in the data.

Note also that we have not discussed the effect of changes to the elements in **A**.

The cure for ill-conditioning is fairly drastic. We can abandon the current equations and try to find some more data – or even abandon the model.

Exercise 37

For each of the following examples, determine the absolute condition number and comment on the conditioning of the problem.

(a) $\mathbf{A} = \begin{pmatrix} 1 & 1 \\ 1 & -2 \end{pmatrix}$, $\mathbf{b} = \begin{pmatrix} 5 \\ -1 \end{pmatrix}$

(b) $\mathbf{A} = \begin{pmatrix} 1.4 & 1 \\ 2 & 1.4 \end{pmatrix}$, $\mathbf{b} = \begin{pmatrix} 3.7 \\ 5.2 \end{pmatrix}$

Learning outcomes

After studying this unit, you should be able to:

- understand how a system of linear equations can be represented using matrices
- solve 2×2 and 3×3 systems of linear equations by the Gaussian elimination method, using essential row interchanges where necessary
- add, subtract and multiply matrices of suitable sizes, and multiply a matrix by a scalar
- understand the terms transpose of a matrix, symmetric matrix, diagonal matrix, upper triangular matrix, lower triangular matrix, zero matrix, identity matrix, inverse matrix, invertible matrix and non-invertible matrix
- understand that a matrix can be used to represent a linear transformation, and know what this means geometrically for a 2×2 matrix
- find the inverse of a 2×2 matrix
- evaluate the determinant of an $n \times n$ matrix, by hand when $n = 2$ or 3, and using the Gaussian elimination method for $n > 3$
- use the determinant of a matrix to evaluate cross products, areas and volumes
- find the interpolating polynomial of degree n passing through $n + 1$ data points, by hand for $n \leq 3$
- understand what is meant by absolute ill-conditioning for a system of linear equations, and know how to determine whether a particular problem is absolutely ill-conditioned.

Solutions to exercises

Solution to Exercise 1

Stage 1(a) We eliminate x_1 using $E_2 - 5E_1$, which gives

$$-3x_2 + 7x_3 = 10, \qquad E_{2a}$$

followed by $E_3 - 4E_1$, which gives

$$-6x_2 + x_3 = 7. \qquad E_{3a}$$

Stage 1(b) We eliminate x_2 using $E_{3a} - 2E_{2a}$, which gives

$$-13x_3 = -13. \qquad E_{3b}$$

Stage 2 The solution is obtained by back substitution. From E_{3b}, we find $x_3 = 1$. Substituting this into E_{2a} gives $-3x_2 + 7 = 10$, hence $x_2 = -1$. From E_1, $x_1 - 1 - 1 = 2$, hence $x_1 = 4$. So the solution is

$$x_1 = 4, \quad x_2 = -1, \quad x_3 = 1.$$

Solution to Exercise 2

(a) $\mathbf{A}|\mathbf{b} = \begin{pmatrix} 3 & -5 & | & 8 \\ 4 & 7 & | & 11 \end{pmatrix}$

(b) $\mathbf{A}|\mathbf{b} = \begin{pmatrix} 1 & 2 & 0 & | & 3 \\ 2 & -1 & 1 & | & 1 \\ 0 & 1 & -1 & | & -1 \end{pmatrix}$

Solution to Exercise 3

The augmented matrix representing these equations is as follows.

$$\begin{pmatrix} 1 & 2 & | & 4 \\ 3 & -1 & | & 5 \end{pmatrix} \begin{matrix} \mathbf{R}_1 \\ \mathbf{R}_2 \end{matrix}$$

Stage 1 We reduce to zero the element below the leading diagonal.

$$\begin{matrix} \\ \mathbf{R}_2 - 3\mathbf{R}_1 \end{matrix} \begin{pmatrix} 1 & 2 & | & 4 \\ 0 & -7 & | & -7 \end{pmatrix} \begin{matrix} \mathbf{R}_1 \\ \mathbf{R}_{2a} \end{matrix}$$

Stage 2 The equations represented by the new matrix are

$$\begin{aligned} x_1 + 2x_2 &= 4, & E_1 \\ -7x_2 &= -7. & E_{2a} \end{aligned}$$

From E_{2a}, we find $x_2 = 1$. Substituting this into E_1, we obtain $x_1 + 2 = 4$. Hence $x_1 = 2$, giving the solution

$$x_1 = 2, \quad x_2 = 1.$$

Solution to Exercise 4

The augmented matrix representing these equations is as follows.

$$\left(\begin{array}{ccc|c} 1 & 1 & -1 & 2 \\ 5 & 2 & 2 & 20 \\ 4 & -2 & -3 & 15 \end{array}\right) \begin{array}{l} \mathbf{R}_1 \\ \mathbf{R}_2 \\ \mathbf{R}_3 \end{array}$$

Stage 1(a)   We reduce the elements below the leading diagonal in column 1 to zero.

$$\begin{array}{l} \\ \mathbf{R}_2 - 5\mathbf{R}_1 \\ \mathbf{R}_3 - 4\mathbf{R}_1 \end{array} \left(\begin{array}{ccc|c} 1 & 1 & -1 & 2 \\ 0 & -3 & 7 & 10 \\ 0 & -6 & 1 & 7 \end{array}\right) \begin{array}{l} \mathbf{R}_1 \\ \mathbf{R}_{2a} \\ \mathbf{R}_{3a} \end{array}$$

Stage 1(b)   We reduce the element below the leading diagonal in column 2 to zero.

$$\begin{array}{l} \\ \\ \mathbf{R}_{3a} - 2\mathbf{R}_{2a} \end{array} \left(\begin{array}{ccc|c} 1 & 1 & -1 & 2 \\ 0 & -3 & 7 & 10 \\ 0 & 0 & -13 & -13 \end{array}\right) \begin{array}{l} \mathbf{R}_1 \\ \mathbf{R}_{2a} \\ \mathbf{R}_{3b} \end{array}$$

Stage 2   The equations represented by the new matrix are

$$\begin{array}{rcrcl} x_1 + x_2 - & x_3 &=& 2, & \qquad E_1 \\ -3x_2 + & 7x_3 &=& 10, & \qquad E_{2a} \\ & -13x_3 &=& -13. & \qquad E_{3b} \end{array}$$

From E_{3b}, we have $x_3 = 1$. From E_{2a}, we have $-3x_2 + 7 = 10$, so $x_2 = -1$. From E_1, we have $x_1 - 1 - 1 = 2$, so $x_1 = 4$. Hence the solution is

$$x_1 = 4, \quad x_2 = -1, \quad x_3 = 1,$$

as we saw in the solution to Exercise 1. As a useful check, note via direct substitution that this solution satisfies E_2 and E_3.

Solution to Exercise 5

The graphs of the four pairs of equations are sketched below.

(a) The two lines are parallel, so there is no solution.

(b) There is one solution, at the intersection of the two lines.

(c) The two lines coincide, so there is an infinite number of solutions, consisting of all the points that lie on the line.

(d) There is one solution, at the intersection of the two lines.

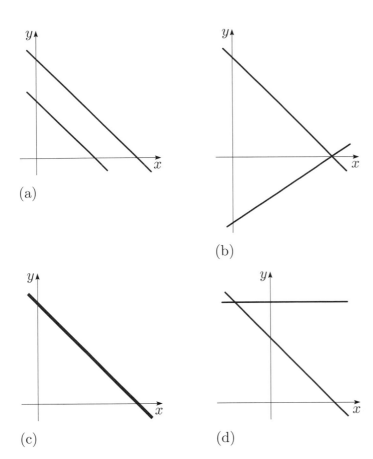

(a)

(b)

(c)

(d)

Solution to Exercise 6

For the two lines to be parallel or coincident, they must have the same slope.

If $b = 0$, the first equation becomes $ax = e$ and the line has infinite slope. Thus we must also have $d = 0$, and the second equation becomes $cx = f$. For a non-trivial solution (i.e. $a \neq 0$ and $c \neq 0$), these lines are coincident if $e/a = f/c$. The same argument applies if we start from $d = 0$.

The remaining case is when $b \neq 0$ and $d \neq 0$. Then the system of equations can be written as

$$y = -\frac{a}{b}x + \frac{e}{b},$$
$$y = -\frac{c}{d}x + \frac{f}{d}.$$

The first line has slope $-a/b$, while the second line has slope $-c/d$. Hence the two lines are parallel if

$$\frac{a}{b} = \frac{c}{d}.$$

The lines are coincident when $e/b = f/d$ also.

Solution to Exercise 7

(a) First, we write down the augmented matrix.

$$\mathbf{A}|\mathbf{b} = \begin{pmatrix} 1 & -2 & 5 & | & 7 \\ 1 & 3 & -4 & | & 20 \\ 1 & 18 & -31 & | & 40 \end{pmatrix} \begin{matrix} \mathbf{R}_1 \\ \mathbf{R}_2 \\ \mathbf{R}_3 \end{matrix}$$

Stage 1(a) We reduce the elements below the leading diagonal in column 1 to zero.

$$\begin{matrix} \\ \mathbf{R}_2 - \mathbf{R}_1 \\ \mathbf{R}_3 - \mathbf{R}_1 \end{matrix} \begin{pmatrix} 1 & -2 & 5 & | & 7 \\ 0 & 5 & -9 & | & 13 \\ 0 & 20 & -36 & | & 33 \end{pmatrix} \begin{matrix} \mathbf{R}_1 \\ \mathbf{R}_{2a} \\ \mathbf{R}_{3a} \end{matrix}$$

Stage 1(b) We reduce the element below the leading diagonal in column 2 to zero.

$$\begin{matrix} \\ \\ \mathbf{R}_{3a} - 4\mathbf{R}_{2a} \end{matrix} \begin{pmatrix} 1 & -2 & 5 & | & 7 \\ 0 & 5 & -9 & | & 13 \\ 0 & 0 & 0 & | & -19 \end{pmatrix} \begin{matrix} \mathbf{R}_1 \\ \mathbf{R}_{2a} \\ \mathbf{R}_{3b} \end{matrix}$$

Stage 2 We try to solve the equations represented by the rows of the above matrix.

Since the rows of $\mathbf{A}$ are linearly dependent but the rows of $\mathbf{A}|\mathbf{b}$ are not, there is no solution.

(b) First, we write down the augmented matrix.

$$\mathbf{A}|\mathbf{b} = \begin{pmatrix} 1 & -2 & 5 & | & 6 \\ 1 & 3 & -4 & | & 7 \\ 2 & 6 & -12 & | & 12 \end{pmatrix} \begin{matrix} \mathbf{R}_1 \\ \mathbf{R}_2 \\ \mathbf{R}_3 \end{matrix}$$

Stage 1(a) We reduce the elements below the leading diagonal in column 1 to zero.

$$\begin{matrix} \\ \mathbf{R}_2 - \mathbf{R}_1 \\ \mathbf{R}_3 - 2\mathbf{R}_1 \end{matrix} \begin{pmatrix} 1 & -2 & 5 & | & 6 \\ 0 & 5 & -9 & | & 1 \\ 0 & 10 & -22 & | & 0 \end{pmatrix} \begin{matrix} \mathbf{R}_1 \\ \mathbf{R}_{2a} \\ \mathbf{R}_{3a} \end{matrix}$$

Stage 1(b) We reduce the element below the leading diagonal in column 2 to zero.

$$\begin{matrix} \\ \\ \mathbf{R}_{3a} - 2\mathbf{R}_{2a} \end{matrix} \begin{pmatrix} 1 & -2 & 5 & | & 6 \\ 0 & 5 & -9 & | & 1 \\ 0 & 0 & -4 & | & -2 \end{pmatrix} \begin{matrix} \mathbf{R}_1 \\ \mathbf{R}_{2a} \\ \mathbf{R}_{3b} \end{matrix}$$

Stage 2 We solve the equations by back substitution.

Since the rows of $\mathbf{A}$ are linearly independent, there is a unique solution. Back substitution gives

$$x_1 = 5.7, \quad x_2 = 1.1, \quad x_3 = 0.5.$$

(c) First, we write down the augmented matrix.

$$\mathbf{A}|\mathbf{b} = \begin{pmatrix} 1 & -4 & 1 & | & 14 \\ 5 & -1 & -1 & | & 2 \\ 6 & 14 & -6 & | & -52 \end{pmatrix} \begin{matrix} \mathbf{R}_1 \\ \mathbf{R}_2 \\ \mathbf{R}_3 \end{matrix}$$

Stage 1(a)   We reduce the elements below the leading diagonal in column 1 to zero.

$$\begin{matrix} \\ \mathbf{R}_2 - 5\mathbf{R}_1 \\ \mathbf{R}_3 - 6\mathbf{R}_1 \end{matrix} \begin{pmatrix} 1 & -4 & 1 & | & 14 \\ 0 & 19 & -6 & | & -68 \\ 0 & 38 & -12 & | & -136 \end{pmatrix} \begin{matrix} \mathbf{R}_1 \\ \mathbf{R}_{2a} \\ \mathbf{R}_{3a} \end{matrix}$$

Stage 1(b)   We reduce the element below the leading diagonal in column 2 to zero.

$$\begin{matrix} \\ \\ \mathbf{R}_{3a} - 2\mathbf{R}_{2a} \end{matrix} \begin{pmatrix} 1 & -4 & 1 & | & 14 \\ 0 & 19 & -6 & | & -68 \\ 0 & 0 & 0 & | & 0 \end{pmatrix} \begin{matrix} \mathbf{R}_1 \\ \mathbf{R}_{2a} \\ \mathbf{R}_{3b} \end{matrix}$$

Stage 2   We solve the equations by back substitution.

Since the rows of $\mathbf{A}|\mathbf{b}$ are linearly dependent, there is an infinite number of solutions. Putting $x_3 = k$, back substitution gives the set of solutions

$$x_1 = (5k - 6)/19, \quad x_2 = (6k - 68)/19, \quad x_3 = k.$$

Here

$$\begin{aligned} \mathbf{R}_{3b} &= \mathbf{R}_{3a} - 2\mathbf{R}_{2a} \\ &= (\mathbf{R}_3 - 6\mathbf{R}_1) - 2(\mathbf{R}_2 - 5\mathbf{R}_1) \\ &= \mathbf{R}_3 - 2\mathbf{R}_2 + 4\mathbf{R}_1 = \mathbf{0}, \end{aligned}$$

which is the required non-trivial linear combination of the rows of $\mathbf{A}|\mathbf{b}$ that gives a row of zeros.

Solution to Exercise 8

(a) $3\mathbf{A} = \begin{pmatrix} 3 & 6 & 9 \\ 12 & 15 & 18 \end{pmatrix}, \quad -\mathbf{A} = \begin{pmatrix} -1 & -2 & -3 \\ -4 & -5 & -6 \end{pmatrix}.$

(b) $\mathbf{A} + \mathbf{B} = \begin{pmatrix} 1+1 & 2+3 & 3+7 \\ 4+4 & 5+(-5) & 6+0 \end{pmatrix} = \begin{pmatrix} 2 & 5 & 10 \\ 8 & 0 & 6 \end{pmatrix},$

$\mathbf{B} + \mathbf{C} = \begin{pmatrix} 1+(-2) & 3+1 & 7+(-6) \\ 4+(-5) & (-5)+3 & 0+3 \end{pmatrix} = \begin{pmatrix} -1 & 4 & 1 \\ -1 & -2 & 3 \end{pmatrix}.$

(c) $(\mathbf{A} + \mathbf{B}) + \mathbf{C} = \begin{pmatrix} 2 & 5 & 10 \\ 8 & 0 & 6 \end{pmatrix} + \begin{pmatrix} -2 & 1 & -6 \\ -5 & 3 & 3 \end{pmatrix} = \begin{pmatrix} 0 & 6 & 4 \\ 3 & 3 & 9 \end{pmatrix},$

$\mathbf{A} + (\mathbf{B} + \mathbf{C}) = \begin{pmatrix} 1 & 2 & 3 \\ 4 & 5 & 6 \end{pmatrix} + \begin{pmatrix} -1 & 4 & 1 \\ -1 & -2 & 3 \end{pmatrix} = \begin{pmatrix} 0 & 6 & 4 \\ 3 & 3 & 9 \end{pmatrix}.$

Thus $(\mathbf{A} + \mathbf{B}) + \mathbf{C} = \mathbf{A} + (\mathbf{B} + \mathbf{C})$.

Solution to Exercise 9

(a) $\mathbf{A} - \mathbf{B} = \begin{pmatrix} 1 & -2 \\ 7 & -3 \end{pmatrix} - \begin{pmatrix} -3 & 0 \\ 4 & -5 \end{pmatrix}$

$= \begin{pmatrix} 1 - (-3) & -2 - 0 \\ 7 - 4 & -3 - (-5) \end{pmatrix} = \begin{pmatrix} 4 & -2 \\ 3 & 2 \end{pmatrix},$

$\mathbf{B} - \mathbf{A} = \begin{pmatrix} -3 & 0 \\ 4 & -5 \end{pmatrix} - \begin{pmatrix} 1 & -2 \\ 7 & -3 \end{pmatrix}$

$= \begin{pmatrix} -3 - 1 & 0 - (-2) \\ 4 - 7 & -5 - (-3) \end{pmatrix} = \begin{pmatrix} -4 & 2 \\ -3 & -2 \end{pmatrix}.$

(b) From part (a) we have $\mathbf{B} - \mathbf{A} = -(\mathbf{A} - \mathbf{B})$.

Solution to Exercise 10

(a) $2\mathbf{A} - 5\mathbf{B} = \begin{pmatrix} 2 & 4 & 6 \\ 8 & 10 & 12 \end{pmatrix} - \begin{pmatrix} 5 & 15 & 35 \\ 20 & -25 & 0 \end{pmatrix} = \begin{pmatrix} -3 & -11 & -29 \\ -12 & 35 & 12 \end{pmatrix}.$

(b) $3(\mathbf{A} + \mathbf{B}) = 3 \begin{pmatrix} 2 & 5 & 10 \\ 8 & 0 & 6 \end{pmatrix} = \begin{pmatrix} 6 & 15 & 30 \\ 24 & 0 & 18 \end{pmatrix},$

$3\mathbf{A} + 3\mathbf{B} = \begin{pmatrix} 3 & 6 & 9 \\ 12 & 15 & 18 \end{pmatrix} + \begin{pmatrix} 3 & 9 & 21 \\ 12 & -15 & 0 \end{pmatrix} = \begin{pmatrix} 6 & 15 & 30 \\ 24 & 0 & 18 \end{pmatrix}.$

Thus $3(\mathbf{A} + \mathbf{B}) = 3\mathbf{A} + 3\mathbf{B}$.

Solution to Exercise 11

(a) $\begin{pmatrix} 1 & 2 \\ 2 & -3 \end{pmatrix} \begin{pmatrix} 1 & 3 \\ 2 & -1 \end{pmatrix} = \begin{pmatrix} 5 & 1 \\ -4 & 9 \end{pmatrix}.$

(b) $\begin{pmatrix} 2 & 1 \end{pmatrix} \begin{pmatrix} 1 & 6 \\ 0 & 2 \end{pmatrix} = \begin{pmatrix} 2 & 14 \end{pmatrix}.$

(c) $\begin{pmatrix} 1 \\ 2 \end{pmatrix} \begin{pmatrix} 3 & 0 & -4 \end{pmatrix} = \begin{pmatrix} 3 & 0 & -4 \\ 6 & 0 & -8 \end{pmatrix}.$

(d) $\begin{pmatrix} 3 & 1 & 2 \\ 0 & 5 & 1 \end{pmatrix} \begin{pmatrix} -2 & 0 & 1 \\ 1 & 3 & 0 \\ 4 & 1 & -1 \end{pmatrix} = \begin{pmatrix} 3 & 5 & 1 \\ 9 & 16 & -1 \end{pmatrix}.$

(e) The product does not exist, because the left-hand matrix has only 1 column, whereas the right-hand matrix has 2 rows.

Solution to Exercise 12

$$\mathbf{Ax} = \begin{pmatrix} 3 & -1 & 5 \\ 6 & 4 & 7 \\ 2 & -3 & 0 \end{pmatrix} \begin{pmatrix} x_1 \\ x_2 \\ x_3 \end{pmatrix} = \begin{pmatrix} 3x_1 - x_2 + 5x_3 \\ 6x_1 + 4x_2 + 7x_3 \\ 2x_1 - 3x_2 \end{pmatrix}.$$

The two matrices $\mathbf{Ax}$ and $\mathbf{b}$ are equal only if

$3x_1 - x_2 + 5x_3 = 2,$
$6x_1 + 4x_2 + 7x_3 = 5,$
$2x_1 - 3x_2 = 6.$

Hence the equation $\mathbf{Ax} = \mathbf{b}$ is equivalent to the system of equations.

Solution to Exercise 13

(a) $\quad \mathbf{AB} = \begin{pmatrix} 1 & 1 \\ 3 & 2 \end{pmatrix} \begin{pmatrix} 1 & 4 \\ 2 & 1 \end{pmatrix} = \begin{pmatrix} 3 & 5 \\ 7 & 14 \end{pmatrix}$,

$\quad\quad \mathbf{BA} = \begin{pmatrix} 1 & 4 \\ 2 & 1 \end{pmatrix} \begin{pmatrix} 1 & 1 \\ 3 & 2 \end{pmatrix} = \begin{pmatrix} 13 & 9 \\ 5 & 4 \end{pmatrix}$.

Thus $\mathbf{AB} \neq \mathbf{BA}$.

(b) $\quad (\mathbf{AB})\mathbf{C} = \begin{pmatrix} 3 & 5 \\ 7 & 14 \end{pmatrix} \begin{pmatrix} 2 & 0 \\ 1 & 5 \end{pmatrix} = \begin{pmatrix} 11 & 25 \\ 28 & 70 \end{pmatrix}$,

$\quad\quad \mathbf{A}(\mathbf{BC}) = \begin{pmatrix} 1 & 1 \\ 3 & 2 \end{pmatrix} \left(\begin{pmatrix} 1 & 4 \\ 2 & 1 \end{pmatrix} \begin{pmatrix} 2 & 0 \\ 1 & 5 \end{pmatrix} \right)$

$\quad\quad\quad = \begin{pmatrix} 1 & 1 \\ 3 & 2 \end{pmatrix} \begin{pmatrix} 6 & 20 \\ 5 & 5 \end{pmatrix} = \begin{pmatrix} 11 & 25 \\ 28 & 70 \end{pmatrix}$.

Thus $(\mathbf{AB})\mathbf{C} = \mathbf{A}(\mathbf{BC})$.

(c) $\quad \mathbf{A}(\mathbf{B}+\mathbf{C}) = \begin{pmatrix} 1 & 1 \\ 3 & 2 \end{pmatrix} \left(\begin{pmatrix} 1 & 4 \\ 2 & 1 \end{pmatrix} + \begin{pmatrix} 2 & 0 \\ 1 & 5 \end{pmatrix} \right)$

$\quad\quad\quad = \begin{pmatrix} 1 & 1 \\ 3 & 2 \end{pmatrix} \begin{pmatrix} 3 & 4 \\ 3 & 6 \end{pmatrix} = \begin{pmatrix} 6 & 10 \\ 15 & 24 \end{pmatrix}$,

$\quad\quad \mathbf{AB} + \mathbf{AC} = \begin{pmatrix} 1 & 1 \\ 3 & 2 \end{pmatrix} \begin{pmatrix} 1 & 4 \\ 2 & 1 \end{pmatrix} + \begin{pmatrix} 1 & 1 \\ 3 & 2 \end{pmatrix} \begin{pmatrix} 2 & 0 \\ 1 & 5 \end{pmatrix}$

$\quad\quad\quad = \begin{pmatrix} 3 & 5 \\ 7 & 14 \end{pmatrix} + \begin{pmatrix} 3 & 5 \\ 8 & 10 \end{pmatrix} = \begin{pmatrix} 6 & 10 \\ 15 & 24 \end{pmatrix}$.

Thus $\mathbf{A}(\mathbf{B}+\mathbf{C}) = \mathbf{AB} + \mathbf{AC}$.

Solution to Exercise 14

(a) $\mathbf{A}^T = \begin{pmatrix} 1 & 3 & 5 \\ 2 & 4 & 6 \end{pmatrix}$, $\quad \mathbf{B}^T = \begin{pmatrix} 2 & -1 & 3 \\ 5 & -4 & 1 \end{pmatrix}$, $\quad \mathbf{C}^T = \begin{pmatrix} 1 & 2 \\ 0 & 3 \end{pmatrix}$.

(b) $(\mathbf{A}+\mathbf{B})^T = \left(\begin{pmatrix} 1 & 2 \\ 3 & 4 \\ 5 & 6 \end{pmatrix} + \begin{pmatrix} 2 & 5 \\ -1 & -4 \\ 3 & 1 \end{pmatrix} \right)^T = \begin{pmatrix} 3 & 7 \\ 2 & 0 \\ 8 & 7 \end{pmatrix}^T = \begin{pmatrix} 3 & 2 & 8 \\ 7 & 0 & 7 \end{pmatrix}$,

$\quad \mathbf{A}^T + \mathbf{B}^T = \begin{pmatrix} 1 & 3 & 5 \\ 2 & 4 & 6 \end{pmatrix} + \begin{pmatrix} 2 & -1 & 3 \\ 5 & -4 & 1 \end{pmatrix} = \begin{pmatrix} 3 & 2 & 8 \\ 7 & 0 & 7 \end{pmatrix}$.

Thus $(\mathbf{A}+\mathbf{B})^T = \mathbf{A}^T + \mathbf{B}^T$.

(c) $(\mathbf{AC})^T = \left(\begin{pmatrix} 1 & 2 \\ 3 & 4 \\ 5 & 6 \end{pmatrix} \begin{pmatrix} 1 & 0 \\ 2 & 3 \end{pmatrix} \right)^T = \begin{pmatrix} 5 & 6 \\ 11 & 12 \\ 17 & 18 \end{pmatrix}^T = \begin{pmatrix} 5 & 11 & 17 \\ 6 & 12 & 18 \end{pmatrix}$,

$\quad \mathbf{C}^T \mathbf{A}^T = \begin{pmatrix} 1 & 2 \\ 0 & 3 \end{pmatrix} \begin{pmatrix} 1 & 3 & 5 \\ 2 & 4 & 6 \end{pmatrix} = \begin{pmatrix} 5 & 11 & 17 \\ 6 & 12 & 18 \end{pmatrix}$.

Thus $(\mathbf{AC})^T = \mathbf{C}^T \mathbf{A}^T$.

(d) From the solution to part (a), we can immediately see that $\mathbf{C}^T \neq \mathbf{C}$ and therefore $\mathbf{C}$ is not symmetric.

(e) Let $\mathbf{D} = \mathbf{CC}^T$. Then, using the rules for transposes of matrices, we have
$$\mathbf{D}^T = (\mathbf{CC}^T)^T = (\mathbf{C}^T)^T\mathbf{C}^T = \mathbf{CC}^T = \mathbf{D},$$
so $\mathbf{D} = \mathbf{CC}^T$ is a symmetric matrix.

This is true for *any* matrix $\mathbf{C}$, but we can verify that this result holds for the $\mathbf{C}$ given here since
$$\mathbf{CC}^T = \begin{pmatrix} 1 & 0 \\ 2 & 3 \end{pmatrix}\begin{pmatrix} 1 & 2 \\ 0 & 3 \end{pmatrix} = \begin{pmatrix} 1 & 2 \\ 2 & 13 \end{pmatrix},$$
which is clearly symmetric.

Solution to Exercise 15

$$\mathbf{AB} = \begin{pmatrix} 1 & 2 & 1 \\ 2 & 3 & -1 \\ 1 & -1 & 0 \end{pmatrix}\begin{pmatrix} 1 & 1 & 0 \\ 1 & 0 & 1 \\ 0 & 1 & 1 \end{pmatrix} = \begin{pmatrix} 3 & 2 & 3 \\ 5 & 1 & 2 \\ 0 & 1 & -1 \end{pmatrix},$$

so we see that $\mathbf{AB}$ is not symmetric.

$$(\mathbf{AB})^T = \begin{pmatrix} 3 & 5 & 0 \\ 2 & 1 & 1 \\ 3 & 2 & -1 \end{pmatrix},$$

$$\mathbf{B}^T\mathbf{A}^T = \mathbf{BA} = \begin{pmatrix} 1 & 1 & 0 \\ 1 & 0 & 1 \\ 0 & 1 & 1 \end{pmatrix}\begin{pmatrix} 1 & 2 & 1 \\ 2 & 3 & -1 \\ 1 & -1 & 0 \end{pmatrix} = \begin{pmatrix} 3 & 5 & 0 \\ 2 & 1 & 1 \\ 3 & 2 & -1 \end{pmatrix},$$

so $(\mathbf{AB})^T = \mathbf{B}^T\mathbf{A}^T$.

Solution to Exercise 16

(a) The matrix is upper triangular.

(b) The matrix is neither upper triangular nor lower triangular, thus cannot be diagonal.

(c) The matrix is upper triangular and lower triangular, and hence is diagonal.

Solution to Exercise 17

(a) $\mathbf{AB} = \begin{pmatrix} 2 & 1 \\ 7 & 8 \end{pmatrix}\begin{pmatrix} \frac{8}{9} & -\frac{1}{9} \\ -\frac{7}{9} & \frac{2}{9} \end{pmatrix} = \begin{pmatrix} 1 & 0 \\ 0 & 1 \end{pmatrix} = \mathbf{I}.$

Since $\mathbf{AB} = \mathbf{I}$, it follows that $\mathbf{B} = \mathbf{A}^{-1}$.

(b) $\mathbf{AB} = \begin{pmatrix} 1 & 3 & -1 \\ -2 & -5 & 1 \\ 4 & 11 & -2 \end{pmatrix}\begin{pmatrix} -1 & -5 & -2 \\ 0 & 2 & 1 \\ -2 & 1 & 1 \end{pmatrix} = \begin{pmatrix} 1 & 0 & 0 \\ 0 & 1 & 0 \\ 0 & 0 & 1 \end{pmatrix} = \mathbf{I}.$

Since $\mathbf{AB} = \mathbf{I}$, it follows that $\mathbf{B} = \mathbf{A}^{-1}$.

Solution to Exercise 18

We form the 4×2 augmented matrix.

$$\begin{pmatrix} a & b & | & 1 & 0 \\ c & d & | & 0 & 1 \end{pmatrix} \begin{matrix} \mathbf{R}_1 \\ \mathbf{R}_2 \end{matrix}$$

First, assume $a \neq 0$. Going through the stages of Procedure 2 in turn (as in Example 7), we obtain the following.

$$\mathbf{R}_2 - \frac{c}{a}\mathbf{R}_1 \begin{pmatrix} a & b & | & 1 & 0 \\ 0 & d - \frac{c}{a}b & | & -\frac{c}{a} & 1 \end{pmatrix} \begin{matrix} \mathbf{R}_1 \\ \mathbf{R}_{2a} \end{matrix}$$

$$\frac{a}{ad-bc}\mathbf{R}_{2a} \begin{pmatrix} a & b & | & 1 & 0 \\ 0 & 1 & | & -\frac{c}{ad-bc} & \frac{a}{ad-bc} \end{pmatrix} \begin{matrix} \mathbf{R}_1 \\ \mathbf{R}_{2b} \end{matrix} \qquad d - \frac{c}{a}b = \frac{ad-bc}{a}$$

$$\mathbf{R}_1 - b\mathbf{R}_{2b} \begin{pmatrix} a & 0 & | & \frac{ad}{ad-bc} & -\frac{ab}{ad-bc} \\ 0 & 1 & | & -\frac{c}{ad-bc} & \frac{a}{ad-bc} \end{pmatrix} \begin{matrix} \mathbf{R}_{1a} \\ \mathbf{R}_{2b} \end{matrix}$$

$$\frac{1}{a}\mathbf{R}_{1a} \begin{pmatrix} 1 & 0 & | & \frac{d}{ad-bc} & -\frac{b}{ad-bc} \\ 0 & 1 & | & -\frac{c}{ad-bc} & \frac{a}{ad-bc} \end{pmatrix} \begin{matrix} \mathbf{R}_{1b} \\ \mathbf{R}_{2b} \end{matrix}$$

Hence

$$\mathbf{A}^{-1} = \frac{1}{ad-bc} \begin{pmatrix} d & -b \\ -c & a \end{pmatrix}.$$

If $a = 0$, we must start by interchanging $\mathbf{R}_1$ and $\mathbf{R}_2$.

$$\mathbf{R}_1 \leftrightarrow \mathbf{R}_2 \begin{pmatrix} c & d & | & 0 & 1 \\ 0 & b & | & 1 & 0 \end{pmatrix} \begin{matrix} \mathbf{R}_{1a} \\ \mathbf{R}_{2a} \end{matrix}$$

Again, going through the stages of Procedure 2 in turn, noting that $bc \neq 0$ since $ad - bc \neq 0$, we obtain the following.

$$\frac{1}{b}\mathbf{R}_{2a} \begin{pmatrix} c & d & | & 0 & 1 \\ 0 & 1 & | & \frac{1}{b} & 0 \end{pmatrix} \begin{matrix} \mathbf{R}_{1a} \\ \mathbf{R}_{2b} \end{matrix}$$

$$\mathbf{R}_{1a} - d\mathbf{R}_{2b} \begin{pmatrix} c & 0 & | & -\frac{d}{b} & 1 \\ 0 & 1 & | & \frac{1}{b} & 0 \end{pmatrix} \begin{matrix} \mathbf{R}_{1b} \\ \mathbf{R}_{2b} \end{matrix}$$

$$\frac{1}{c}\mathbf{R}_{1b} \begin{pmatrix} 1 & 0 & | & -\frac{d}{bc} & \frac{1}{c} \\ 0 & 1 & | & \frac{1}{b} & 0 \end{pmatrix} \begin{matrix} \mathbf{R}_{1c} \\ \mathbf{R}_{2b} \end{matrix}$$

This gives the same inverse matrix as substituting $a = 0$ into the inverse matrix found earlier.

Solution to Exercise 19

(a) Since $\det \mathbf{A} = (7 \times 3) - (4 \times 5) = 1$,

$$\mathbf{A}^{-1} = \begin{pmatrix} 3 & -4 \\ -5 & 7 \end{pmatrix}.$$

(b) Since $\det \mathbf{A} = (6 \times 3) - (2 \times 9) = 0$, $\mathbf{A}^{-1}$ does not exist.

(c) Since $\det \mathbf{A} = (4 \times 3) - (2 \times 5) = 2$,

$$\mathbf{A}^{-1} = \tfrac{1}{2} \begin{pmatrix} 3 & -2 \\ -5 & 4 \end{pmatrix} = \begin{pmatrix} \frac{3}{2} & -1 \\ -\frac{5}{2} & 2 \end{pmatrix}.$$

Solution to Exercise 20

(a) We have

$$(\mathbf{B}^{-1}\mathbf{A}^{-1})(\mathbf{AB}) = \mathbf{B}^{-1}(\mathbf{A}^{-1}\mathbf{A})\mathbf{B} = \mathbf{B}^{-1}\mathbf{IB} = \mathbf{B}^{-1}\mathbf{B} = \mathbf{I}$$

and

$$(\mathbf{AB})(\mathbf{B}^{-1}\mathbf{A}^{-1}) = \mathbf{A}(\mathbf{BB}^{-1})\mathbf{A}^{-1} = \mathbf{AIA}^{-1} = \mathbf{AA}^{-1} = \mathbf{I},$$

hence $(\mathbf{AB})^{-1} = \mathbf{B}^{-1}\mathbf{A}^{-1}$.

(b) Since $\det \mathbf{A} = 2$, we have

$$\mathbf{A}^{-1} = \tfrac{1}{2} \begin{pmatrix} 5 & -2 \\ -4 & 2 \end{pmatrix} = \begin{pmatrix} \frac{5}{2} & -1 \\ -2 & 1 \end{pmatrix}.$$

Since $\det \mathbf{B} = -2$, we have

$$\mathbf{B}^{-1} = \tfrac{1}{-2} \begin{pmatrix} -2 & -4 \\ 1 & 3 \end{pmatrix} = \begin{pmatrix} 1 & 2 \\ -\frac{1}{2} & -\frac{3}{2} \end{pmatrix}.$$

(c) $$(\mathbf{A}+\mathbf{B})^{-1} = \begin{pmatrix} 5 & 6 \\ 3 & 3 \end{pmatrix}^{-1} = \tfrac{1}{-3} \begin{pmatrix} 3 & -6 \\ -3 & 5 \end{pmatrix} = \begin{pmatrix} -1 & 2 \\ 1 & -\frac{5}{3} \end{pmatrix},$$

$$\mathbf{A}^{-1}+\mathbf{B}^{-1} = \begin{pmatrix} \frac{5}{2} & -1 \\ -2 & 1 \end{pmatrix} + \begin{pmatrix} 1 & 2 \\ -\frac{1}{2} & -\frac{3}{2} \end{pmatrix} = \begin{pmatrix} \frac{7}{2} & 1 \\ -\frac{5}{2} & -\frac{1}{2} \end{pmatrix}.$$

Thus $(\mathbf{A}+\mathbf{B})^{-1} \neq \mathbf{A}^{-1}+\mathbf{B}^{-1}$.

(d) $$(\mathbf{AB})^{-1} = \left(\begin{pmatrix} 2 & 2 \\ 4 & 5 \end{pmatrix} \begin{pmatrix} 3 & 4 \\ -1 & -2 \end{pmatrix} \right)^{-1}$$

$$= \begin{pmatrix} 4 & 4 \\ 7 & 6 \end{pmatrix}^{-1} = \tfrac{1}{-4} \begin{pmatrix} 6 & -4 \\ -7 & 4 \end{pmatrix} = \begin{pmatrix} -\frac{3}{2} & 1 \\ \frac{7}{4} & -1 \end{pmatrix},$$

$$\mathbf{B}^{-1}\mathbf{A}^{-1} = \begin{pmatrix} 1 & 2 \\ -\frac{1}{2} & -\frac{3}{2} \end{pmatrix} \begin{pmatrix} \frac{5}{2} & -1 \\ -2 & 1 \end{pmatrix} = \begin{pmatrix} -\frac{3}{2} & 1 \\ \frac{7}{4} & -1 \end{pmatrix}.$$

Thus $(\mathbf{AB})^{-1} = \mathbf{B}^{-1}\mathbf{A}^{-1}$.

Solution to Exercise 21

(a) $\mathbf{A} = \begin{pmatrix} 1 & 2 \\ 3 & 4 \end{pmatrix}$.

(b) (i) $\mathbf{A} \begin{pmatrix} 3 \\ 1 \end{pmatrix} = \begin{pmatrix} 1 & 2 \\ 3 & 4 \end{pmatrix} \begin{pmatrix} 3 \\ 1 \end{pmatrix} = \begin{pmatrix} 5 \\ 13 \end{pmatrix}$.

(ii) $\mathbf{A} \begin{pmatrix} -1 \\ 1 \end{pmatrix} = \begin{pmatrix} 1 & 2 \\ 3 & 4 \end{pmatrix} \begin{pmatrix} -1 \\ 1 \end{pmatrix} = \begin{pmatrix} 1 \\ 1 \end{pmatrix}$.

(iii) $\mathbf{A} \begin{pmatrix} 0 \\ 0 \end{pmatrix} = \begin{pmatrix} 1 & 2 \\ 3 & 4 \end{pmatrix} \begin{pmatrix} 0 \\ 0 \end{pmatrix} = \begin{pmatrix} 0 \\ 0 \end{pmatrix}$.

Solution to Exercise 22

(a) In each case, the area of the parallelogram is the magnitude of det $\mathbf{A}$. (Note that in each case the parallelogram is a rectangle!)

In this case, det $\mathbf{A} = 2$.

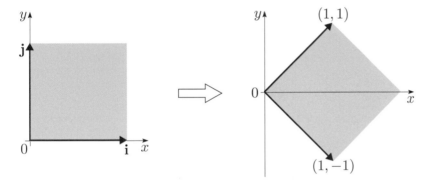

From the figure, the area of the parallelogram is the area of a square of side $\sqrt{1+1} = \sqrt{2}$. That is, the area is 2, agreeing with the value of $|\det \mathbf{A}|$.

(b) In this case, det $\mathbf{A} = -20$.

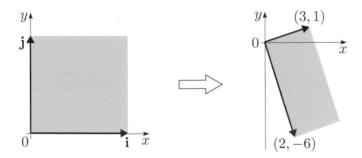

From the figure, the area of the parallelogram is the area of a rectangle with sides $\sqrt{3^2 + 1^2} = \sqrt{10}$ and $\sqrt{2^2 + (-6)^2} = \sqrt{40} = 2\sqrt{10}$. That is, the area is 20, agreeing with the value of $|\det \mathbf{A}|$.

(c) In this case, $\det \mathbf{A} = 0$.

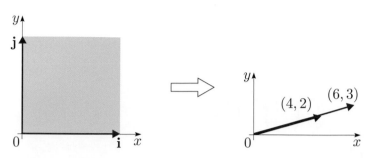

From the figure, the area of the parallelogram must be 0, because the vectors defining it are parallel. This agrees with the value of $|\det \mathbf{A}|$.

Solution to Exercise 23

$\det \mathbf{A} = 1 - (-2) = 3$ and $\mathbf{A}^{-1} = \frac{1}{3} \begin{pmatrix} 1 & -2 \\ 1 & 1 \end{pmatrix}$.

Putting $\mathbf{x} = (x \quad y)^T$ and $\mathbf{b} = (1 \quad -1)^T$, we need to solve $\mathbf{A}\mathbf{x} = \mathbf{b}$. Multiplying both sides on the left by $\mathbf{A}^{-1}$, we obtain $\mathbf{A}^{-1}\mathbf{A}\mathbf{x} = \mathbf{A}^{-1}\mathbf{b}$. This simplifies to

$$\mathbf{x} = \mathbf{A}^{-1}\mathbf{b} = \frac{1}{3} \begin{pmatrix} 1 & -2 \\ 1 & 1 \end{pmatrix} \begin{pmatrix} 1 \\ -1 \end{pmatrix} = \begin{pmatrix} 1 \\ 0 \end{pmatrix},$$

so $x = 1$ and $y = 0$.

Solution to Exercise 24

(a) $\begin{vmatrix} a & 0 \\ c & d \end{vmatrix} = \begin{vmatrix} a & b \\ 0 & d \end{vmatrix} = \begin{vmatrix} a & 0 \\ 0 & d \end{vmatrix} = ad.$

(b) $\begin{vmatrix} c & d \\ a & b \end{vmatrix} = \begin{vmatrix} b & a \\ d & c \end{vmatrix} = bc - ad = -(ad - bc) = -\det \mathbf{A}.$

(c) $\det \mathbf{A}^T = \begin{vmatrix} a & c \\ b & d \end{vmatrix} = ad - bc = \det \mathbf{A}.$

(d) $\begin{vmatrix} a & b \\ a & b \end{vmatrix} = \begin{vmatrix} a & a \\ c & c \end{vmatrix} = 0.$

(e) $\begin{vmatrix} ka & kb \\ c & d \end{vmatrix} = \begin{vmatrix} ka & b \\ kc & d \end{vmatrix} = k(ad - bc) = k \det \mathbf{A}.$

(f) $\det(k\mathbf{A}) = \begin{vmatrix} ka & kb \\ kc & kd \end{vmatrix} = k^2(ad - bc) = k^2 \det \mathbf{A}.$

(g) $\begin{vmatrix} a & b \\ c - ma & d - mb \end{vmatrix} = ad - amb - bc + bma = ad - bc = \det \mathbf{A},$

$\begin{vmatrix} a - mc & b - md \\ c & d \end{vmatrix} = ad - mcd - bc + mdc = ad - bc = \det \mathbf{A}.$

(h) From part (f) with $k = (ad - bc)^{-1}$, we have

$$\det \mathbf{A}^{-1} = \begin{vmatrix} \dfrac{d}{ad-bc} & -\dfrac{b}{ad-bc} \\ -\dfrac{c}{ad-bc} & \dfrac{a}{ad-bc} \end{vmatrix}$$

$$= \frac{1}{(ad-bc)^2} \begin{vmatrix} d & -b \\ -c & a \end{vmatrix}$$

$$= \frac{1}{ad-bc}$$

$$= \frac{1}{\det \mathbf{A}}.$$

Solution to Exercise 25

(a) $\begin{vmatrix} 4 & 1 & 0 \\ 0 & 2 & -1 \\ 2 & 3 & 1 \end{vmatrix} = 4\begin{vmatrix} 2 & -1 \\ 3 & 1 \end{vmatrix} - 1\begin{vmatrix} 0 & -1 \\ 2 & 1 \end{vmatrix} + 0\begin{vmatrix} 0 & 2 \\ 2 & 3 \end{vmatrix}$

$$= (4 \times 5) - (1 \times 2) + 0$$
$$= 18.$$

(b) $\begin{vmatrix} 1 & 2 & 3 \\ 4 & 5 & 6 \\ 7 & 8 & 9 \end{vmatrix} = 1\begin{vmatrix} 5 & 6 \\ 8 & 9 \end{vmatrix} - 2\begin{vmatrix} 4 & 6 \\ 7 & 9 \end{vmatrix} + 3\begin{vmatrix} 4 & 5 \\ 7 & 8 \end{vmatrix}$

$$= (1 \times (-3)) - (2 \times (-6)) + (3 \times (-3))$$
$$= -3 + 12 - 9$$
$$= 0.$$

(c) $\begin{vmatrix} 1 & 2 & 3 \\ 0 & 4 & 5 \\ 0 & 0 & 6 \end{vmatrix} = 1\begin{vmatrix} 4 & 5 \\ 0 & 6 \end{vmatrix} - 2\begin{vmatrix} 0 & 5 \\ 0 & 6 \end{vmatrix} + 3\begin{vmatrix} 0 & 4 \\ 0 & 0 \end{vmatrix}$

$$= (1 \times 24) - (2 \times 0) + (3 \times 0)$$
$$= 24.$$

Solution to Exercise 26

(a) Expanding by the second row, we have

$$\begin{vmatrix} 2 & 1 & 3 \\ 0 & 2 & 1 \\ 3 & 1 & 6 \end{vmatrix} = -0\begin{vmatrix} 1 & 3 \\ 1 & 6 \end{vmatrix} + 2\begin{vmatrix} 2 & 3 \\ 3 & 6 \end{vmatrix} - 1\begin{vmatrix} 2 & 1 \\ 3 & 1 \end{vmatrix}$$

$$= (2 \times 3) - (1 \times (-1))$$
$$= 6 + 1$$
$$= 7.$$

(b) (i) We obtain -7 (interchanging two rows).

(ii) We obtain 7 (taking the transpose).

(iii) We obtain -21 (interchanging two rows, as in part (b)(i), then multiplying column 2 by 3).

(c) Expanding by the first column, we have

$$\det \mathbf{A} = 1 \begin{vmatrix} 1 & -1 \\ 2 & 3 \end{vmatrix} - 0 \begin{vmatrix} 3 & 2 \\ 2 & 3 \end{vmatrix} + 0 \begin{vmatrix} 3 & 2 \\ 1 & -1 \end{vmatrix} = 5.$$

We obtain

$$\mathbf{U} = \begin{pmatrix} 1 & 3 & 2 \\ 0 & 1 & -1 \\ 0 & 0 & 5 \end{pmatrix},$$

then (expanding by the first column)

$$\det \mathbf{U} = 1 \begin{vmatrix} 1 & -1 \\ 0 & 5 \end{vmatrix} - 0 \begin{vmatrix} 3 & 2 \\ 0 & 5 \end{vmatrix} + 0 \begin{vmatrix} 3 & 2 \\ 1 & -1 \end{vmatrix} = 5.$$

The product of the diagonal elements of $\mathbf{U}$ is also $1 \times 1 \times 5 = 5$.

Note that $\det \mathbf{U} = \det \mathbf{A}$, which follows from rule (g) above.

Solution to Exercise 27

We have

$$\det \mathbf{A} = \begin{vmatrix} 1 & -4 & 2 \\ 3 & -2 & 3 \\ 8 & -2 & 9 \end{vmatrix} = 1 \begin{vmatrix} -2 & 3 \\ -2 & 9 \end{vmatrix} - (-4) \begin{vmatrix} 3 & 3 \\ 8 & 9 \end{vmatrix} + 2 \begin{vmatrix} 3 & -2 \\ 8 & -2 \end{vmatrix}$$

$$= -12 + 12 + 20 = 20$$

and

$$\det \mathbf{U} = \begin{vmatrix} 1 & -4 & 2 \\ 0 & 10 & -3 \\ 0 & 0 & 2 \end{vmatrix} = 1 \times 10 \times 2 = 20.$$

Thus $\det \mathbf{A} = \det \mathbf{U}$.

Solution to Exercise 28

By selecting the third column in the expansion of the determinant, we have

$$\begin{vmatrix} 1 & -2 & 0 & 3 \\ 4 & -5 & 0 & 6 \\ -2 & -1 & 10 & 4 \\ 5 & -7 & 0 & 9 \end{vmatrix} = 10 \begin{vmatrix} 1 & -2 & 3 \\ 4 & -5 & 6 \\ 5 & -7 & 9 \end{vmatrix} = 10 \begin{vmatrix} 1 & -2 & 3 \\ 5 & -7 & 9 \\ 5 & -7 & 9 \end{vmatrix} = 0,$$

where the second equality followed by adding Row 1 to Row 2, and using the rule that such an operation leaves the determinant unchanged. The final equality to zero follows from rule (d) about two linearly dependent rows.

Solution to Exercise 29

Using equation (22) and the result of Exercise 26(a),

$$\mathbf{a} \cdot (\mathbf{b} \times \mathbf{c}) = \begin{vmatrix} 2 & 1 & 3 \\ 0 & 2 & 1 \\ 3 & 1 & 6 \end{vmatrix} = 7.$$

Solution to Exercise 30

The volume is

$$\left| \det \begin{pmatrix} 1 & 0 & 1 \\ 1 & 2 & 0 \\ 0 & 1 & 3 \end{pmatrix} \right| = \left| 1 \times \det \begin{pmatrix} 2 & 0 \\ 1 & 3 \end{pmatrix} - 0 \times \det \begin{pmatrix} 1 & 0 \\ 0 & 3 \end{pmatrix} + 1 \times \det \begin{pmatrix} 1 & 2 \\ 0 & 1 \end{pmatrix} \right|$$

$$= \left| (1 \times 6) - 0 + (1 \times 1) \right| = 7.$$

Solution to Exercise 31

(a)
$$\mathbf{b} \times \mathbf{c} = \begin{vmatrix} \mathbf{i} & \mathbf{j} & \mathbf{k} \\ 3 & 2 & -4 \\ 1 & -1 & 3 \end{vmatrix}$$

$$= \begin{vmatrix} 2 & -4 \\ -1 & 3 \end{vmatrix} \mathbf{i} - \begin{vmatrix} 3 & -4 \\ 1 & 3 \end{vmatrix} \mathbf{j} + \begin{vmatrix} 3 & 2 \\ 1 & -1 \end{vmatrix} \mathbf{k}$$

$$= 2\mathbf{i} - 13\mathbf{j} - 5\mathbf{k}.$$

(b)
$$\mathbf{b} \times \mathbf{c} = \begin{vmatrix} \mathbf{i} & \mathbf{j} & \mathbf{k} \\ 1 & 2 & 3 \\ 6 & 5 & 4 \end{vmatrix}$$

$$= \begin{vmatrix} 2 & 3 \\ 5 & 4 \end{vmatrix} \mathbf{i} - \begin{vmatrix} 1 & 3 \\ 6 & 4 \end{vmatrix} \mathbf{j} + \begin{vmatrix} 1 & 2 \\ 6 & 5 \end{vmatrix} \mathbf{k}$$

$$= -7\mathbf{i} + 14\mathbf{j} - 7\mathbf{k}.$$

Solution to Exercise 32

The area is

$$\frac{1}{2} \left| \det \begin{pmatrix} 1 & 1 & 1 \\ 3 & 1 & 2 \\ 1 & 2 & -1 \end{pmatrix} \right| = \frac{1}{2} \left| 1 \times \det \begin{pmatrix} 1 & 2 \\ 2 & -1 \end{pmatrix} - 1 \times \det \begin{pmatrix} 3 & 2 \\ 1 & -1 \end{pmatrix} \right.$$

$$\left. + 1 \times \det \begin{pmatrix} 3 & 1 \\ 1 & 2 \end{pmatrix} \right|$$

$$= \frac{1}{2} |-5 + 5 + 5| = 2.5.$$

Solution to Exercise 33

Suppose that the line is $y = a_0 + a_1 x$, so the interpolation equations are

$$a_0 + 0.6a_1 = 1.856,$$
$$a_0 + 0.8a_1 = 2.3472.$$

The solution of this pair of equations is $a_0 = 0.3824$ and $a_1 = 2.456$, so the equation of the interpolating straight line is

$$y = 0.3824 + 2.456x.$$

Thus $y(0.65) = 1.9788$ and $y(0.47) = 1.53672$.

Solution to Exercise 34

Suppose that the quadratic is $y = a_0 + a_1 x + a_2 x^2$, so the interpolation equations are

$$a_0 + 0.2a_1 + (0.2)^2 a_2 = 1.2,$$
$$a_0 + 0.4a_1 + (0.4)^2 a_2 = 1.48,$$
$$a_0 + 0.6a_1 + (0.6)^2 a_2 = 1.856.$$

The augmented matrix form of these equations is

$$\mathbf{X}|\mathbf{y} = \begin{pmatrix} 1 & 0.2 & 0.04 & \bigm| & 1.2 \\ 1 & 0.4 & 0.16 & \bigm| & 1.48 \\ 1 & 0.6 & 0.36 & \bigm| & 1.856 \end{pmatrix}.$$

After Stage 1 of the Gaussian elimination method, we have

$$\mathbf{U}|\mathbf{c} = \begin{pmatrix} 1 & 0.2 & 0.04 & \bigm| & 1.2 \\ 0 & 0.2 & 0.12 & \bigm| & 0.28 \\ 0 & 0 & 0.08 & \bigm| & 0.096 \end{pmatrix}.$$

Back substitution gives $\mathbf{a} = (1.016 \quad 0.68 \quad 1.2)^T$, so the equation of the interpolating quadratic is

$$y = 1.016 + 0.68x + 1.2x^2.$$

This gives $y(0.47) = 1.600\,68$. This estimate is very close to the value $1.598\,496$ obtained in Example 10. However, since the three points closest to $x = 0.47$ are 0.2, 0.4 and 0.6, the value $1.600\,68$ would be regarded as the most reliable of the four estimates that we have computed, in Examples 9 and 10, and Exercises 33 and 34.

Solution to Exercise 35

The change in $\mathbf{x}$ is

$$\delta\mathbf{x} = \overline{\mathbf{x}} - \mathbf{x} = (0.04 \quad 0.03 \quad -0.05)^T,$$

so the absolute change is

$$\|\delta\mathbf{x}\| = 0.05.$$

Solution to Exercise 36

(a) The row sums of the magnitudes of the elements of $\mathbf{A}^{-1}$ are 20, 74 and 59. Hence the absolute condition number is $k_a = 74$.

(b) Now,

$$\delta\mathbf{x} = \mathbf{A}^{-1}\delta\mathbf{b} = \begin{pmatrix} 6 & 6 & -8 \\ -20 & -24 & 30 \\ 15 & 20 & -24 \end{pmatrix} \begin{pmatrix} \varepsilon_1 \\ \varepsilon_2 \\ \varepsilon_3 \end{pmatrix}$$
$$= \begin{pmatrix} 6\varepsilon_1 + 6\varepsilon_2 - 8\varepsilon_3 \\ -20\varepsilon_1 - 24\varepsilon_2 + 30\varepsilon_3 \\ 15\varepsilon_1 + 20\varepsilon_2 - 24\varepsilon_3 \end{pmatrix}.$$

From this we can see that the largest element of $\delta\mathbf{x}$ takes its maximum value when $\varepsilon_1 = -\varepsilon$, $\varepsilon_2 = -\varepsilon$ and $\varepsilon_3 = \varepsilon$, so that $\delta\mathbf{b}$ takes the form

$$\delta\mathbf{b} = (-\varepsilon \quad -\varepsilon \quad \varepsilon)^T.$$

This gives $\delta\mathbf{x} = (-20\varepsilon \quad 74\varepsilon \quad -59\varepsilon)^T$, so $\|\delta\mathbf{x}\| = 74\varepsilon$. Since $\|\delta\mathbf{b}\| = \varepsilon$, the maximum value of $\|\delta\mathbf{x}\|/\|\delta\mathbf{b}\|$ is 74, as required.

Solution to Exercise 37

(a) The inverse matrix is

$$\mathbf{A}^{-1} = \begin{pmatrix} \frac{2}{3} & \frac{1}{3} \\ \frac{1}{3} & -\frac{1}{3} \end{pmatrix}.$$

The problem is absolutely well-conditioned, since $k_a = 1$.

(The solution is

$$\mathbf{x} = \mathbf{A}^{-1} \begin{pmatrix} 5 \\ -1 \end{pmatrix} = \begin{pmatrix} 3 \\ 2 \end{pmatrix},$$

though you were not asked to find it.)

(b) The inverse matrix is

$$\mathbf{A}^{-1} = \begin{pmatrix} -35 & 25 \\ 50 & -35 \end{pmatrix}.$$

The problem is absolutely ill-conditioned, since $k_a = 85$.

(The solution is

$$\mathbf{x} = \mathbf{A}^{-1} \begin{pmatrix} 3.7 \\ 5.2 \end{pmatrix} = \begin{pmatrix} 0.5 \\ 3 \end{pmatrix},$$

though you were not asked to find it.)

Unit 5

Eigenvalues and eigenvectors

Introduction

Consider the following simplified migration problem.

The towns Exton and Wyeville have a regular interchange of population: each year, one-tenth of Exton's population migrates to Wyeville, while one-fifth of Wyeville's population migrates to Exton (see Figure 1). Other changes in population, such as births, deaths and other migrations, cancel each other thus can be ignored. If x_n and y_n denote, respectively, the populations of Exton and Wyeville at the beginning of year n, then the corresponding populations at the beginning of year $n+1$ are given by

$$x_{n+1} = 0.9x_n + 0.2y_n,$$
$$y_{n+1} = 0.1x_n + 0.8y_n,$$

or, in matrix form,

$$\begin{pmatrix} x_{n+1} \\ y_{n+1} \end{pmatrix} = \begin{pmatrix} 0.9 & 0.2 \\ 0.1 & 0.8 \end{pmatrix} \begin{pmatrix} x_n \\ y_n \end{pmatrix}.$$

This is an example of an *iterative process*, in which the values associated with the $(n+1)$th iterate can be determined from the values associated with the nth iterate.

Suppose that initially the population of Exton is 10 000 and that of Wyeville is 8000, that is, $x_0 = 10\,000$ and $y_0 = 8000$. Then after one year the populations are given by

$$\begin{pmatrix} x_1 \\ y_1 \end{pmatrix} = \begin{pmatrix} 0.9 & 0.2 \\ 0.1 & 0.8 \end{pmatrix} \begin{pmatrix} 10\,000 \\ 8\,000 \end{pmatrix} = \begin{pmatrix} 10\,600 \\ 7\,400 \end{pmatrix},$$

and after two years they are given by

$$\begin{pmatrix} x_2 \\ y_2 \end{pmatrix} = \begin{pmatrix} 0.9 & 0.2 \\ 0.1 & 0.8 \end{pmatrix} \begin{pmatrix} 10\,600 \\ 7\,400 \end{pmatrix} = \begin{pmatrix} 11\,020 \\ 6\,980 \end{pmatrix};$$

we can continue this process as far as we wish, provided that the underlying assumptions do not change.

What happens in the long term? Do the populations eventually stabilise? Using a computer algebra package, we can verify that the populations after 30 years are $x_{30} = 12\,000$ and $y_{30} = 6000$. It follows that after 31 years the populations are given by

$$\begin{pmatrix} x_{31} \\ y_{31} \end{pmatrix} = \begin{pmatrix} 0.9 & 0.2 \\ 0.1 & 0.8 \end{pmatrix} \begin{pmatrix} 12\,000 \\ 6\,000 \end{pmatrix}$$
$$= \begin{pmatrix} 0.9 \times 12\,000 + 0.2 \times 6000 \\ 0.1 \times 12\,000 + 0.8 \times 6000 \end{pmatrix} = \begin{pmatrix} 12\,000 \\ 6\,000 \end{pmatrix}.$$

So if $x_{30} = 12\,000$ and $y_{30} = 6000$, then $x_{31} = x_{30}$ and $y_{31} = y_{30}$, and the sizes of the populations of the two towns do not change. Moreover, the sizes of the populations will not change in any subsequent year.

Figure 1 Population flow

A matrix such as $\begin{pmatrix} 0.9 & 0.2 \\ 0.1 & 0.8 \end{pmatrix}$ is called a *transition matrix*.

The elements of such a matrix are all non-negative, and the elements in each column sum to 1.

There are situations, such as in the above migration problem, where a particular non-zero vector does not change under a linear transformation. However, this is more the exception than the rule. It is more useful to investigate vectors that are transformed to *scalar multiples* of themselves – geometrically, this means that each such vector is transformed into another vector in the same or opposite direction. Such vectors are called *eigenvectors*, and the corresponding scalar multipliers are called *eigenvalues*.

Section 1 considers the eigenvectors and eigenvalues associated with various linear transformations of the plane. We also outline situations where eigenvectors and eigenvalues are useful.

In many problems, such as in the above migration problem, the appropriate linear transformation is given in matrix form. In Sections 2 and 3 we investigate the various types of eigenvalue that can arise for 2×2 and 3×3 matrices.

Here 'steady-state' refers to the fact that the populations no longer change.

In the migration problem, we iterated to obtain the 'steady-state' population. Section 4 uses a similar method in order to calculate the eigenvalues and eigenvectors of a matrix. Although our discussion is mainly about 2×2 and 3×3 matrices, many of the ideas can be extended to the much larger matrices that often arise from practical applications.

1 Introducing eigenvectors

We first investigate the eigenvectors and eigenvalues that arise from various linear transformations of the plane – in particular, scaling, reflection and rotation. Do not worry about how we construct the transformation matrices – that is not important. It is the geometric properties of these matrices, and the relevance of these properties to eigenvectors and eigenvalues, that are important here. Later in this section we outline another use of eigenvectors and eigenvalues.

1.1 Eigenvectors in the plane

Consider the linear transformation of the plane specified by the matrix

$$\mathbf{A} = \begin{pmatrix} 3 & 2 \\ 1 & 4 \end{pmatrix}.$$

Using matrix multiplication, we can find the image under this linear transformation of any given vector in the plane. For example, to find the image of the vector $\mathbf{v} = (2 \ \ 1)^T$, we calculate

$$\mathbf{Av} = \begin{pmatrix} 3 & 2 \\ 1 & 4 \end{pmatrix} \begin{pmatrix} 2 \\ 1 \end{pmatrix} = \begin{pmatrix} 8 \\ 6 \end{pmatrix},$$

so the required image is $(8 \ \ 6)^T$, as shown in Figure 2.

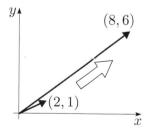

Figure 2 A linear transformation acting on the vector $(2 \ \ 1)^T$

In general, to find the image under this linear transformation of the vector $\mathbf{v} = (x \quad y)^T$, we calculate

$$\mathbf{Av} = \begin{pmatrix} 3 & 2 \\ 1 & 4 \end{pmatrix} \begin{pmatrix} x \\ y \end{pmatrix} = \begin{pmatrix} 3x + 2y \\ x + 4y \end{pmatrix},$$

so the required image is $(3x + 2y \quad x + 4y)^T$.

This is a linear transformation because each component of the vector $(3x + 2y \quad x + 4y)^T$ is a linear function of x and y. Recall the definition of a linear transformation from Subsection 2.2 of Unit 4.

Exercise 1

Find the image of each of the vectors

$$\mathbf{w} = \begin{pmatrix} 3 \\ -1 \end{pmatrix}, \quad \mathbf{x} = \begin{pmatrix} 1 \\ 1 \end{pmatrix}, \quad \mathbf{y} = \begin{pmatrix} -2 \\ 1 \end{pmatrix}, \quad \mathbf{z} = \begin{pmatrix} 0 \\ 0 \end{pmatrix}$$

under the transformation matrix $\mathbf{A} = \begin{pmatrix} 3 & 2 \\ 1 & 4 \end{pmatrix}$.

In Exercise 1 you saw that the image of $\mathbf{x} = (1 \quad 1)^T$ is $(5 \quad 5)^T$. This image is a vector in the same direction as $\mathbf{x}$, but with five times the magnitude, as shown in Figure 3. In symbols, we write this transformation as $\mathbf{Ax} = 5\mathbf{x}$.

Figure 3 The vector $(1, 1)$ is transformed to the vector $(5, 5)$

In fact, as you can easily check, *any* vector in the same direction as $\mathbf{x} = (1 \quad 1)^T$ (or in the direction opposite to $\mathbf{x}$) is transformed into another vector in the same (or opposite) direction, but with five times the magnitude, as shown in Figure 4. Non-zero vectors that are transformed to scalar multiples of themselves are called *eigenvectors*; the corresponding scalar multipliers are called *eigenvalues*. For the 2×2 matrix $\mathbf{A}$ in Exercise 1, $(1 \quad 1)^T$ is an eigenvector, with corresponding eigenvalue 5, since

$$\begin{pmatrix} 3 & 2 \\ 1 & 4 \end{pmatrix} \begin{pmatrix} 1 \\ 1 \end{pmatrix} = \begin{pmatrix} 5 \\ 5 \end{pmatrix} = 5 \begin{pmatrix} 1 \\ 1 \end{pmatrix}.$$

Similarly, since (from Exercise 1)

$$\begin{pmatrix} 3 & 2 \\ 1 & 4 \end{pmatrix} \begin{pmatrix} -2 \\ 1 \end{pmatrix} = \begin{pmatrix} -4 \\ 2 \end{pmatrix} = 2 \begin{pmatrix} -2 \\ 1 \end{pmatrix},$$

we can see that $(-2 \quad 1)^T$ is also an eigenvector, with corresponding eigenvalue 2.

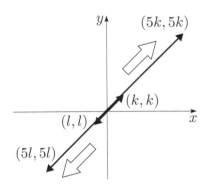

Figure 4 Any scalar multiple of $(1, 1)$ is transformed to the same scalar multiple of $(5, 5)$

Eigenvalues and eigenvectors

Let $\mathbf{A}$ be any square matrix. A non-zero vector $\mathbf{v}$ is an **eigenvector** of $\mathbf{A}$ if $\mathbf{Av} = \lambda\mathbf{v}$ for some number λ. The number λ is the corresponding **eigenvalue**.

Because $\mathbf{A}(k\mathbf{v}) = k(\mathbf{Av}) = k(\lambda\mathbf{v}) = \lambda(k\mathbf{v})$ for any scalar k, any non-zero multiple of an eigenvector is also an eigenvector with the same eigenvalue.

For example, if $\mathbf{A} = \begin{pmatrix} 3 & 2 \\ 1 & 4 \end{pmatrix}$, then for any non-zero number k, each vector $(k \quad k)^T$ is an eigenvector corresponding to the eigenvalue 5, because

$$\begin{pmatrix} 3 & 2 \\ 1 & 4 \end{pmatrix} \begin{pmatrix} k \\ k \end{pmatrix} = 5 \begin{pmatrix} k \\ k \end{pmatrix};$$

also, each vector $(-2k \quad k)^T$ is an eigenvector corresponding to the eigenvalue 2, because

$$\begin{pmatrix} 3 & 2 \\ 1 & 4 \end{pmatrix} \begin{pmatrix} -2k \\ k \end{pmatrix} = 2 \begin{pmatrix} -2k \\ k \end{pmatrix}.$$

We defined linear dependence for the rows of a matrix in Unit 4. The concept may be extended to any collection of vectors as follows.

Linear dependence and linear independence

The vectors $\mathbf{v}_1, \mathbf{v}_2, \ldots, \mathbf{v}_n$ are **linearly dependent** if a non-trivial linear combination of these vectors is equal to the zero vector, that is,

$$q_1 \mathbf{v}_1 + q_2 \mathbf{v}_2 + \cdots + q_n \mathbf{v}_n = \mathbf{0}, \tag{1}$$

where the numbers $q_1, q_2, \ldots, q_n$ are not all zero.

Vectors that are not linearly dependent are **linearly independent**.

Example 1

Consider the two-dimensional vectors

$$\mathbf{v}_1 = \mathbf{i}, \quad \mathbf{v}_2 = \mathbf{i} + \mathbf{j}, \quad \mathbf{v}_3 = 5\mathbf{i} - 3\mathbf{j}.$$

Recall that the two-dimensional Cartesian unit vectors $\mathbf{i}$ and $\mathbf{j}$ may be written as column vectors as $\mathbf{i} = (1 \quad 0)^T$ and $\mathbf{j} = (0 \quad 1)^T$.

(a) Show that $\mathbf{v}_1$ and $\mathbf{v}_2$ are linearly independent.

(b) Show that $\mathbf{v}_1$, $\mathbf{v}_2$ and $\mathbf{v}_3$ are linearly dependent.

Solution

(a) For linear dependence, we need to find q_1 and q_2, not both zero, such that $q_1 \mathbf{v}_1 + q_2 \mathbf{v}_2 = \mathbf{0}$. But

$$q_1 \mathbf{v}_1 + q_2 \mathbf{v}_2 = (q_1 + q_2)\mathbf{i} + q_2 \mathbf{j},$$

and it is not possible to find q_1 and q_2, not both zero, such that the right-hand side of this equation is equal to $\mathbf{0}$. Therefore $\mathbf{v}_1$ and $\mathbf{v}_2$ are linearly independent.

(b) We need to find q_1, q_2 and q_3, not all zero, such that $q_1 \mathbf{v}_1 + q_2 \mathbf{v}_2 + q_3 \mathbf{v}_3 = \mathbf{0}$. But

$$q_1 \mathbf{v}_1 + q_2 \mathbf{v}_2 + q_3 \mathbf{v}_3 = (q_1 + q_2 + 5q_3)\mathbf{i} + (q_2 - 3q_3)\mathbf{j}.$$

Start by choosing $q_3 = 1$. Then for the coefficient of $\mathbf{j}$ to be zero we require $q_2 = 3$, and for the coefficient of $\mathbf{i}$ to be zero we require $q_1 + 3 + 5 = 0$, so $q_1 = -8$.

Hence

$$-8\mathbf{v}_1 + 3\mathbf{v}_2 + \mathbf{v}_3 = \mathbf{0},$$

so $\mathbf{v}_1$, $\mathbf{v}_2$ and $\mathbf{v}_3$ are linearly dependent.

Example 2

Consider the three-dimensional vectors

$$\mathbf{v}_1 = \mathbf{i} + \mathbf{j} + \mathbf{k}, \quad \mathbf{v}_2 = 2\mathbf{i} + \mathbf{j} + \mathbf{k}, \quad \mathbf{v}_3 = 3\mathbf{i} + 2\mathbf{j} + 3\mathbf{k}.$$

Show that $\mathbf{v}_1$, $\mathbf{v}_2$ and $\mathbf{v}_3$ are linearly independent.

Recall that the three-dimensional Cartesian unit vectors $\mathbf{i}$, $\mathbf{j}$ and $\mathbf{k}$ may be written as column vectors as $\mathbf{i} = (1 \quad 0 \quad 0)^T$, $\mathbf{j} = (0 \quad 1 \quad 0)^T$ and $\mathbf{k} = (0 \quad 0 \quad 1)^T$.

Solution

If $\mathbf{v}_1$, $\mathbf{v}_2$ and $\mathbf{v}_3$ were linearly dependent, it would be possible to find q_1, q_2 and q_3, not all zero, such that $q_1\mathbf{v}_1 + q_2\mathbf{v}_2 + q_3\mathbf{v}_3 = \mathbf{0}$. But

$$q_1\mathbf{v}_1 + q_2\mathbf{v}_2 + q_3\mathbf{v}_3 = (q_1 + 2q_2 + 3q_3)\mathbf{i} + (q_1 + q_2 + 2q_3)\mathbf{j}$$
$$+ (q_1 + q_2 + 3q_3)\mathbf{k}.$$

It is not possible to set all the coefficients of $\mathbf{i}$, $\mathbf{j}$ and $\mathbf{k}$ to zero without having $q_1 = q_2 = q_3 = 0$. To see this, note that for the coefficient of $\mathbf{j}$ to be zero, we require $q_1 + q_2 = -2q_3$. Then for the coefficient of $\mathbf{k}$ to be zero, we require $q_1 + q_2 + 3q_3 = -2q_3 + 3q_3 = q_3 = 0$, which means that $q_1 + q_2 = -2q_3 = 0$, so $q_1 = -q_2$. Finally, for the coefficient of $\mathbf{i}$ to be zero, we require $q_1 + 2q_2 + 3q_3 = -q_2 + 2q_2 + 3 \times 0 = q_2 = 0$, hence $q_1 = -q_2 = 0$; and we already have $q_3 = 0$. Thus $\mathbf{v}_1$, $\mathbf{v}_2$ and $\mathbf{v}_3$ are linearly independent.

The nature of the eigenvectors of a matrix is closely bound to the notion of linear dependence.

Consider two (non-zero) vectors $\mathbf{v}_1$ and $\mathbf{v}_2$. If these vectors are linearly dependent, then we can write

$$q_1\mathbf{v}_1 + q_2\mathbf{v}_2 = \mathbf{0}$$

with q_1 and q_2 not both zero. If $q_1 \neq 0$, then

$$\mathbf{v}_1 = -\frac{q_2}{q_1}\mathbf{v}_2.$$

Similarly, if $q_2 \neq 0$, then

$$\mathbf{v}_2 = -\frac{q_1}{q_2}\mathbf{v}_1.$$

Thus one of the vectors is a multiple of the other.

On the other hand, if one of the vectors is a multiple of the other, say $\mathbf{v}_2 = k\mathbf{v}_1$ ($k \neq 0$), then

$$q_1\mathbf{v}_1 + q_2\mathbf{v}_2 = (q_1 + kq_2)\mathbf{v}_1,$$

and choosing $q_1 = k$, $q_2 = -1$ shows that the vectors are linearly dependent.

So we have shown that two (non-zero) vectors are linearly dependent if and only if one is a multiple of the other.

Thus the vectors $(1 \quad 1)^T$ and $(2 \quad 2)^T$ are linearly dependent, as are all the eigenvectors of the form $(k \quad k)^T$ corresponding to the eigenvalue 5 of the matrix $\mathbf{A}$ considered in Exercise 1. Similarly, all the eigenvectors of the form $(-2k \quad k)^T$ corresponding to the eigenvalue 2 of $\mathbf{A}$ are linearly dependent. However, the eigenvectors $(1 \quad 1)^T$ and $(-2 \quad 1)^T$ are linearly independent, since one is clearly not a multiple of the other.

The following exercise, concerning the eigenvectors of $\mathbf{A}$, illustrates a property of linearly independent vectors that will prove useful later.

Exercise 2

The vectors $\mathbf{v}_1 = (1 \quad 1)^T$ and $\mathbf{v}_2 = (-2 \quad 1)^T$ are linearly independent. Show that for any vector $\mathbf{v} = (x \quad y)^T$, there are numbers α and β such that $\mathbf{v} = \alpha\mathbf{v}_1 + \beta\mathbf{v}_2$. (In other words, show that any two-dimensional vector $\mathbf{v}$ can be written as a linear combination of $\mathbf{v}_1$ and $\mathbf{v}_2$.)

The result generalises further. If $\mathbf{v}_1, \mathbf{v}_2, \ldots, \mathbf{v}_n$ are any n linearly independent n-dimensional vectors and $\mathbf{v}$ is any n-dimensional vector, then we can find numbers $\alpha_1, \alpha_2, \ldots, \alpha_n$ such that

$$\mathbf{v} = \alpha_1\mathbf{v}_1 + \alpha_2\mathbf{v}_2 + \cdots + \alpha_n\mathbf{v}_n.$$

We do not prove this result here.

The result in Exercise 2 generalises to *any* two linearly independent vectors. That is, if $\mathbf{v}_1$ and $\mathbf{v}_2$ are any pair of linearly independent two-dimensional vectors and $\mathbf{v}$ is any two-dimensional vector, then we can find numbers α and β such that $\mathbf{v} = \alpha\mathbf{v}_1 + \beta\mathbf{v}_2$.

Returning to eigenvectors, we require an eigenvector to be non-zero. This is because $\mathbf{A}\mathbf{0} = \mathbf{0}$ for *every* square matrix $\mathbf{A}$, so $\mathbf{0}$ would otherwise be an eigenvector for *all* square matrices. Thus there is no point in including $\mathbf{0}$ as an eigenvector. However, it is possible for an eigenvalue to be 0. For example, if we choose $\mathbf{A} = \begin{pmatrix} 2 & 1 \\ 4 & 2 \end{pmatrix}$ and $\mathbf{v} = \begin{pmatrix} 1 \\ -2 \end{pmatrix}$, then

$$\mathbf{A}\mathbf{v} = \begin{pmatrix} 2 & 1 \\ 4 & 2 \end{pmatrix}\begin{pmatrix} 1 \\ -2 \end{pmatrix} = \begin{pmatrix} 0 \\ 0 \end{pmatrix} = 0\begin{pmatrix} 1 \\ -2 \end{pmatrix},$$

so $(1 \quad -2)^T$ is an eigenvector of $\mathbf{A}$ with eigenvalue 0.

Exercise 3

In each of the following cases, verify that $\mathbf{v}$ is an eigenvector of $\mathbf{A}$, and write down the corresponding eigenvalue.

(a) $\mathbf{A} = \begin{pmatrix} 2 & 3 \\ 2 & 1 \end{pmatrix}, \quad \mathbf{v} = \begin{pmatrix} 3 \\ 2 \end{pmatrix}$ (b) $\mathbf{A} = \begin{pmatrix} 2 & 3 \\ 2 & 1 \end{pmatrix}, \quad \mathbf{v} = \begin{pmatrix} 1 \\ -1 \end{pmatrix}$

(c) $\mathbf{A} = \begin{pmatrix} 2 & 0 \\ 1 & 2 \end{pmatrix}, \quad \mathbf{v} = \begin{pmatrix} 0 \\ 6 \end{pmatrix}$ (d) $\mathbf{A} = \begin{pmatrix} 12 & 3 \\ -8 & -2 \end{pmatrix}, \quad \mathbf{v} = \begin{pmatrix} 1 \\ -4 \end{pmatrix}$

Exercise 4

Write down an eigenvector and the corresponding eigenvalue for the matrix associated with the migration problem in the Introduction, that is,

$$\begin{pmatrix} 0.9 & 0.2 \\ 0.1 & 0.8 \end{pmatrix}.$$

Exercise 5

Show that $\begin{pmatrix} 2 \\ -3 \end{pmatrix}$ and $\begin{pmatrix} 2 \\ 3 \end{pmatrix}$ are eigenvectors of the matrix $\begin{pmatrix} 1 & 4 \\ 9 & 1 \end{pmatrix}$, and find the corresponding eigenvalues.

Very occasionally it is possible to determine information about the eigenvectors and eigenvalues of a given matrix from its geometric properties. This is so for each of the cases in Figure 5 (where the image of the unit square is used in each case to indicate the behaviour of the transformation).

The unit square has vertices $(0,0)$, $(1,0)$, $(1,1)$ and $(0,1)$.

Matrix	Comment	Transformation of the unit square	Eigenvectors	Eigenvalues
$\begin{pmatrix} 3 & 0 \\ 0 & 2 \end{pmatrix}$	A scaling by 3 in the x-direction and by 2 in the y-direction (i.e. a $(3,2)$ scaling)		$(1 \quad 0)^T$ $(0 \quad 1)^T$	3 2
$\begin{pmatrix} 1 & 0 \\ 0 & -1 \end{pmatrix}$	A reflection in the x-axis		$(1 \quad 0)^T$ $(0 \quad 1)^T$	1 -1
$\begin{pmatrix} \frac{1}{\sqrt{2}} & -\frac{1}{\sqrt{2}} \\ \frac{1}{\sqrt{2}} & \frac{1}{\sqrt{2}} \end{pmatrix}$	A rotation through $\frac{\pi}{4}$ anticlockwise about the origin		No real eigenvalues	No real eigenvectors

Figure 5 Three matrices representing transformations of the plane, together with their real eigenvectors and corresponding eigenvalues

In the case of the matrix $\begin{pmatrix} 3 & 0 \\ 0 & 2 \end{pmatrix}$, it is clear from the geometric properties of the linear transformation that vectors along the coordinate axes are eigenvectors, as these are transformed to vectors in the same directions.

In the case of the matrix $\begin{pmatrix} 1 & 0 \\ 0 & -1 \end{pmatrix}$, we see that reflection in the x-axis leaves the vector $(1 \quad 0)^T$ unchanged, and reverses the direction of $(0 \quad 1)^T$, so these must be eigenvectors.

In the third case (rotation through $\pi/4$ anticlockwise about the origin), we do not expect to find any real eigenvectors because the direction of every vector is changed by the linear transformation. Surprisingly, even this matrix has eigenvectors of a kind, namely complex ones, but we would have to adopt the algebraic approach of Section 2 in order to find them.

Exercise 6

The matrix $\mathbf{A} = \begin{pmatrix} 0 & 1 \\ 1 & 0 \end{pmatrix}$ represents reflection in a line through the origin at an angle $\pi/4$ to the x-axis. What are the eigenvectors of $\mathbf{A}$ and their corresponding eigenvalues?

(*Hint*: Find two lines through the origin that are transformed to themselves, then consider what happens to a point on each line.)

Exercise 7

The matrix $\mathbf{A} = \begin{pmatrix} -1 & 0 \\ 0 & 1 \end{pmatrix}$ represents reflection in the y-axis. Write down two eigenvectors and the corresponding eigenvalues.

(*Hint*: Find two lines through the origin that are transformed to themselves, then consider what happens to a point on each line.)

1.2 Simultaneous differential equations

We conclude this section by outlining another application of eigenvectors and eigenvalues that you will meet again in Unit 6.

Many mathematical models give rise to systems of simultaneous differential equations relating two or more functions and their derivatives. A simple case is shown in Example 3; we will discuss the relevance of eigenvectors and eigenvalues to these equations after we have solved them.

Example 3

Determine the general solution of the pair of differential equations

$\dot{x}$ is dx/dt, $\dot{y}$ is dy/dt.

$$\dot{x} = 3x + 2y, \tag{2}$$
$$\dot{y} = x + 4y, \tag{3}$$

where $x(t)$ and $y(t)$ are functions of the independent variable t.

Solution

In order to solve such a system of equations, we need to find specific formulas for x and y in terms of t.

From equation (3) we have

$$x = \dot{y} - 4y, \tag{4}$$

and differentiating this equation with respect to t gives

$$\dot{x} = \ddot{y} - 4\dot{y}. \tag{5}$$

Substituting for x and $\dot{x}$ in equation (2) using equations (4) and (5), we obtain $\ddot{y} - 4\dot{y} = 3(\dot{y} - 4y) + 2y$, which simplifies to

$$\ddot{y} - 7\dot{y} + 10y = 0.$$

The general solution of this equation is obtained by solving the auxiliary equation $\lambda^2 - 7\lambda + 10 = 0$. This has solutions $\lambda = 5$ and $\lambda = 2$, so the required general solution for y is

$$y = Ae^{5t} + Be^{2t},$$

where A and B are arbitrary constants.

It follows from equation (4) that

$$
\begin{aligned}
x &= \dot{y} - 4y \\
&= (5Ae^{5t} + 2Be^{2t}) - 4(Ae^{5t} + Be^{2t}) \\
&= Ae^{5t} - 2Be^{2t}.
\end{aligned}
$$

Thus the general solution of the system of equations is

$$\begin{cases} x = Ae^{5t} - 2Be^{2t}, \\ y = Ae^{5t} + Be^{2t}. \end{cases} \tag{6}$$

> This is a type of differential equation that you should recognise from Unit 1.

What is the connection between eigenvalues and eigenvectors, and the equations of Example 3? The differential equations (2) and (3) can be written in matrix form as

$$\begin{pmatrix} \dot{x} \\ \dot{y} \end{pmatrix} = \begin{pmatrix} 3 & 2 \\ 1 & 4 \end{pmatrix} \begin{pmatrix} x \\ y \end{pmatrix}. \tag{7}$$

The 2×2 matrix in equation (7) has eigenvectors $(1 \quad 1)^T$ and $(-2 \quad 1)^T$ with corresponding eigenvalues 5 and 2, respectively, as we saw in Subsection 1.1.

These eigenvectors and eigenvalues appear in the matrix form of the general solution given in equations (6):

$$\begin{pmatrix} x \\ y \end{pmatrix} = A \begin{pmatrix} 1 \\ 1 \end{pmatrix} e^{5t} + B \begin{pmatrix} -2 \\ 1 \end{pmatrix} e^{2t}.$$

The first term on the right-hand side involves $(1 \quad 1)^T$, an eigenvector of the matrix of coefficients $\begin{pmatrix} 3 & 2 \\ 1 & 4 \end{pmatrix}$, and a term e^{5t}, where 5 is the corresponding eigenvalue.

The second term on the right-hand side is of the same form, but it involves the other eigenvector and corresponding eigenvalue. That the general solution of a system of differential equations can be written explicitly in terms of eigenvectors and eigenvalues is no coincidence, as we will explain in Unit 6.

2 Eigenvalues and eigenvectors of 2×2 matrices

In Section 1 we considered the linear transformation of the plane specified by the matrix $\mathbf{A} = \begin{pmatrix} 3 & 2 \\ 1 & 4 \end{pmatrix}$. We saw that $(1 \quad 1)^T$ and $(-2 \quad 1)^T$ are eigenvectors of $\mathbf{A}$, with corresponding eigenvalues 5 and 2, respectively.

We did not show in Section 1 that these are the *only* possible eigenvalues of $\mathbf{A}$, nor did we show you how to find the eigenvectors and corresponding eigenvalues for an arbitrary matrix. In this section we use algebraic techniques to show you how to calculate *all* the eigenvalues and eigenvectors of any given 2×2 matrix. We also investigate the three situations that arise when the eigenvalues are:

For example:

5 and 2,

2 and 2,

i and $-i$, where $i^2 = -1$.

- distinct real numbers
- one real number repeated
- complex numbers.

Before we begin the discussion, we need to remind you of some results from Unit 4.

Often, a pair of equations with zero right-hand sides, such as

$$\begin{cases} 2x + 3y = 0, \\ x - y = 0, \end{cases} \tag{8}$$

has just one solution $x = 0$, $y = 0$. But this is not the case for every pair of equations of this type. For example, the equations

$$\begin{cases} x - 2y = 0, \\ -2x + 4y = 0, \end{cases} \tag{9}$$

have a solution $x = 2$, $y = 1$, and another solution $x = 6$, $y = 3$. In fact, $x = 2k$, $y = k$ is a solution for every value of k, that is, there is an infinite number of solutions. This is because the equations $x - 2y = 0$ and $-2x + 4y = 0$ are essentially the same equation, since either one of the equations can be obtained from the other by multiplying by a suitable factor.

Example 4

The second equation can be obtained from the first equation by multiplying it by -2.

Find a solution (other than $x = y = 0$) of the equations

$$3x - 5y = 0,$$
$$-6x + 10y = 0.$$

Solution

There is an infinite number of solutions. For example, choosing $x = 5$, we find (from either equation) that $y = 3$, which gives us a solution of the pair of equations. (Any other non-zero choice of x would give another solution.)

The general solution is $x = 5k$, $y = 3k$, for any constant k.

You saw in Unit 4 that a system of linear equations $\mathbf{Ax} = \mathbf{b}$ has a unique solution if and only if the matrix of coefficients $\mathbf{A}$ is invertible. So if the system has an infinite number of solutions, then the matrix $\mathbf{A}$ must be non-invertible.

Thus the coefficient matrix $\begin{pmatrix} 1 & -2 \\ -2 & 4 \end{pmatrix}$ of equations (9) must be non-invertible, as must be the coefficient matrix $\begin{pmatrix} 3 & -5 \\ -6 & 10 \end{pmatrix}$ of Example 4, whereas the coefficient matrix $\begin{pmatrix} 2 & 3 \\ 1 & -1 \end{pmatrix}$ of equations (8) must be invertible. Recall from Unit 4 that a matrix $\mathbf{A}$ is non-invertible if and only if $\det \mathbf{A} = 0$. You may like to check that the determinants of the first two matrices are zero, but the determinant of the last matrix is non-zero.

2.1 Basic method

We now look at a method for finding the eigenvalues and corresponding eigenvectors of an arbitrary 2×2 matrix. Consider the following example.

Example 5

Find the eigenvalues and corresponding eigenvectors of the matrix

$$\mathbf{A} = \begin{pmatrix} 3 & 2 \\ 1 & 4 \end{pmatrix}.$$

This matrix was discussed in Subsection 1.1.

Solution

We wish to find those non-zero vectors $\mathbf{v}$ that satisfy the equation

$$\mathbf{Av} = \lambda\mathbf{v}, \tag{10}$$

for some number λ. Writing $\mathbf{v} = (x \quad y)^T$, we have

$$\begin{pmatrix} 3 & 2 \\ 1 & 4 \end{pmatrix} \begin{pmatrix} x \\ y \end{pmatrix} = \lambda \begin{pmatrix} x \\ y \end{pmatrix},$$

that is, x and y must satisfy the simultaneous linear equations

$$\begin{cases} 3x + 2y = \lambda x, \\ x + 4y = \lambda y. \end{cases}$$

We are interested in only non-zero vectors $\mathbf{v}$, so x and y are not both zero. These equations will have such a solution for only certain values of λ – the eigenvalues of the matrix – and our first task is to find these values of λ. The above equations are a pair of linear equations in the unknowns x and y, where λ is a constant that has yet to be determined.

Transferring the terms λx and λy to the left-hand side, we obtain

$$\begin{cases} (3-\lambda)x + 2y = 0, \\ x + (4-\lambda)y = 0, \end{cases} \tag{11}$$

which can be written as

$$(\mathbf{A} - \lambda\mathbf{I})\mathbf{v} = \mathbf{0}. \tag{12}$$

To see this, notice that equation (10) can be rewritten as $\mathbf{A}\mathbf{v} = \lambda\mathbf{I}\mathbf{v}$ (where $\mathbf{I}$ is the 2×2 identity matrix), which in turn can be rewritten as $\mathbf{A}\mathbf{v} - \lambda\mathbf{I}\mathbf{v} = \mathbf{0}$ and hence as $(\mathbf{A} - \lambda\mathbf{I})\mathbf{v} = \mathbf{0}$.

It is convenient to refer to equations (11) as the *eigenvector equations*.

Do not lose sight of the fact that we require $\mathbf{v} \neq \mathbf{0}$. In Unit 4 we saw that if such a non-zero solution $\mathbf{v}$ exists, then the matrix $\mathbf{A} - \lambda\mathbf{I}$ in equation (12) must be non-invertible, so $\det(\mathbf{A} - \lambda\mathbf{I}) = 0$, that is,

$$\begin{vmatrix} 3-\lambda & 2 \\ 1 & 4-\lambda \end{vmatrix} = 0. \tag{13}$$

Recall that $\begin{vmatrix} a & b \\ c & d \end{vmatrix} = ad - bc.$

Our conclusion at this stage is that equation (10) can hold for only certain values of λ, and these values must satisfy equation (13). Expanding the determinant in equation (13) gives

$$(3-\lambda)(4-\lambda) - 2 = 0,$$

which simplifies to

$$\lambda^2 - 7\lambda + 10 = 0.$$

Since $\lambda^2 - 7\lambda + 10 = (\lambda - 5)(\lambda - 2)$, we deduce that $\lambda = 5$ or $\lambda = 2$.

Thus it is only when $\lambda = 5$ or $\lambda = 2$ that equation (10) has a non-zero solution $\mathbf{v}$, that is, 5 and 2 are the *only* eigenvalues of $\mathbf{A}$.

In order to find the corresponding eigenvectors, we substitute each of these eigenvalues into equations (11) and solve the resulting eigenvector equations, as follows.

The matrix $\mathbf{A} - \lambda\mathbf{I}$, i.e.
$$\begin{pmatrix} 3-\lambda & 2 \\ 1 & 4-\lambda \end{pmatrix},$$
is non-invertible, as stated above, so the equivalent eigenvector equations are linearly dependent – hence represent a *single* equation. This is equivalent to the property of non-invertible matrices having linearly dependent rows, as explained in Unit 4.

- For $\lambda = 5$, the eigenvector equations (11) become $-2x + 2y = 0$ and $x - y = 0$, and both are equivalent to the single equation $y = x$. It follows that an eigenvector corresponding to $\lambda = 5$ is $(1 \quad 1)^T$.

- For $\lambda = 2$, the eigenvector equations (11) become $x + 2y = 0$ and $x + 2y = 0$, and both are equivalent to the single equation $-2y = x$. It follows that an eigenvector corresponding to $\lambda = 2$ is $(-2 \quad 1)^T$.

Thus $(1 \quad 1)^T$ is an eigenvector of $\mathbf{A}$ with corresponding eigenvalue 5, and $(-2 \quad 1)^T$ is an eigenvector of $\mathbf{A}$ with corresponding eigenvalue 2.

In this case, the matrix $\mathbf{A}$ has two distinct eigenvalues, and these correspond to two linearly independent eigenvectors.

In Example 5 we found an eigenvector $(1 \quad 1)^T$ corresponding to the eigenvalue 5, and an eigenvector $(-2 \quad 1)^T$ corresponding to the eigenvalue 2, but these vectors are not unique. We could have chosen $(2 \quad 2)^T$ as the eigenvector corresponding to the eigenvalue 5, and $(6 \quad -3)^T$ as the eigenvector corresponding to the eigenvalue 2. However, *all* the eigenvectors corresponding to 5 are multiples of $(1 \quad 1)^T$, and *all* the eigenvectors corresponding to 2 are multiples of $(-2 \quad 1)^T$.

Thus, in a sense, $(1 \quad 1)^T$ and $(2 \quad 2)^T$ represent the 'same' eigenvector, as do $(-2 \quad 1)^T$ and $(6 \quad -3)^T$.

Exercise 8

Use the method of Example 5 to find the eigenvalues and corresponding eigenvectors of the matrix $\mathbf{A} = \begin{pmatrix} 5 & 2 \\ 2 & 5 \end{pmatrix}$.

As we will see shortly, there is a result involving the diagonal elements of a matrix that provides a useful check on calculations. To state this result succinctly, we will need the following definition.

> **Trace of a matrix**
>
> The sum of the elements on the leading diagonal of a square matrix $\mathbf{A}$ is known as the **trace** of $\mathbf{A}$ and is written as $\operatorname{tr}\mathbf{A}$.

In Example 5 we found the eigenvalues of the matrix

$$\mathbf{A} = \begin{pmatrix} 3 & 2 \\ 1 & 4 \end{pmatrix}$$

by solving the equation $\det(\mathbf{A} - \lambda\mathbf{I}) = 0$, that is,

$$\begin{vmatrix} 3 - \lambda & 2 \\ 1 & 4 - \lambda \end{vmatrix} = 0,$$

which gives a quadratic equation in λ.

More generally, we find the eigenvalues of the 2×2 matrix

$$\mathbf{A} = \begin{pmatrix} a & b \\ c & d \end{pmatrix}$$

by solving the equation $\det(\mathbf{A} - \lambda\mathbf{I}) = 0$, that is,

$$\begin{vmatrix} a - \lambda & b \\ c & d - \lambda \end{vmatrix} = 0,$$

for λ. Expanding this determinant gives

$$(a - \lambda)(d - \lambda) - bc = 0,$$

which is equivalent to the quadratic equation

$$\lambda^2 - (a + d)\lambda + (ad - bc) = 0. \tag{14}$$

Writing this equation in the form

$$(\lambda - \lambda_1)(\lambda - \lambda_2) = 0$$

gives

$$\lambda^2 - (\lambda_1 + \lambda_2)\lambda + \lambda_1\lambda_2 = 0.$$

So the roots λ_1 and λ_2 of equation (14) are the eigenvalues of $\mathbf{A}$ and satisfy

$$\lambda_1\lambda_2 = ad - bc = \det \mathbf{A} \quad \text{and} \quad \lambda_1 + \lambda_2 = a + d = \operatorname{tr} \mathbf{A}. \tag{15}$$

Equation (14) is called the **characteristic equation** of $\mathbf{A}$. Note that by combining the results in equations (15) with equation (14), the characteristic equation for the 2×2 matrix $\mathbf{A}$ can be expressed as

$$\lambda^2 - (\operatorname{tr} \mathbf{A})\lambda + \det \mathbf{A} = 0.$$

This can have distinct real roots, a repeated real root or complex roots, depending on the values of a, b, c and d. We investigate these three possibilities in the next subsection.

Using Example 5 and the above discussion as a model, we can now give the following procedures for determining the eigenvalues and eigenvectors of a given 2×2 matrix.

Procedure 1   Finding eigenvalues of a 2×2 matrix

Let $\mathbf{A} = \begin{pmatrix} a & b \\ c & d \end{pmatrix}$. To find the *eigenvalues* of $\mathbf{A}$, write down the *characteristic equation* $\det(\mathbf{A} - \lambda \mathbf{I}) = 0$. Expand this as

$$\begin{vmatrix} a - \lambda & b \\ c & d - \lambda \end{vmatrix} = \lambda^2 - (a + d)\lambda + (ad - bc) = 0. \tag{16}$$

Solve this quadratic equation for λ.

Using equations (15) to determine the characteristic equation leads to the same quadratic equation.

Procedure 2   Finding eigenvectors of a 2×2 matrix

Let $\mathbf{A} = \begin{pmatrix} a & b \\ c & d \end{pmatrix}$. To find an *eigenvector* corresponding to the eigenvalue λ, write down the **eigenvector equations**

$$\begin{cases} (a - \lambda)x + by = 0, \\ cx + (d - \lambda)y = 0. \end{cases} \tag{17}$$

These equations reduce to a single equation of the form $py = qx$, with solution $x = p$, $y = q$, so $(p \quad q)^T$ is an eigenvector. Any non-zero multiple $(kp \quad kq)^T$ is also an eigenvector corresponding to the same eigenvalue.

Note that in the equation $py = qx$, the coefficient of y gives the first component of the eigenvector, and the coefficient of x gives the second component.

Example 6

Find the eigenvalues and corresponding eigenvectors of the matrix

$$\mathbf{A} = \begin{pmatrix} 2 & 3 \\ 2 & 1 \end{pmatrix},$$

following Procedures 1 and 2.

Solution

The characteristic equation is

$$\begin{vmatrix} 2 - \lambda & 3 \\ 2 & 1 - \lambda \end{vmatrix} = (2 - \lambda)(1 - \lambda) - 6 = 0,$$

which simplifies to $\lambda^2 - 3\lambda - 4 = 0$. Using the formula for solving a quadratic equation, we deduce that the eigenvalues are $\lambda = 4$ and $\lambda = -1$.

- For $\lambda = 4$, the eigenvector equations become $-2x + 3y = 0$ and $2x - 3y = 0$, which reduce to the single equation $3y = 2x$ (so $p = 3$ and $q = 2$ in Procedure 2). Thus an eigenvector corresponding to $\lambda = 4$ is $(3 \quad 2)^T$.

- For $\lambda = -1$, the eigenvector equations become $3x + 3y = 0$ and $2x + 2y = 0$, which reduce to the single equation $-y = x$ (so $p = -1$ and $q = 1$ in Procedure 2). Thus an eigenvector corresponding to $\lambda = -1$ is $(-1 \quad 1)^T$.

We check that $\operatorname{tr} \mathbf{A} = 2 + 1 = 3$ and $\lambda_1 + \lambda_2 = 4 - 1 = 3$, as required, and $\det \mathbf{A} = 2 \times 1 - 3 \times 2 = -4$ and $\lambda_1 \lambda_2 = 4 \times (-1) = -4$, as required.

Alternatively, you may have noticed that
$$\lambda^2 - 3\lambda - 4 = (\lambda - 4)(\lambda + 1).$$

In Example 6 we have two distinct real eigenvalues, and these correspond to two linearly independent eigenvectors.

Exercise 9

Use Procedures 1 and 2 to find the eigenvalues and corresponding eigenvectors of each of the following matrices.

(a) $\mathbf{A} = \begin{pmatrix} 1 & 4 \\ 1 & -2 \end{pmatrix}$ (b) $\mathbf{A} = \begin{pmatrix} 8 & -5 \\ 10 & -7 \end{pmatrix}$ (c) $\mathbf{A} = \begin{pmatrix} -1 & 0 \\ 9 & 2 \end{pmatrix}$

From equations (15), the sum of the eigenvalues is $a + d = \operatorname{tr} \mathbf{A}$ and the product is $ad - bc = \det \mathbf{A}$. It is useful to check that these properties hold whenever you have calculated the eigenvalues of a given matrix. If they do not hold, then you have made a mistake, which you should rectify before proceeding to calculate the eigenvectors.

Similar results are true for all square matrices, of any size.

Exercise 10

Verify the properties in equations (15) for the matrices in the following.

(a) Example 5 (b) Exercise 8 (c) Exercise 9

2.2 Three types of eigenvalue

The characteristic equation of a matrix is a quadratic equation, and this has distinct real, repeated real or distinct complex roots depending on whether the discriminant of the quadratic equation is positive, zero or negative. We illustrate each of these three cases below.

See equation (14).

See Unit 1, Section 2.

Distinct real eigenvalues

In the following exercises, the eigenvalues are real and distinct.

Exercise 11

Calculate the eigenvalues and corresponding eigenvectors of the matrix $\begin{pmatrix} p & 0 \\ 0 & q \end{pmatrix}$ with $p \neq q$. Check that your answers agree with those obtained by geometric considerations in Section 1 (see Figure 5).

Exercise 12

This matrix is associated with the migration problem discussed in the Introduction.

Calculate the eigenvalues and corresponding eigenvectors of the matrix

$$\mathbf{A} = \begin{pmatrix} 0.9 & 0.2 \\ 0.1 & 0.8 \end{pmatrix}.$$

This is true in general, though we do not prove it here except for the case of real symmetric matrices, which is left until Subsection 3.3.

Notice that whenever we have two distinct real eigenvalues, we also have two linearly independent eigenvectors.

Repeated eigenvalue

In the following exercise, the eigenvalue is repeated.

Exercise 13

Calculate the eigenvalues and corresponding eigenvectors of the following matrices.

(a) $\begin{pmatrix} a & 0 \\ 0 & a \end{pmatrix}$, where $a \neq 0$ (b) $\begin{pmatrix} a & 1 \\ 0 & a \end{pmatrix}$, where $a \neq 0$

In fact, it is always true that if a 2×2 matrix has a repeated eigenvalue, then either we can select any two linearly independent vectors as eigenvectors, as is the case for diagonal matrices (Exercise 13(a)), or there is only one linearly independent eigenvector, as exemplified by Exercise 13(b). Indeed, one can show that if any *non-diagonal* 2×2 matrix has a repeated eigenvalue, then it has only one linearly independent eigenvector, although we do not prove this here.

Complex eigenvalues

Although we discuss complex eigenvalues, in this module the *elements* of a matrix $\mathbf{A}$ will always be real, so that $\mathbf{A}$ is a *real* matrix.

For 2×2 matrices, complex eigenvalues arise when there are no fixed directions under the corresponding linear transformation as, for example, in an anticlockwise rotation through $\pi/4$ about the origin (see Figure 5 and the discussion about it). They can occur for matrices of all sizes, but for real matrices they always occur in complex conjugate pairs (i.e. if $\lambda_1 = a + ib$ is an eigenvalue, then $\lambda_2 = a - ib$ is also an eigenvalue). The following example illustrates one of the simplest cases.

Example 7

Calculate the eigenvalues and corresponding eigenvectors of the matrix

$$\mathbf{A} = \begin{pmatrix} 0 & -1 \\ 1 & 0 \end{pmatrix}.$$

Solution

The characteristic equation is $\lambda^2 + 1 = 0$. This equation has no real solutions, so there are no real eigenvalues. However, it has complex solutions

$$\lambda = i \quad \text{and} \quad \lambda = -i, \quad \text{where } i^2 = -1.$$

Check: sum $= \operatorname{tr}\mathbf{A} = 0$; product $= \det\mathbf{A} = 1$.

Thus the matrix $\mathbf{A}$ has the complex eigenvalues i and $-i$.

The eigenvector equations are $-\lambda x - y = 0$ and $x - \lambda y = 0$ (using equations (17)).

- For $\lambda = i$, the eigenvector equations become $-ix - y = 0$ and $x - iy = 0$, which reduce to the single equation $y = -ix$ (so $p = 1$ and $q = -i$ in Procedure 2). Thus an eigenvector corresponding to the eigenvalue $\lambda = i$ is $(1 \quad -i)^T$.

  The second equation is i times the first.

- For $\lambda = -i$, the eigenvector equations become $ix - y = 0$ and $x + iy = 0$, which reduce to the single equation $y = ix$ (so $p = 1$ and $q = i$ in Procedure 2). Thus an eigenvector corresponding to the eigenvalue $\lambda = -i$ is $(1 \quad i)^T$.

  The second equation is $-i$ times the first.

In Example 7 the eigenvectors are complex, but nevertheless are linearly independent. It remains true that any two eigenvectors corresponding to distinct eigenvalues, whether real or complex, are linearly independent.

Exercise 14

Calculate the eigenvalues and corresponding eigenvectors of the matrix

$$\mathbf{A} = \begin{pmatrix} 3 & -1 \\ 2 & 1 \end{pmatrix}.$$

2.3 Some results on eigenvalues

In this subsection we list some general results that will be needed later. Although we introduce them in the context of 2×2 matrices, they hold for square matrices of any size.

We consider the eigenvalues of various types of matrix: triangular, symmetric and non-invertible.

Triangular matrices

See Unit 4.

A matrix is *triangular* if all the elements above (or below) the leading diagonal are 0. Thus a 2×2 triangular matrix has one of the forms

$$\begin{pmatrix} a & b \\ 0 & d \end{pmatrix}, \qquad \begin{pmatrix} a & 0 \\ c & d \end{pmatrix}, \qquad \begin{pmatrix} a & 0 \\ 0 & d \end{pmatrix}.$$

(upper triangular)   (lower triangular)   (diagonal)

The above triangular matrices all have characteristic equation

$$(a - \lambda)(d - \lambda) = 0,$$

and eigenvalues $\lambda = a$ and $\lambda = d$.

Thus the eigenvalues of a triangular matrix are the diagonal entries.

Exercise 15

Find the eigenvalues and corresponding eigenvectors of the upper triangular matrix $\begin{pmatrix} 1 & 3 \\ 0 & 2 \end{pmatrix}$.

Symmetric matrices

See Unit 4.

A matrix is *symmetric* if it is equal to its transpose – that is, if the entries are symmetric about the leading diagonal. Thus a 2×2 symmetric matrix has the form

$$\mathbf{A} = \begin{pmatrix} a & b \\ b & d \end{pmatrix}.$$

It has characteristic equation

$$\lambda^2 - (a + d)\lambda + (ad - b^2) = 0,$$

and eigenvalues

$$\lambda = \tfrac{1}{2}\left(a + d \pm \sqrt{(a + d)^2 - 4(ad - b^2)}\right).$$

The discriminant is

In this module, $\mathbf{A}$ is always a real matrix, so a, b and d are real numbers.

$$(a + d)^2 - 4(ad - b^2) = (a^2 + 2ad + d^2) - 4ad + 4b^2 = (a - d)^2 + 4b^2,$$

which is the sum of two squares and therefore cannot be negative.

It follows that the eigenvalues of a real symmetric matrix are real. In Subsection 3.3, this result will be shown to hold for general $n \times n$ real symmetric matrices, along with an important property of their eigenvectors.

Exercise 16

Under what circumstances can a symmetric matrix $\begin{pmatrix} a & b \\ b & d \end{pmatrix}$ have a repeated eigenvalue?

Non-invertible matrices

A matrix is *non-invertible* if and only if its determinant is 0. Thus a 2×2 non-invertible matrix has the form

$$\mathbf{A} = \begin{pmatrix} a & b \\ c & d \end{pmatrix} \quad \text{where } ad - bc = 0.$$

See Unit 4.

However, we know that if λ_1 and λ_2 are the eigenvalues of $\mathbf{A}$, then

$$\lambda_1 \lambda_2 = \det \mathbf{A} = 0.$$

See equations (15).

It follows that a matrix is non-invertible if and only if at least one of its eigenvalues is 0. Also, a matrix is invertible if and only if all its eigenvalues are non-zero.

For example, if $\mathbf{A} = \begin{pmatrix} 2 & 1 \\ 4 & 2 \end{pmatrix}$, then $\det \mathbf{A} = 0$ and hence 0 is an eigenvalue of $\mathbf{A}$, as we saw in the discussion immediately before Exercise 3.

Since $\lambda_1 + \lambda_2 = \operatorname{tr} \mathbf{A} = 4$, the other eigenvalue is 4.

Non-invertible matrices

A square matrix $\mathbf{A}$ is non-invertible if and only if any of the following equivalent conditions holds:

- its determinant is zero
- its rows are linearly dependent
- its columns are linearly dependent
- the equation $\mathbf{Ax} = \mathbf{0}$ has a non-zero solution
- at least one of its eigenvalues is zero.

The third condition follows immediately from the second, since $\det \mathbf{A} = \det(\mathbf{A}^T)$.

Summary

We can summarise the results about eigenvalues in this section so far.

Eigenvalues − summary

- The eigenvalues of a triangular matrix are the diagonal entries.
- The eigenvalues of a real symmetric matrix are real.
- The sum of the eigenvalues of $\mathbf{A}$ is $\operatorname{tr} \mathbf{A}$.
- The product of the eigenvalues of $\mathbf{A}$ is $\det \mathbf{A}$.

Exercise 17

Without solving the characteristic equation, what can you say about the eigenvalues of each of the following matrices?

(a) $\mathbf{A} = \begin{pmatrix} 67 & 72 \\ 72 & -17 \end{pmatrix}$ (b) $\mathbf{A} = \begin{pmatrix} 67 & 72 \\ 0 & -17 \end{pmatrix}$ (c) $\mathbf{A} = \begin{pmatrix} 288 & 72 \\ 72 & 18 \end{pmatrix}$

2.4 Eigenvalues of related matrices

For the rest of this section, we compare the eigenvalues of a matrix $\mathbf{A}$ with the eigenvalues of some related matrices. The results of our investigations are needed in Section 4. The following exercise leads our discussion.

Exercise 18

Let $\mathbf{A} = \begin{pmatrix} 3 & 2 \\ 1 & 4 \end{pmatrix}$. In Example 5 you saw that $(1 \quad 1)^T$ is an eigenvector of $\mathbf{A}$ corresponding to the eigenvalue 5, and that $(-2 \quad 1)^T$ is an eigenvector corresponding to the eigenvalue 2.

(a) Evaluate the following matrices. In each case, solve the characteristic equation, determine the eigenvalues, and compare these eigenvalues with the eigenvalues of $\mathbf{A}$.

    (i) $\mathbf{A}^2$ (ii) $\mathbf{A}^{-1}$ (iii) $\mathbf{A} + 2\mathbf{I}$ (iv) $(\mathbf{A} - 4\mathbf{I})^{-1}$ (v) $3\mathbf{A}$

(b) Verify that the given eigenvectors of $\mathbf{A}$ are also eigenvectors of the matrices in part (a).

Exercise 18 illustrates some general results.

- If $\mathbf{v}$ is an eigenvector of a matrix $\mathbf{A}$ with eigenvalue λ, then $\mathbf{A}\mathbf{v} = \lambda\mathbf{v}$. It follows that

$$\mathbf{A}^2\mathbf{v} = \mathbf{A}(\mathbf{A}\mathbf{v}) = \mathbf{A}(\lambda\mathbf{v}) = \lambda(\mathbf{A}\mathbf{v}) = \lambda(\lambda\mathbf{v}) = \lambda^2\mathbf{v},$$

  which shows that $\mathbf{v}$ is an eigenvector of $\mathbf{A}^2$, with eigenvalue λ^2.

  More generally, if $\mathbf{v}$ is an eigenvector of a matrix $\mathbf{A}$ with eigenvalue λ, then $\mathbf{v}$ is also an eigenvector of $\mathbf{A}^k$ (for any positive integer k), with eigenvalue λ^k.

- If $\mathbf{v}$ is an eigenvector of a matrix $\mathbf{A}$ with eigenvalue λ, then $\mathbf{A}\mathbf{v} = \lambda\mathbf{v}$. It follows that (provided that $\mathbf{A}$ is invertible, so $\mathbf{A}^{-1}$ exists)

$$\mathbf{A}^{-1}(\mathbf{A}\mathbf{v}) = \mathbf{A}^{-1}(\lambda\mathbf{v}) = \lambda\mathbf{A}^{-1}\mathbf{v},$$

  so $\mathbf{v} = \lambda\mathbf{A}^{-1}\mathbf{v}$. Dividing by λ (which cannot be zero since $\mathbf{A}$ is invertible) gives

$$\mathbf{A}^{-1}\mathbf{v} = (1/\lambda)\mathbf{v},$$

  which shows that $\mathbf{v}$ is an eigenvector of $\mathbf{A}^{-1}$, with eigenvalue $1/\lambda$.

- If $\mathbf{v}$ is an eigenvector of a matrix $\mathbf{A}$ with eigenvalue λ, then $\mathbf{A}\mathbf{v} = \lambda\mathbf{v}$. If p is any number, it follows that

$$(\mathbf{A} - p\mathbf{I})\mathbf{v} = \mathbf{A}\mathbf{v} - p\mathbf{I}\mathbf{v} = \lambda\mathbf{v} - p\mathbf{v} = (\lambda - p)\mathbf{v},$$

  which shows that $\mathbf{v}$ is an eigenvector of $\mathbf{A} - p\mathbf{I}$, with eigenvalue $\lambda - p$.

If the number p is *not* an eigenvalue of $\mathbf{A}$, then the eigenvalues $\lambda - p$ of $\mathbf{A} - p\mathbf{I}$ are non-zero, so $\mathbf{A} - p\mathbf{I}$ is invertible. Therefore we can multiply both sides of the equation

$$(\mathbf{A} - p\mathbf{I})\mathbf{v} = (\lambda - p)\mathbf{v}$$

on the left by $(\mathbf{A} - p\mathbf{I})^{-1}$ to obtain

$$\mathbf{v} = (\mathbf{A} - p\mathbf{I})^{-1}(\lambda - p)\mathbf{v},$$

and, dividing by $\lambda - p$,

$$(\mathbf{A} - p\mathbf{I})^{-1}\mathbf{v} = (\lambda - p)^{-1}\mathbf{v}.$$

This shows that $\mathbf{v}$ is also an eigenvector of $(\mathbf{A} - p\mathbf{I})^{-1}$, with eigenvalue $(\lambda - p)^{-1}$.

- If $\mathbf{v}$ is an eigenvector of a matrix $\mathbf{A}$ with eigenvalue λ, then $\mathbf{A}\mathbf{v} = \lambda\mathbf{v}$. It follows that for any number p, $p(\mathbf{A}\mathbf{v}) = p\lambda\mathbf{v}$, so $(p\mathbf{A})\mathbf{v} = (p\lambda)\mathbf{v}$, which shows that $\mathbf{v}$ is an eigenvector of $p\mathbf{A}$ with eigenvalue $p\lambda$.

Eigenvalues and eigenvectors of associated matrices

If $\mathbf{A}$ is an arbitrary matrix and λ is one of its eigenvalues, then:

- λ^k is an eigenvalue of $\mathbf{A}^k$ for any positive integer k
- if $\mathbf{A}$ is invertible, then λ^{-1} is an eigenvalue of $\mathbf{A}^{-1}$
- $\lambda - p$ is an eigenvalue of $\mathbf{A} - p\mathbf{I}$, for any number p
- $(\lambda - p)^{-1}$ is an eigenvalue of $(\mathbf{A} - p\mathbf{I})^{-1}$, for any number p that is not an eigenvalue of $\mathbf{A}$
- $p\lambda$ is an eigenvalue of $p\mathbf{A}$ for any number p.

In each case, an eigenvector of $\mathbf{A}$ is also an eigenvector of the associated matrix.

We will need these results in Section 4 and in later units of the module.

Exercise 19

(a) The eigenvalues of $\mathbf{A} = \begin{pmatrix} 2 & 3 \\ 2 & 1 \end{pmatrix}$ are 4 and -1. Write down the eigenvalues of each of the following.

    (i) $\mathbf{A}^3$ (ii) $\mathbf{A}^{-1}$ (iii) $\mathbf{A} - 6\mathbf{I}$ (iv) $(\mathbf{A} + 3\mathbf{I})^{-1}$

(b) What can you say about the eigenvalues of $\mathbf{A} - 4\mathbf{I}$? What can you say about the inverse of $\mathbf{A} - 4\mathbf{I}$?

Exercise 20

(a) Find the eigenvalues and corresponding eigenvectors of the matrix
$\mathbf{A} = \begin{pmatrix} 1 & 2 \\ 3 & -4 \end{pmatrix}$. Write down the eigenvalues and corresponding
eigenvectors of the matrix $\mathbf{A}^{10}$.

(b) Write down the eigenvalues and corresponding eigenvectors of the
matrix $\begin{pmatrix} 3 & 2 \\ 3 & -2 \end{pmatrix}$.

(*Hint*: Compare this matrix with the matrix $\mathbf{A}$ in part (a).)

Exercise 21

(a) Let θ be an angle that is not an integer multiple of π. Calculate the
eigenvalues and eigenvectors of the matrix

$$\mathbf{A} = \begin{pmatrix} \cos\theta & -\sin\theta \\ \sin\theta & \cos\theta \end{pmatrix},$$

which represents an anticlockwise rotation through the angle θ.

(b) If θ is an integer multiple of π, what can be stated about the matrix $\mathbf{A}$?
What can be deduced about the eigenvalues and eigenvectors of $\mathbf{A}$?

3 Eigenvalues and eigenvectors of 3×3 matrices

In this section we extend the ideas of Section 2 to deal with 3×3 matrices.
In fact, it is possible to extend the treatment to $n \times n$ matrices, and with
this in mind it is convenient to use the notation x_1, x_2 and x_3 (rather than
x, y and z).

So we are interested in finding the eigenvalues and corresponding
eigenvectors of a matrix such as

$$\begin{pmatrix} -2 & 1 & 0 \\ 1 & -2 & 1 \\ 0 & 1 & -2 \end{pmatrix}.$$

As in the case of 2×2 matrices, we can verify that a given vector is an
eigenvector. For example, $(1 \quad 0 \quad -1)^T$ is an eigenvector of the above
matrix, since

$$\begin{pmatrix} -2 & 1 & 0 \\ 1 & -2 & 1 \\ 0 & 1 & -2 \end{pmatrix} \begin{pmatrix} 1 \\ 0 \\ -1 \end{pmatrix} = \begin{pmatrix} -2 \\ 0 \\ 2 \end{pmatrix} = -2 \begin{pmatrix} 1 \\ 0 \\ -1 \end{pmatrix},$$

and the corresponding eigenvalue is -2.

Exercise 22

Verify that $\begin{pmatrix} 0 \\ 1 \\ 1 \end{pmatrix}$ and $\begin{pmatrix} 0 \\ 1 \\ -1 \end{pmatrix}$ are eigenvectors of $\begin{pmatrix} 5 & 0 & 0 \\ 1 & 2 & 1 \\ 1 & 1 & 2 \end{pmatrix}$, and find the corresponding eigenvalues.

The above exercise should have convinced you that it is easy to *verify* that a given vector is an eigenvector, but how are we to *find* such eigenvectors? Moreover, how are we to deal with the more general case of an $n \times n$ matrix? This section examines these questions.

3.1 Basic method

In this subsection we look at a method for finding the eigenvalues and corresponding eigenvectors of an arbitrary 3×3 matrix. Consider the following example.

Example 8

Find the eigenvalues and corresponding eigenvectors of the matrix

$$\mathbf{A} = \begin{pmatrix} 3 & 2 & 2 \\ 2 & 2 & 0 \\ 2 & 0 & 4 \end{pmatrix}.$$

Solution

We wish to find those non-zero vectors $\mathbf{v}$ that satisfy the equation

$$\mathbf{A}\mathbf{v} = \lambda\mathbf{v}$$

for some number λ. Writing $\mathbf{v} = (x_1 \ \ x_2 \ \ x_3)^T$, we have

$$\begin{pmatrix} 3 & 2 & 2 \\ 2 & 2 & 0 \\ 2 & 0 & 4 \end{pmatrix} \begin{pmatrix} x_1 \\ x_2 \\ x_3 \end{pmatrix} = \lambda \begin{pmatrix} x_1 \\ x_2 \\ x_3 \end{pmatrix},$$

which gives

$$\begin{cases} (3-\lambda)x_1 + \qquad 2x_2 + \qquad 2x_3 = 0, \\ \qquad 2x_1 + (2-\lambda)x_2 \qquad\qquad = 0, \\ \qquad 2x_1 \qquad\qquad + (4-\lambda)x_3 = 0, \end{cases} \qquad (18)$$

These are the *eigenvector equations*.

which can be written as $(\mathbf{A} - \lambda\mathbf{I})\mathbf{v} = \mathbf{0}$. We are interested in non-zero solutions of these equations (i.e. solutions in which x_1, x_2 and x_3 are not all 0). The condition for such solutions to exist is that the determinant of the coefficient matrix $\mathbf{A} - \lambda\mathbf{I}$ is 0, that is,

$$\begin{vmatrix} 3-\lambda & 2 & 2 \\ 2 & 2-\lambda & 0 \\ 2 & 0 & 4-\lambda \end{vmatrix} = 0.$$

Expanding this determinant by the middle row gives

$$-2\begin{vmatrix} 2 & 2 \\ 0 & 4-\lambda \end{vmatrix} + (2-\lambda)\begin{vmatrix} 3-\lambda & 2 \\ 2 & 4-\lambda \end{vmatrix} - 0\begin{vmatrix} 3-\lambda & 2 \\ 2 & 0 \end{vmatrix} = 0,$$

hence

$$-4(4-\lambda) + (2-\lambda)[(3-\lambda)(4-\lambda) - 4] = 0,$$

This is the *characteristic equation* of **A**. For *any* 3×3 matrix, it will be a cubic equation.

which simplifies to the cubic equation

$$\lambda^3 - 9\lambda^2 + 18\lambda = 0.$$

We must now solve this equation. In general, it is difficult to solve a cubic equation algebraically, unless you use a computer algebra package. However, if you can spot one of the roots, then the task becomes considerably easier. In this case,

$$\lambda^3 - 9\lambda^2 + 18\lambda = \lambda(\lambda^2 - 9\lambda + 18),$$

One way of solving the quadratic equation is to notice that
$$\lambda^2 - 9\lambda + 18 = (\lambda - 3)(\lambda - 6).$$

so $\lambda = 0$ is one of the roots. The others are obtained by solving the quadratic equation $\lambda^2 - 9\lambda + 18 = 0$ to give the roots 3 and 6. So the eigenvalues are 0, 3 and 6.

In order to find the corresponding eigenvectors, we substitute each of these eigenvalues into the eigenvector equations (18) as follows.

- For $\lambda = 6$, the matrix form of the eigenvector equations (18) is

$$\begin{pmatrix} -3 & 2 & 2 \\ 2 & -4 & 0 \\ 2 & 0 & -2 \end{pmatrix} \begin{pmatrix} x_1 \\ x_2 \\ x_3 \end{pmatrix} = \begin{pmatrix} 0 \\ 0 \\ 0 \end{pmatrix}.$$

We saw in Subsection 2.3 that an equation of the form $\mathbf{Ax} = \mathbf{0}$ has a non-zero solution (and hence infinitely many solutions) if and only if the rows of **A** are linearly dependent. Here, this means that at least one of the following equations may be obtained from the other two:

While it may appear that we have three equations in the three unknowns x_1, x_2 and x_3, only two of the equations are distinct. You may recall a similar occurrence in Exercise 7(c) of Unit 4.

$$-3x_1 + 2x_2 + 2x_3 = 0,$$
$$2x_1 - 4x_2 \qquad = 0,$$
$$2x_1 \qquad - 2x_3 = 0.$$

We should check that these values satisfy the original equations.

So we can find our desired solution by considering just two of the equations. Using the second and third, we have $x_1 - 2x_2 = 0$ and $x_1 - x_3 = 0$. Putting $x_3 = k$ and solving for x_1 and x_2, we obtain $x_1 = k$, $x_2 = \frac{1}{2}k$. Choosing $k = 2$ gives an answer avoiding fractions: $x_1 = 2$, $x_2 = 1$, $x_3 = 2$. This means that $(2 \quad 1 \quad 2)^T$ is an eigenvector corresponding to the eigenvalue $\lambda = 6$.

Gaussian elimination is a more cumbersome process than the previous method, but it is illuminating. At the final stage of the elimination process, the bottom row of the augmented matrix consists entirely of zeros – and this must be the case because the rows of $\mathbf{A} - \lambda\mathbf{I}$ are linearly dependent.

Alternatively, we may solve the eigenvector equations by Gaussian elimination. In this case, we have the following augmented matrix.

$$\begin{pmatrix} -3 & 2 & 2 & | & 0 \\ 2 & -4 & 0 & | & 0 \\ 2 & 0 & -2 & | & 0 \end{pmatrix} \begin{matrix} \mathbf{R}_1 \\ \mathbf{R}_2 \\ \mathbf{R}_3 \end{matrix}$$

Stage 1(a)   We reduce to zero the elements below the leading diagonal in column 1.

$$\begin{array}{c} \\ \mathbf{R}_2 + \frac{2}{3}\mathbf{R}_1 \\ \mathbf{R}_3 + \frac{2}{3}\mathbf{R}_1 \end{array} \left(\begin{array}{ccc|c} -3 & 2 & 2 & 0 \\ 0 & -\frac{8}{3} & \frac{4}{3} & 0 \\ 0 & \frac{4}{3} & -\frac{2}{3} & 0 \end{array}\right) \begin{array}{c} \mathbf{R}_1 \\ \mathbf{R}_{2a} \\ \mathbf{R}_{3a} \end{array}$$

Stage 1(b)   We reduce to zero the element below the leading diagonal in column 2.

$$\begin{array}{c} \\ \\ \mathbf{R}_{3a} + \frac{1}{2}\mathbf{R}_{2a} \end{array} \left(\begin{array}{ccc|c} -3 & 2 & 2 & 0 \\ 0 & -\frac{8}{3} & \frac{4}{3} & 0 \\ 0 & 0 & 0 & 0 \end{array}\right)$$

Stage 2   Back substitution gives $x_2 = \frac{1}{2}x_3$ and $x_1 = \frac{2}{3}(x_2 + x_3) = x_3$. We are free to choose x_3 as we please, so putting $x_3 = 2$, we find that $(2 \quad 1 \quad 2)^T$ is an eigenvector (as before).

- For $\lambda = 3$, substituting $\lambda = 3$ into equations (18), the eigenvector equations become $2x_2 + 2x_3 = 0$, $2x_1 - x_2 = 0$ and $2x_1 + x_3 = 0$. The first and second equations reduce to $x_3 = -x_2$ and $x_2 = 2x_1$. It follows that $(1 \quad 2 \quad -2)^T$ is an eigenvector corresponding to the eigenvalue 3.

  Choose, for example, $x_1 = 1$, and use this to calculate x_2 and x_3.

- For $\lambda = 0$, substituting $\lambda = 0$ into equations (18), the eigenvector equations become $3x_1 + 2x_2 + 2x_3 = 0$, $2x_1 + 2x_2 = 0$ and $2x_1 + 4x_3 = 0$. These equations reduce to $x_2 = -x_1$ and $x_1 = -2x_3$. It follows that $(-2 \quad 2 \quad 1)^T$ is an eigenvector corresponding to the eigenvalue 0.

  Choose, for example, $x_3 = 1$, and use this to calculate x_1 and x_2.

It is always worth checking that the values of x_1, x_2 and x_3 satisfy each equation.

In Example 8, we first found the eigenvalues by solving a cubic equation, then used these eigenvalues and the eigenvector equations to find the corresponding eigenvectors. We found the eigenvalues of the matrix

$$\mathbf{A} = \begin{pmatrix} 3 & 2 & 2 \\ 2 & 2 & 0 \\ 2 & 0 & 4 \end{pmatrix}$$

by solving the equation

$$\begin{vmatrix} 3 - \lambda & 2 & 2 \\ 2 & 2 - \lambda & 0 \\ 2 & 0 & 4 - \lambda \end{vmatrix} = 0.$$

Since the left-hand side of this equation is $\det(\mathbf{A} - \lambda\mathbf{I})$, it can be written in the form $\det(\mathbf{A} - \lambda\mathbf{I}) = 0$.

As in the case of a 2×2 matrix, the values of $\operatorname{tr}\mathbf{A}$ and $\det\mathbf{A}$ provide a useful check on the calculations.

For Example 8, we see that $\operatorname{tr} \mathbf{A} = 3 + 2 + 4 = 9$, and the sum of the eigenvalues is also 9. Also, expanding by the middle row, we have

$$\det \mathbf{A} = -2 \begin{vmatrix} 2 & 2 \\ 0 & 4 \end{vmatrix} + 2 \begin{vmatrix} 3 & 2 \\ 2 & 4 \end{vmatrix} - 0 \begin{vmatrix} 3 & 2 \\ 2 & 0 \end{vmatrix} = -16 + 16 = 0,$$

and the product of the eigenvalues is also 0.

We can extend and generalise Procedures 1 and 2 to $n \times n$ matrices.

Procedure 3 Finding eigenvalues and eigenvectors of an $n \times n$ matrix

To find the eigenvalues and eigenvectors of an $n \times n$ matrix $\mathbf{A}$, carry out the following steps.

1. Solve the characteristic equation

$$\det(\mathbf{A} - \lambda \mathbf{I}) = 0$$

to determine the eigenvalues $\lambda_1, \lambda_2, \ldots, \lambda_n$.

2. Solve the corresponding eigenvector equations $(\mathbf{A} - \lambda_i \mathbf{I})\mathbf{v}_i = \mathbf{0}$ for each eigenvalue λ_i, to find a corresponding eigenvector $\mathbf{v}_i$.

The characteristic equation of an $n \times n$ matrix has n solutions (some of which may be repeated). If there are n distinct solutions, then there will be n linearly independent eigenvectors (but there may be fewer if any eigenvalue is repeated).

Exercise 23

The eigenvalues of the matrix

$$\mathbf{A} = \begin{pmatrix} 1 & 0 & -1 \\ 1 & 2 & 1 \\ 2 & 2 & 3 \end{pmatrix}$$

are $\lambda = 1$, $\lambda = 2$ and $\lambda = 3$. Write down the eigenvector equations, and determine corresponding eigenvectors.

Exercise 24

Determine the characteristic equation of the matrix

$$\mathbf{A} = \begin{pmatrix} 0 & 0 & 6 \\ \frac{1}{2} & 0 & 0 \\ 0 & \frac{1}{3} & 0 \end{pmatrix}.$$

Verify that $\lambda = 1$ is an eigenvalue of $\mathbf{A}$, and find a corresponding eigenvector. (You do not need to find any other eigenvalues.)

3.2 Finding eigenvalues by hand

For the matrices that arise from real applications, it is often impossible to calculate the eigenvalues and eigenvectors by hand (as opposed to using a computer), and we would generally use numerical techniques such as those discussed in the next section. However, finding eigenvalues and eigenvectors by hand is an important part of the learning process. In this module you can divide the exercises into two types: those for which it is easy to find the eigenvalues by hand, and the rest (for which you will probably need to use a computer algebra package). The examples and exercises in this section have been carefully chosen to be of the former kind.

Example 9

Find the eigenvalues of the matrix
$$\mathbf{A} = \begin{pmatrix} 5 & 0 & 0 \\ 1 & 2 & 1 \\ 1 & 1 & 2 \end{pmatrix}.$$

Solution

The characteristic equation is
$$\begin{vmatrix} 5-\lambda & 0 & 0 \\ 1 & 2-\lambda & 1 \\ 1 & 1 & 2-\lambda \end{vmatrix} = 0.$$

Expanding the determinant by the first row gives
$$(5-\lambda)\begin{vmatrix} 2-\lambda & 1 \\ 1 & 2-\lambda \end{vmatrix} = 0,$$

hence $(5-\lambda)(\lambda^2 - 4\lambda + 3) = 0$. So $5 - \lambda = 0$ or $\lambda^2 - 4\lambda + 3 = 0$. Hence one solution is $\lambda = 5$. The quadratic equation $\lambda^2 - 4\lambda + 3 = 0$ has roots 1 and 3.

Thus the eigenvalues are $\lambda = 5$, $\lambda = 3$ and $\lambda = 1$.

Exercise 25

Find the eigenvalues of each of the following matrices.

(a) $\mathbf{A} = \begin{pmatrix} 0 & 0 & 1 \\ 0 & 0 & 0 \\ 1 & 0 & 0 \end{pmatrix}$ (b) $\mathbf{A} = \begin{pmatrix} 1 & 0 & 0 \\ 6 & 2 & 0 \\ 5 & 4 & 3 \end{pmatrix}$

Often the most arduous part of such problems is the expansion of the determinant, but a judicious choice of which row or column to expand by can reduce the work, as the following example shows.

Example 10

Find the eigenvalues of the matrix
$$\mathbf{A} = \begin{pmatrix} 5 & 2 & 0 \\ 2 & 5 & 0 \\ -3 & 4 & 6 \end{pmatrix}.$$

Solution

The characteristic equation is
$$\begin{vmatrix} 5-\lambda & 2 & 0 \\ 2 & 5-\lambda & 0 \\ -3 & 4 & 6-\lambda \end{vmatrix} = 0.$$

Since the third column contains two zeros, we expand the determinant by the third column to give
$$(6-\lambda) \begin{vmatrix} 5-\lambda & 2 \\ 2 & 5-\lambda \end{vmatrix} = 0,$$

hence $(6-\lambda)((5-\lambda)^2 - 4) = 0$. So $\lambda - 6 = 0$ or $(5-\lambda)^2 - 4 = 0$. Hence one solution is $\lambda = 6$. The quadratic equation $(5-\lambda)^2 - 4 = 0$ can be rewritten as $(5-\lambda)^2 = 4$, so $5 - \lambda = \pm 2$, and the two other solutions are $\lambda = 7$ and $\lambda = 3$.

Thus the eigenvalues are $\lambda = 6$, $\lambda = 7$ and $\lambda = 3$.

Exercise 26

Find the eigenvalues of the matrix
$$\mathbf{A} = \begin{pmatrix} 8 & 0 & -5 \\ 9 & 3 & -6 \\ 10 & 0 & -7 \end{pmatrix}.$$

Exercise 27

See Subsection 2.3.

Verify that the eigenvalues of the triangular matrices
$$\begin{pmatrix} a & 0 & 0 \\ d & b & 0 \\ e & f & c \end{pmatrix} \quad \text{and} \quad \begin{pmatrix} a & d & e \\ 0 & b & f \\ 0 & 0 & c \end{pmatrix}$$
are the diagonal entries a, b and c.

Exercise 28

Verify that the sum of the eigenvalues is $\operatorname{tr} \mathbf{A}$ for the matrices $\mathbf{A}$ in the following. In each case, find the value of $\det \mathbf{A}$, and verify that this is the product of the eigenvalues.

(a) Example 9   (b) Example 10

(c) Exercise 23   (d) Exercise 25   (e) Exercise 26

The eigenvalues of a 3×3 matrix can be real and distinct (as in Exercise 23), or real and repeated (as in Exercise 26), or one may be real and the other two form a complex conjugate pair – as in the following example.

Repeated real eigenvalues may be repeated once,
$$\lambda_1 = \lambda_2 \neq \lambda_3,$$
or twice,
$$\lambda_1 = \lambda_2 = \lambda_3.$$

Example 11

Find the eigenvalues and corresponding eigenvectors of the matrix
$$\begin{pmatrix} 1 & 0 & 0 \\ 0 & 0 & 1 \\ 0 & -1 & 0 \end{pmatrix}.$$

Solution

The characteristic equation is
$$\begin{vmatrix} 1-\lambda & 0 & 0 \\ 0 & -\lambda & 1 \\ 0 & -1 & -\lambda \end{vmatrix} = 0.$$

Expanding the determinant by the first row gives
$$(1-\lambda) \begin{vmatrix} -\lambda & 1 \\ -1 & -\lambda \end{vmatrix} = (1-\lambda)(\lambda^2 + 1) = 0,$$

so $1 - \lambda = 0$ or $\lambda^2 + 1 = 0$. The quadratic equation $\lambda^2 + 1 = 0$ has roots $\lambda = i$ and $\lambda = -i$, where $i^2 = -1$. Thus the eigenvalues are $\lambda = 1$, $\lambda = i$ and $\lambda = -i$.

The eigenvector equations are
$$\begin{aligned}
(1-\lambda)x_1 \quad\quad\quad &= 0, \\
-\lambda x_2 + x_3 &= 0, \\
-x_2 - \lambda x_3 &= 0.
\end{aligned}$$

- For $\lambda = 1$, the eigenvector equations become $0 = 0$, $-x_2 + x_3 = 0$ and $-x_2 - x_3 = 0$, which reduce to the equations $x_2 = 0$ and $x_3 = 0$. However, there is no constraint on the value of x_1, so we may choose it as we please provided that it is non-zero. It follows that a corresponding eigenvector is $(1 \;\; 0 \;\; 0)^T$.

- For $\lambda = i$, the eigenvector equations become $(1-i)x_1 = 0$, $-ix_2 + x_3 = 0$ and $-x_2 - ix_3 = 0$, which reduce to the equations $x_1 = 0$ and $ix_2 = x_3$. It follows that a corresponding eigenvector is $(0 \;\; 1 \;\; i)^T$.

- For $\lambda = -i$, the eigenvector equations become $(1+i)x_1 = 0$, $ix_2 + x_3 = 0$ and $-x_2 + ix_3 = 0$, which reduce to the equations $x_1 = 0$ and $-ix_2 = x_3$. It follows that a corresponding eigenvector is $(0 \;\; 1 \;\; -i)^T$.

In Example 11 we have three distinct eigenvalues and three distinct eigenvectors, but only the real eigenvalue $\lambda = 1$ gives rise to a real eigenvector.

Exercise 29

Calculate the eigenvalues and corresponding eigenvectors of the following matrices.

(a) $\begin{pmatrix} 0 & 0 & 1 \\ 0 & 1 & 0 \\ 1 & 0 & 0 \end{pmatrix}$ 　(b) $\begin{pmatrix} \frac{1}{\sqrt{2}} & 0 & \frac{1}{\sqrt{2}} \\ 0 & 1 & 0 \\ -\frac{1}{\sqrt{2}} & 0 & \frac{1}{\sqrt{2}} \end{pmatrix}$ 　(c) $\begin{pmatrix} 2 & 1 & -1 \\ 0 & -3 & 2 \\ 0 & 0 & 4 \end{pmatrix}$

(d) $\begin{pmatrix} 0 & 2 & 0 \\ -2 & 0 & 0 \\ 0 & 0 & 1 \end{pmatrix}$ 　(e) $\begin{pmatrix} 1 & 0 & 0 \\ 0 & 1 & 2 \\ 0 & -2 & 5 \end{pmatrix}$ 　(f) $\begin{pmatrix} 1 & 0 & 0 \\ 0 & 1 & 0 \\ 1 & 1 & -2 \end{pmatrix}$

We have dealt with 3×3 matrices for which the eigenvalues can be found easily, and it is reasonable to solve such problems by hand. Generally, the larger matrices that arise in practical problems are better dealt with in an entirely different fashion, as we will see in Section 4. However, our experience of finding the eigenvalues and eigenvectors of the simpler kinds of 2×2 and 3×3 matrices will not be wasted, for it will allow us to see what types of solution we may expect for larger matrices.

In each of the cases considered in this section, if a 3×3 matrix has three distinct eigenvalues, then the corresponding eigenvectors are linearly independent. More generally, any $n \times n$ matrix with n distinct eigenvalues has n linearly independent eigenvectors, although we do not prove this here.

If eigenvalues are repeated, then the situation becomes more complicated. We leave that discussion to the next unit, when we return to this topic in the context of solving systems of differential equations.

3.3   Real symmetric matrices

The eigenvalues and eigenvectors of any real symmetric $n \times n$ matrix have some important properties, which we now investigate: namely, that their eigenvalues are real and that their eigenvectors are mutually *orthogonal* – that is, perpendicular to one another – or can be made orthogonal.

> ### Orthogonal vectors
>
> If two non-zero vectors $\mathbf{u}$ and $\mathbf{v}$ satisfy the condition
>
> $$\mathbf{u}^T \mathbf{v} = u_1 v_1 + u_2 v_2 + \cdots + u_n v_n = 0,$$
>
> then they are said to be **orthogonal** to one another.

You may think of $\mathbf{u}^T\mathbf{v}$ as a $1 \times n$ matrix multiplying an $n \times 1$ matrix.

Recall from Unit 2 that the component form of the dot product (generalised to n-component vectors) is

$$\mathbf{u} \cdot \mathbf{v} = u_1 v_1 + u_2 v_2 + \cdots + u_n v_n,$$

so

$$\mathbf{u}^T \mathbf{v} = \mathbf{u} \cdot \mathbf{v} = |\mathbf{u}|\,|\mathbf{v}| \cos \theta,$$

where θ $(0 \leq \theta \leq \pi)$ is the angle between $\mathbf{u}$ and $\mathbf{v}$. Thus the orthogonality condition $\mathbf{u}^T \mathbf{v} = \mathbf{u} \cdot \mathbf{v} = 0$ implies that $\theta = \pi/2$, that is, $\mathbf{u}$ and $\mathbf{v}$ are perpendicular.

We begin by showing that the eigenvalues of a real symmetric matrix are real. This was already demonstrated for 2×2 real symmetric matrices in Subsection 2.3, but we now show that the property holds for general $n \times n$ real symmetric matrices.

We start from the eigenvalue equation

$$\mathbf{A}\mathbf{v} = \lambda \mathbf{v}, \tag{19}$$

where $\mathbf{A}$ is a real symmetric $n \times n$ matrix, and assume that the eigenvalues are in general complex, but we will eventually arrive at an expression that can be satisfied only if they are real.

Premultiply both sides of equation (19) by the transpose of the complex conjugate of $\mathbf{v}$ to obtain

$$\overline{\mathbf{v}}^T \mathbf{A} \mathbf{v} = \lambda \overline{\mathbf{v}}^T \mathbf{v}. \tag{20}$$

Note that $\overline{\mathbf{v}}$ denotes the complex conjugate of $\mathbf{v}$, i.e. if $\mathbf{v} = \mathbf{a} + i\mathbf{b}$, then $\overline{\mathbf{v}} = \mathbf{a} - i\mathbf{b}$, where $\mathbf{a}$ and $\mathbf{b}$ are real vectors.

Now transpose both sides of equation (19), which gives

$$\mathbf{v}^T \mathbf{A}^T = \lambda \mathbf{v}^T,$$

where we have used the transpose property $(\mathbf{AB})^T = \mathbf{B}^T \mathbf{A}^T$ as explained in Subsection 2.1 of Unit 4 (rules for transposes of matrices). Taking the complex conjugate of this last equation, and noting that $\mathbf{A}$ is real so that $\overline{\mathbf{A}} = \mathbf{A}$, gives

$$\overline{\mathbf{v}}^T \mathbf{A}^T = \overline{\lambda}\,\overline{\mathbf{v}}^T,$$

and then postmultiplying both sides by $\mathbf{v}$ yields

$$\overline{\mathbf{v}}^T \mathbf{A}^T \mathbf{v} = \overline{\lambda}\,\overline{\mathbf{v}}^T \mathbf{v}. \tag{21}$$

In this module, we only ever consider real matrices (apart from complex vectors). However, if $\mathbf{A}$ is complex, then its complex conjugate $\overline{\mathbf{A}}$ is obtained by replacing every element in $\mathbf{A}$ by the element's complex conjugate. An example of a complex matrix is $\mathbf{A} = \begin{pmatrix} 2 - 3i & 2 \\ 4i & 0 \end{pmatrix}$, in which case $\overline{\mathbf{A}} = \begin{pmatrix} 2 + 3i & 2 \\ -4i & 0 \end{pmatrix}$.

Subtracting equation (21) from equation (20) gives

$$\overline{\mathbf{v}}^T \mathbf{A} \mathbf{v} - \overline{\mathbf{v}}^T \mathbf{A}^T \mathbf{v} = \lambda \overline{\mathbf{v}}^T \mathbf{v} - \overline{\lambda}\,\overline{\mathbf{v}}^T \mathbf{v}. \tag{22}$$

But $\mathbf{A}$ is symmetric, which means that $\mathbf{A}^T = \mathbf{A}$, so the left-hand side of equation (22) is zero, and

$$\lambda \overline{\mathbf{v}}^T \mathbf{v} - \overline{\lambda}\,\overline{\mathbf{v}}^T \mathbf{v} = (\lambda - \overline{\lambda})\overline{\mathbf{v}}^T \mathbf{v} = 0. \tag{23}$$

Finally, by writing $\mathbf{v} = \mathbf{a} + i\mathbf{b} \neq \mathbf{0}$, where $\mathbf{a}$ and $\mathbf{b}$ are real vectors, and noting that $(\mathbf{a} - i\mathbf{b})^T = \mathbf{a}^T - i\mathbf{b}^T$ and $\mathbf{a}^T \mathbf{b} = \mathbf{b}^T \mathbf{a}$, we have

$$\overline{\mathbf{v}}^T \mathbf{v} = (\mathbf{a} - i\mathbf{b})^T (\mathbf{a} + i\mathbf{b}) = \mathbf{a}^T \mathbf{a} - i\mathbf{b}^T \mathbf{a} + i\mathbf{a}^T \mathbf{b} + \mathbf{b}^T \mathbf{b}$$
$$= \mathbf{a}^T \mathbf{a} + \mathbf{b}^T \mathbf{b} > 0,$$

so equation (23) can be satisfied only if $\overline{\lambda} = \lambda$, which holds *only* if λ is real.

At least one of $\mathbf{a}$ and $\mathbf{b}$ is not the zero vector, so at least one of $\mathbf{a}^T \mathbf{a}$ and $\mathbf{b}^T \mathbf{b}$ is non-zero (and in fact positive, since $\mathbf{u}^T \mathbf{u} = \mathbf{u} \cdot \mathbf{u} = |\mathbf{u}|^2 > 0$ for any non-zero vector $\mathbf{u}$.

Having established that the eigenvalues of general real symmetric matrices are real, we now move on to the second property by first showing that the eigenvectors corresponding to *distinct* eigenvalues of a real symmetric matrix are orthogonal.

Let λ_i be an eigenvalue of the real symmetric matrix $\mathbf{A}$ with corresponding eigenvector $\mathbf{v}_i$, and let λ_j be an eigenvalue with corresponding eigenvector $\mathbf{v}_j$ such that $\lambda_i \neq \lambda_j$. Thus we have

$$\mathbf{A}\mathbf{v}_i = \lambda_i \mathbf{v}_i, \tag{24}$$
$$\mathbf{A}\mathbf{v}_j = \lambda_j \mathbf{v}_j. \tag{25}$$

Premultiplying both sides of equation (24) by $\mathbf{v}_j^T$ gives

$$\mathbf{v}_j^T \mathbf{A}\mathbf{v}_i = \lambda_i \mathbf{v}_j^T \mathbf{v}_i, \tag{26}$$

and taking the transpose of equation (25) followed by postmultiplying by $\mathbf{v}_i$ gives

$$\mathbf{v}_j^T \mathbf{A}^T \mathbf{v}_i = \lambda_j \mathbf{v}_j^T \mathbf{v}_i. \tag{27}$$

Finally, subtracting equation (27) from equation (26), and using the fact that $\mathbf{A}^T = \mathbf{A}$, leads to

$$(\lambda_i - \lambda_j)\mathbf{v}_j^T \mathbf{v}_i = 0,$$

and since $\lambda_i \neq \lambda_j$, it must follow that $\mathbf{v}_j^T \mathbf{v}_i = 0$ or, in other words, $\mathbf{v}_i$ and $\mathbf{v}_j$ are orthogonal.

Now, we have established that eigenvectors corresponding to *distinct* eigenvalues of a symmetric matrix are orthogonal. It turns out that eigenvectors corresponding to a repeated eigenvalue (of general multiplicity) of a symmetric matrix are linearly independent and can be selected to be mutually orthogonal. The proof of this for general $n \times n$ matrices is beyond the scope of this module. However, recall from Exercise 16 that a 2×2 symmetric matrix with a repeated eigenvalue must necessarily be a scalar multiple of the 2×2 identity matrix, for which any two linearly independent vectors are eigenvectors and we are free to select two that are orthogonal, such as $(1 \quad 0)^T$ and $(0 \quad 1)^T$.

Eigenvalues and eigenvectors of real symmetric matrices

If $\mathbf{A}$ is a real symmetric $n \times n$ matrix, then:

- the eigenvalues of $\mathbf{A}$ are real
- the eigenvectors corresponding to distinct eigenvalues of $\mathbf{A}$ are orthogonal, and those corresponding to repeated eigenvalues are linearly independent and can be chosen to be orthogonal.

These properties of the eigenvalues and eigenvectors of real symmetric matrices are important in their own right and have many applications in applied mathematics. For this module, they are used in Unit 7 for classifying the stationary points of functions of several variables.

You saw an example of a real symmetric matrix having real eigenvalues and orthogonal eigenvectors in Exercise 8. Some more examples are given in the following exercises.

Exercise 30

Determine the eigenvalues and eigenvectors of the following matrices, and verify that their eigenvalues are real and that their eigenvectors are orthogonal.

(a) $\mathbf{A} = \begin{pmatrix} 1 & 2 \\ 2 & 1 \end{pmatrix}$ (b) $\mathbf{A} = \begin{pmatrix} 4 & -2 \\ -2 & 1 \end{pmatrix}$ (c) $\mathbf{A} = \begin{pmatrix} 2 & 0 & 0 \\ 0 & 0 & 1 \\ 0 & 1 & 0 \end{pmatrix}$

Exercise 31

Determine the eigenvalues and eigenvectors of the matrix

$$\begin{pmatrix} 2 & 0 & 1 \\ 0 & 3 & 0 \\ 1 & 0 & 2 \end{pmatrix},$$

and verify that the eigenvalues are real. In the case of a repeated eigenvalue, show that it has two linearly independent eigenvectors that can be chosen to be orthogonal, and that these are orthogonal to the eigenvector corresponding to the other eigenvalue.

4 Iterative methods

Finding the eigenvalues and eigenvectors of a 3×3 matrix using the method of Section 3 can be a quite laborious process, and the calculations become progressively more difficult for larger matrices.

In this section we show how we can often find approximations to real eigenvectors and their corresponding eigenvalues by iteration – that is, by choosing a vector and applying the matrix repeatedly.

4.1 Approximating eigenvectors

In the Introduction we considered a migration problem in which the towns Exton and Wyeville have a regular interchange of population. We saw that if x_n and y_n denote the respective populations of Exton and Wyeville at the beginning of year n, then the corresponding populations at the beginning of year $n + 1$ are given by the matrix equation

$$\begin{pmatrix} x_{n+1} \\ y_{n+1} \end{pmatrix} = \begin{pmatrix} 0.9 & 0.2 \\ 0.1 & 0.8 \end{pmatrix} \begin{pmatrix} x_n \\ y_n \end{pmatrix}.$$

Using this equation, we saw that if the initial populations are $x_0 = 10\,000$ and $y_0 = 8000$, then the populations in successive years are

$$\begin{pmatrix} x_0 \\ y_0 \end{pmatrix} = \begin{pmatrix} 10\,000 \\ 8\,000 \end{pmatrix}, \quad \begin{pmatrix} x_1 \\ y_1 \end{pmatrix} = \begin{pmatrix} 10\,600 \\ 7\,400 \end{pmatrix}, \quad \begin{pmatrix} x_2 \\ y_2 \end{pmatrix} = \begin{pmatrix} 11\,020 \\ 6\,980 \end{pmatrix}, \quad \ldots$$

As n increases, the sequence of vectors $(x_n \quad y_n)^T$ converges to the vector $(x \quad y)^T = (12\,000 \quad 6000)^T$, which is an eigenvector of the above 2×2 matrix.

More generally, suppose that we wish to find the eigenvectors of a given matrix $\mathbf{A}$, and that we have an initial estimate $\mathbf{e}_0$ for an eigenvector.

It may happen that $\mathbf{e}_0$ is an eigenvector of $\mathbf{A}$, and $\mathbf{A}\mathbf{e}_0$ is in the same direction as $\mathbf{e}_0$, as in Figure 6.

Figure 6   Finding $\mathbf{A}\mathbf{e}_0$ when $\mathbf{e}_0$ is an eigenvector

If, as usually happens, $\mathbf{e}_0$ is not an eigenvector, then we calculate the vector $\mathbf{e}_1 = \mathbf{A}\mathbf{e}_0$ and then another vector $\mathbf{e}_2$, defined by $\mathbf{e}_2 = \mathbf{A}\mathbf{e}_1 = \mathbf{A}^2\mathbf{e}_0$. Continuing in this way, we obtain a sequence of vectors

$$\mathbf{e}_0, \quad \mathbf{e}_1 = \mathbf{A}\mathbf{e}_0, \quad \mathbf{e}_2 = \mathbf{A}^2\mathbf{e}_0, \quad \mathbf{e}_3 = \mathbf{A}^3\mathbf{e}_0, \quad \mathbf{e}_4 = \mathbf{A}^4\mathbf{e}_0, \quad \ldots,$$

as shown in Figure 7, where each vector in the sequence is obtained from the previous one by multiplying by the matrix $\mathbf{A}$. Often this simple method of repeatedly applying the matrix $\mathbf{A}$ produces a sequence of vectors that converges to an eigenvector.

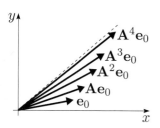

Figure 7   Repeatedly applying $\mathbf{A}$ to $\mathbf{e}_0$ converges to an eigenvector (along the dashed line)

Exercise 32

Given

$$\mathbf{A} = \begin{pmatrix} 3 & 2 \\ 1 & 4 \end{pmatrix}, \quad \mathbf{e}_0 = \begin{pmatrix} 1 \\ 0 \end{pmatrix}, \quad \mathbf{e}_{n+1} = \mathbf{A}\mathbf{e}_n, \ n = 0, 1, 2, \ldots,$$

calculate $\mathbf{e}_1, \mathbf{e}_2, \mathbf{e}_3$ and $\mathbf{e}_4$.

From Example 5 we know that for $\mathbf{A} = \begin{pmatrix} 3 & 2 \\ 1 & 4 \end{pmatrix}$, $\mathbf{v}_1 = (1 \quad 1)^T$ is an eigenvector corresponding to the eigenvalue 5, and $\mathbf{v}_2 = (-2 \quad 1)^T$ is an eigenvector corresponding to the eigenvalue 2. We may suspect that the sequence $\mathbf{e}_1, \mathbf{e}_2, \mathbf{e}_3, \mathbf{e}_4, \ldots$ in Exercise 32 converges to a scalar multiple of the eigenvector $(1 \quad 1)^T$, but how can we be *sure* that it does?

Since $\mathbf{v}_1$ and $\mathbf{v}_2$ are linearly independent eigenvectors, we can express any other vector as a linear combination of them (see Exercise 2 and the text following that exercise). So let us express our initial vector $\mathbf{e}_0 = (1 \quad 0)^T$ as $\mathbf{e}_0 = \alpha\mathbf{v}_1 + \beta\mathbf{v}_2$ for some numbers α and β. Then

α and β are known as the *components* of $\mathbf{v}_1$ and $\mathbf{v}_2$ in $\mathbf{e}_0$.

$$\mathbf{e}_0 = \begin{pmatrix} 1 \\ 0 \end{pmatrix} = \alpha \begin{pmatrix} 1 \\ 1 \end{pmatrix} + \beta \begin{pmatrix} -2 \\ 1 \end{pmatrix} = \begin{pmatrix} 1 & -2 \\ 1 & 1 \end{pmatrix} \begin{pmatrix} \alpha \\ \beta \end{pmatrix},$$

so

$$\begin{pmatrix} 1 & -2 \\ 1 & 1 \end{pmatrix} \begin{pmatrix} \alpha \\ \beta \end{pmatrix} = \begin{pmatrix} 1 \\ 0 \end{pmatrix}.$$

Multiplying both sides of this equation on the left by the inverse of the matrix on the left-hand side, we see that

$$\begin{pmatrix} \alpha \\ \beta \end{pmatrix} = \tfrac{1}{3} \begin{pmatrix} 1 & 2 \\ -1 & 1 \end{pmatrix} \begin{pmatrix} 1 \\ 0 \end{pmatrix} = \begin{pmatrix} \tfrac{1}{3} \\ -\tfrac{1}{3} \end{pmatrix},$$

so $\alpha = \tfrac{1}{3}$, $\beta = -\tfrac{1}{3}$ and

$$\mathbf{e}_0 = \tfrac{1}{3}\mathbf{v}_1 - \tfrac{1}{3}\mathbf{v}_2.$$

A matrix formed from linearly independent vectors in this way always has an inverse.

We can now express $\mathbf{e}_1, \mathbf{e}_2, \ldots$ in terms of $\mathbf{v}_1$ and $\mathbf{v}_2$. Since $\mathbf{v}_1$ and $\mathbf{v}_2$ are eigenvectors, and we know that $\mathbf{A}\mathbf{v}_1 = 5\mathbf{v}_1$ and $\mathbf{A}\mathbf{v}_2 = 2\mathbf{v}_2$, we have

$$\mathbf{e}_1 = \mathbf{A}\mathbf{e}_0 = \tfrac{1}{3}\mathbf{A}\mathbf{v}_1 - \tfrac{1}{3}\mathbf{A}\mathbf{v}_2 = \tfrac{1}{3}(5\mathbf{v}_1) - \tfrac{1}{3}(2\mathbf{v}_2).$$

Applying $\mathbf{A}$ repeatedly gives

$$\mathbf{e}_2 = \mathbf{A}^2\mathbf{e}_0 = \tfrac{1}{3}(5\mathbf{A}\mathbf{v}_1) - \tfrac{1}{3}(2\mathbf{A}\mathbf{v}_2) = \tfrac{1}{3}(5^2\mathbf{v}_1) - \tfrac{1}{3}(2^2\mathbf{v}_2),$$

$$\mathbf{e}_3 = \mathbf{A}^3\mathbf{e}_0 = \tfrac{1}{3}(5^2\mathbf{A}\mathbf{v}_1) - \tfrac{1}{3}(2^2\mathbf{A}\mathbf{v}_2) = \tfrac{1}{3}(5^3\mathbf{v}_1) - \tfrac{1}{3}(2^3\mathbf{v}_2),$$

$$\mathbf{e}_2 = \mathbf{A}\mathbf{e}_1 = \mathbf{A}^2\mathbf{e}_0$$

and so on.

In general, we can write

$$\mathbf{e}_n = \mathbf{A}^n\mathbf{e}_0 = \tfrac{1}{3}(5^n\mathbf{v}_1) - \tfrac{1}{3}(2^n\mathbf{v}_2).$$

For example,

$$\begin{aligned} \mathbf{e}_{10} = \mathbf{A}^{10}\mathbf{e}_0 &= \tfrac{1}{3}(5^{10}\mathbf{v}_1) - \tfrac{1}{3}(2^{10}\mathbf{v}_2) \\ &\simeq 3\,255\,208\mathbf{v}_1 - 341\mathbf{v}_2 \\ &\simeq 3\,255\,208(\mathbf{v}_1 - 0.000\,105\mathbf{v}_2). \end{aligned}$$

As you can see, the powers of 5 rapidly become much larger than the powers of 2, and for large values of n we can ignore the latter, to give the approximation

$$\mathbf{e}_n = \mathbf{A}^n\mathbf{e}_0 \simeq \tfrac{1}{3}(5^n\mathbf{v}_1).$$

This is a scalar multiple of an eigenvector that corresponds to the eigenvalue of larger magnitude.

Thus repeatedly applying $\mathbf{A}$ leads to an approximation of an eigenvector – an eigenvector corresponding to the eigenvalue of larger magnitude.

Taking another example, you can show that the matrix

$$\begin{pmatrix} 4 & 2 \\ -7 & -5 \end{pmatrix}$$

has eigenvalues -3 and 2, and that the above method will give approximations to an eigenvector corresponding to the eigenvalue -3 because powers of -3 eventually dominate powers of 2.

Exercise 33

Consider

$$\mathbf{A} = \begin{pmatrix} 2 & 1 \\ 1 & 2 \end{pmatrix}, \quad \mathbf{e}_0 = \begin{pmatrix} 1 \\ 0 \end{pmatrix}, \quad \mathbf{e}_{n+1} = \mathbf{A}\mathbf{e}_n, \quad n = 0, 1, 2, \ldots.$$

(a) Calculate $\mathbf{e}_1$, $\mathbf{e}_2$ and $\mathbf{e}_3$.

(b) Given $\mathbf{e}_{10} = (29\,525 \quad 29\,524)^T$, calculate $\mathbf{e}_{11}$.

(c) Use Procedures 1 and 2 to find the eigenvalues λ_1 and λ_2, and corresponding eigenvectors $\mathbf{v}_1$ and $\mathbf{v}_2$, of $\mathbf{A}$.

(d) Express $\mathbf{e}_0$ as a linear combination of $\mathbf{v}_1$ and $\mathbf{v}_2$.

(e) Express $\mathbf{e}_1$, $\mathbf{e}_2$, and hence $\mathbf{e}_n$, as linear combinations of $\mathbf{v}_1$ and $\mathbf{v}_2$.

(f) To which eigenvector does the sequence $\{\mathbf{e}_n\}$ provide an approximation?

The above technique provides us with increasingly accurate approximations to one of the eigenvectors of a 2×2 matrix. But the most significant aspect of the method is that it is possible to extend it to matrices of *any* size. However, there are difficulties, and you should be aware of them before we proceed. You may have noticed in the previous exercise that the components of an approximation to an eigenvector may be quite large and, had we attempted to calculate $\mathbf{e}_{20}$, we would have found that $\mathbf{e}_{20} = (1\,743\,392\,201 \quad 1\,743\,392\,200)^T$. For larger values of n, $\mathbf{e}_n$ involves even larger numbers. We will see that this difficulty is easily overcome, but there are other difficulties. Table 1 shows five examples, each exhibiting a different problem.

The $\mathbf{e}_0$ are normally chosen rather arbitrarily.

Table 1

	Matrix	Eigenvalues	Corresponding eigenvectors	Initial vector and nth approximation
(a)	$\begin{pmatrix} 1 & 4 \\ 9 & 1 \end{pmatrix}$	7 -5	$\mathbf{v}_1 = (2 \quad 3)^T$ $\mathbf{v}_2 = (2 \quad -3)^T$	$\mathbf{e}_0 = (1 \quad 0)^T$ $\mathbf{e}_n = \frac{1}{4}(7)^n\mathbf{v}_1 + \frac{1}{4}(-5)^n\mathbf{v}_2$
(b)	$\begin{pmatrix} 2 & 0 \\ 0 & -2 \end{pmatrix}$	2 -2	$\mathbf{v}_1 = (1 \quad 0)^T$ $\mathbf{v}_2 = (0 \quad 1)^T$	$\mathbf{e}_0 = (1 \quad 1)^T$ $\mathbf{e}_n = 2^n\mathbf{v}_1 + (-2)^n\mathbf{v}_2$
(c)	$\begin{pmatrix} 1.2 & -0.2 \\ 0.3 & 0.7 \end{pmatrix}$	1 0.9	$\mathbf{v}_1 = (1 \quad 1)^T$ $\mathbf{v}_2 = (2 \quad 3)^T$	$\mathbf{e}_0 = (1 \quad 0)^T$ $\mathbf{e}_n = 3\mathbf{v}_1 - (0.9)^n\mathbf{v}_2$
(d)	$\begin{pmatrix} 0 & -1 \\ 1 & 0 \end{pmatrix}$	i $-i$	$\mathbf{v}_1 = (1 \quad -i)^T$ $\mathbf{v}_2 = (1 \quad i)^T$	$\mathbf{e}_0 = (1 \quad 0)^T$ $\mathbf{e}_n = \frac{1}{2}(i)^n\mathbf{v}_1 + \frac{1}{2}(-i)^n\mathbf{v}_2$
(e)	$\begin{pmatrix} 3 & 0 & 0 \\ 0 & 2 & 0 \\ 0 & 0 & 1 \end{pmatrix}$	3 2 1	$\mathbf{v}_1 = (1 \quad 0 \quad 0)^T$ $\mathbf{v}_2 = (0 \quad 1 \quad 0)^T$ $\mathbf{v}_3 = (0 \quad 0 \quad 1)^T$	$\mathbf{e}_0 = (0 \quad 1 \quad 1)^T$ $\mathbf{e}_n = 2^n\mathbf{v}_2 + \mathbf{v}_3$

In row (a) of the table, the elements of $\mathbf{e}_n$ become very large: for example,

$$\mathbf{e}_5 = (6841 \quad 14\,949)^T$$

and

$$\mathbf{e}_{10} = (146\,120\,437 \quad 204\,532\,218)^T.$$

This may cause difficulties in the calculations. You may already suspect how this difficulty may be overcome. We are interested in only the *directions* of the vectors, and rescaling a vector does not change its direction. So dividing both components of $\mathbf{e}_{10}$ by $204\,532\,218$, we obtain the vector $(0.7144 \quad 1)^T$ (to four decimal places) as the estimate of an eigenvector.

In row (b) we have a rather more fundamental problem. The eigenvalues have the same magnitude, so as n increases, neither the term involving $\mathbf{v}_1$ nor the term involving $\mathbf{v}_2$ becomes dominant, thus the iteration does not converge.

The eigenvalues in row (c) are certainly not equal, but they are similar in magnitude. This means that we need to choose a very large value of n in order to obtain a good approximation to $\mathbf{v}_1$ (the eigenvector corresponding to the eigenvalue of larger magnitude).

In row (d) we have complex eigenvalues, and as you might expect, a sequence of real vectors cannot converge to a complex eigenvector.

You always generate a real sequence (unless you start with a complex $\mathbf{e}_0$).

In row (e) we see that the sequence $\mathbf{e}_n$ converges to the eigenvector $\mathbf{v}_2$, when we might expect it to converge to $\mathbf{v}_1$ (the eigenvector corresponding to the eigenvalue of largest magnitude). This is because the original estimate $\mathbf{e}_0$ contains no component of $\mathbf{v}_1$, so the same is true of all subsequent estimates. (Such a difficulty is unlikely to arise in practice because rounding errors in the calculation of the iterates will normally ensure that the component of $\mathbf{v}_1$ is not exactly zero.)

Exercise 34

In the migration problem first discussed in the Introduction, we have

$$\mathbf{A} = \begin{pmatrix} 0.9 & 0.2 \\ 0.1 & 0.8 \end{pmatrix}, \quad \mathbf{e}_0 = \begin{pmatrix} 10\,000 \\ 8\,000 \end{pmatrix}.$$

Eigenvectors of $\mathbf{A}$ are $\mathbf{v}_1 = (2 \quad 1)^T$ with corresponding eigenvalue 1, and $\mathbf{v}_2 = (1 \quad -1)^T$ with corresponding eigenvalue 0.7.

You found these eigenvalues and eigenvectors in Exercise 12.

(a) Write $\mathbf{e}_0$ as a linear combination of $\mathbf{v}_1$ and $\mathbf{v}_2$.

(b) Obtain an expression for $\mathbf{e}_n = \mathbf{A}^n \mathbf{e}_0$ as a linear combination of $\mathbf{v}_1$ and $\mathbf{v}_2$.

(c) Explain what happens as n becomes large.

4.2 Iterative techniques

Suppose that we are given a square matrix whose eigenvalues are known to be real and distinct in magnitude. Though we do not know their values, assume that the eigenvalues are listed in decreasing order of magnitude. For example, eigenvalues 5, -1 and -4 would be listed in the order

$$\lambda_1 = 5, \quad \lambda_2 = -4, \quad \lambda_3 = -1.$$

$|5| > |-4| > |-1|$

Using the ideas of the previous subsection, together with the results at the end of Section 2, we can approximate all the eigenvalues and corresponding eigenvectors. We start with the eigenvector corresponding to the eigenvalue of largest magnitude, then we show how the other eigenvectors and eigenvalues are approximated.

Eigenvalue of largest magnitude: direct iteration

In order to approximate an eigenvector corresponding to the eigenvalue $\lambda_{\max}$ of largest magnitude, we use the approach that we employed at the beginning of the previous subsection. We start with a square matrix $\mathbf{A}$ and a vector $\mathbf{e}_0$, and successively calculate the new vectors

$$\mathbf{e}_1 = \mathbf{A}\mathbf{e}_0, \quad \mathbf{e}_2 = \mathbf{A}\mathbf{e}_1, \quad \mathbf{e}_3 = \mathbf{A}\mathbf{e}_2, \quad \ldots,$$

which is equivalent to writing $\mathbf{e}_n = \mathbf{A}^n \mathbf{e}_0$, $n = 1, 2, 3, \ldots$.

For example, if

$$\mathbf{A} = \begin{pmatrix} 3 & 2 \\ 1 & 4 \end{pmatrix} \quad \text{and} \quad \mathbf{e}_0 = \begin{pmatrix} 1 \\ 0 \end{pmatrix},$$

then, as you saw in Exercise 32,

$$\mathbf{e}_1 = \begin{pmatrix} 3 \\ 1 \end{pmatrix}, \quad \mathbf{e}_2 = \begin{pmatrix} 11 \\ 7 \end{pmatrix}, \quad \mathbf{e}_3 = \begin{pmatrix} 47 \\ 39 \end{pmatrix}, \quad \mathbf{e}_4 = \begin{pmatrix} 219 \\ 203 \end{pmatrix}, \quad \ldots.$$

The main difficulty with this method is that the components of $\mathbf{e}_n$ can rapidly become very large (or very small). But we can overcome this problem by setting α_n to be the component of largest magnitude in $\mathbf{e}_n$. Then dividing the vector $\mathbf{e}_n$ by α_n ensures that the vector $\mathbf{e}_n/\alpha_n$ has components that are less than, or equal to, 1 in magnitude. This process is called *scaling*, giving a *scaled vector*.

For the above vectors, $\alpha_1 = 3$, $\alpha_2 = 11$, $\alpha_3 = 47$ and $\alpha_4 = 219$, and we obtain the sequence of vectors

$$\begin{pmatrix} 1 \\ \frac{1}{3} \end{pmatrix}, \quad \begin{pmatrix} 1 \\ \frac{7}{11} \end{pmatrix}, \quad \begin{pmatrix} 1 \\ \frac{39}{47} \end{pmatrix}, \quad \begin{pmatrix} 1 \\ \frac{203}{219} \end{pmatrix}$$

(with the same directions as the sequence found in Exercise 32).

The components of our final answer will now be of reasonable size. If this scaling process is applied only at the final stage, we may still encounter very large components in the intermediate calculations. This difficulty is avoided by applying the scaling process at each step of the calculation, as in the following procedure.

Procedure 4   Direct iteration

For any square matrix $\mathbf{A}$ for which the eigenvalue $\lambda_{\max}$ of largest magnitude is real (and distinct in magnitude from any other eigenvalue), choose any vector $\mathbf{e}_0$.

For $n = 0, 1, 2, \ldots$, carry out the following steps.

1.   Calculate $\mathbf{z}_{n+1} = \mathbf{A}\mathbf{e}_n$.

2.   Find α_{n+1}, the component of largest magnitude of $\mathbf{z}_{n+1}$.

3.   Put $\mathbf{e}_{n+1} = \mathbf{z}_{n+1}/\alpha_{n+1}$.

For sufficiently large n, $\mathbf{e}_n$ will be a good approximation to an eigenvector corresponding to the eigenvalue of largest magnitude, provided that $\mathbf{e}_0$ has a non-zero component of the required eigenvector. If the sequence α_n converges, then it converges to $\lambda_{\max}$.

For example, a matrix with eigenvalues 3 and -3 would not qualify, because the eigenvalues are equal in magnitude.

If $\lambda_{\max}$ is complex, then its complex conjugate will also be an eigenvalue of the same magnitude, so this procedure works only when the eigenvalue of largest magnitude is real.

The final sentence of the above procedure can be deduced from the fact that at each stage of the calculation we have $\mathbf{A}\mathbf{e}_n = \mathbf{z}_{n+1} = \alpha_{n+1}\mathbf{e}_{n+1}$. If $\mathbf{e}_n$ converges to a vector $\mathbf{e}$ and α_n converges to a number α, then, in the limit, we have $\mathbf{A}\mathbf{e} = \alpha\mathbf{e}$, so $\mathbf{e}$ is an eigenvector corresponding to the eigenvalue α. But we know that $\mathbf{e}$ is an eigenvector corresponding to the eigenvalue of largest magnitude, so α must be this eigenvalue.

Example 12

Given

$$\mathbf{A} = \begin{pmatrix} 3 & 2 \\ 1 & 4 \end{pmatrix} \quad \text{and} \quad \mathbf{e}_0 = \begin{pmatrix} 1 \\ 0 \end{pmatrix},$$

use Procedure 4 to find $\mathbf{e}_1$, $\mathbf{e}_2$ and $\mathbf{e}_3$. (From Example 5, the eigenvalues of $\mathbf{A}$ are 5 and 2, with corresponding eigenvectors $(1 \quad 1)^T$ and $(-2 \quad 1)^T$, respectively.)

Solution

First iteration:

$$\mathbf{z}_1 = \mathbf{A}\mathbf{e}_0 = \begin{pmatrix} 3 & 2 \\ 1 & 4 \end{pmatrix} \begin{pmatrix} 1 \\ 0 \end{pmatrix} = \begin{pmatrix} 3 \\ 1 \end{pmatrix},$$

$$\alpha_1 = 3,$$

$$\mathbf{e}_1 = \frac{\mathbf{z}_1}{\alpha_1} = \tfrac{1}{3} \begin{pmatrix} 3 \\ 1 \end{pmatrix} = \begin{pmatrix} 1 \\ \tfrac{1}{3} \end{pmatrix}.$$

Second iteration:

$$\mathbf{z}_2 = \mathbf{A}\mathbf{e}_1 = \begin{pmatrix} 3 & 2 \\ 1 & 4 \end{pmatrix} \begin{pmatrix} 1 \\ \frac{1}{3} \end{pmatrix} = \begin{pmatrix} \frac{11}{3} \\ \frac{7}{3} \end{pmatrix},$$

$$\alpha_2 = \frac{11}{3},$$

$$\mathbf{e}_2 = \frac{\mathbf{z}_2}{\alpha_2} = \frac{3}{11} \begin{pmatrix} \frac{11}{3} \\ \frac{7}{3} \end{pmatrix} = \begin{pmatrix} 1 \\ \frac{7}{11} \end{pmatrix}.$$

Third iteration:

$$\mathbf{z}_3 = \mathbf{A}\mathbf{e}_2 = \begin{pmatrix} 3 & 2 \\ 1 & 4 \end{pmatrix} \begin{pmatrix} 1 \\ \frac{7}{11} \end{pmatrix} = \begin{pmatrix} \frac{47}{11} \\ \frac{39}{11} \end{pmatrix},$$

$$\alpha_3 = \frac{47}{11},$$

$$\mathbf{e}_3 = \frac{\mathbf{z}_3}{\alpha_3} = \frac{11}{47} \begin{pmatrix} \frac{47}{11} \\ \frac{39}{11} \end{pmatrix} = \begin{pmatrix} 1 \\ \frac{39}{47} \end{pmatrix}.$$

If we were to continue the process in Example 12, we would find that the sequence of vectors $\mathbf{e}_n$ converges to the eigenvector $(1 \quad 1)^T$, and the sequence α_n converges to the corresponding eigenvalue 5.

Exercise 35

Given

$$\mathbf{A} = \begin{pmatrix} 3 & 6 \\ 4 & 8 \end{pmatrix} \quad \text{and} \quad \mathbf{e}_0 = (1 \quad 0)^T,$$

use Procedure 4 to calculate $\mathbf{e}_1$, $\mathbf{e}_2$ and $\mathbf{e}_3$. What can you deduce about the eigenvalues and eigenvectors of $\mathbf{A}$?

Eigenvalue of smallest magnitude: inverse iteration

In order to approximate an eigenvector corresponding to the eigenvalue of *smallest* magnitude, we adapt the above method of direct iteration.

If $\mathbf{A}$ is invertible, then $\mathbf{A}^{-1}$ exists and the eigenvalues are non-zero (see Subsection 2.3).

Consider an invertible matrix $\mathbf{A}$ whose eigenvalues are real and distinct in magnitude. Suppose again that the eigenvalues of $\mathbf{A}$ are listed in decreasing order of magnitude. It follows that their reciprocals must appear in increasing order of magnitude. But by the results of Subsection 2.4, the numbers λ^{-1} are the eigenvalues of the inverse matrix $\mathbf{A}^{-1}$ with the same eigenvectors as the matrix $\mathbf{A}$. So the problem of approximating the eigenvalue of smallest magnitude λ of $\mathbf{A}$ is the same as that of approximating the eigenvalue of largest magnitude λ^{-1} of $\mathbf{A}^{-1}$.

It follows that repeatedly applying the matrix $\mathbf{A}^{-1}$ produces an eigenvector corresponding to the eigenvalue of smallest magnitude, assuming that it is real and distinct in magnitude from any other eigenvalue of $\mathbf{A}$.

For any square matrix $\mathbf{A}$ with non-zero real eigenvalues, we find an eigenvector corresponding to an eigenvalue of smallest magnitude by choosing a vector $\mathbf{e}_0$ and successively calculating the vectors $\mathbf{e}_1, \mathbf{e}_2, \mathbf{e}_3, \ldots$ using the formula

$$\mathbf{e}_{n+1} = \mathbf{A}^{-1}\mathbf{e}_n, \quad n = 0, 1, 2, \ldots.$$

In practice, such calculations can suffer from the same difficulties as direct iteration. We solve the problem of very large or very small vectors as before, by scaling, writing

$$\mathbf{z}_{n+1} = \mathbf{A}^{-1}\mathbf{e}_n, \quad \mathbf{e}_{n+1} = \frac{\mathbf{z}_{n+1}}{\alpha_{n+1}}, \quad n = 0, 1, 2, \ldots,$$

where α_{n+1} is the component of largest magnitude of $\mathbf{z}_{n+1}$. However, there is a further complication – the calculation of the inverse matrix can be very time consuming for large matrices. A more practical approach is based on solving the equations $\mathbf{A}\mathbf{z}_{n+1} = \mathbf{e}_n$ for $\mathbf{z}_{n+1}$ by Gaussian elimination and then putting $\mathbf{e}_{n+1} = \mathbf{z}_{n+1}/\alpha_{n+1}$.

Procedure 5   Inverse iteration

For any invertible (square) matrix $\mathbf{A}$ for which the eigenvalue $\lambda_{\min}$ of smallest magnitude is real and distinct in magnitude from any other eigenvalue, choose any vector $\mathbf{e}_0$.

The fact that $\mathbf{A}$ is invertible ensures that $\lambda_{\min} \neq 0$ and that $\mathbf{A}^{-1}$ exists.

(a) For $n = 0, 1, 2, \ldots$, carry out the following steps.

1. Calculate $\mathbf{z}_{n+1} = \mathbf{A}^{-1}\mathbf{e}_n$.
2. Find α_{n+1}, the component of largest magnitude of $\mathbf{z}_{n+1}$.
3. Put $\mathbf{e}_{n+1} = \mathbf{z}_{n+1}/\alpha_{n+1}$.

(b) The above method is inefficient for large matrices due to the difficulty of calculating $\mathbf{A}^{-1}$. In such cases, for $n = 0, 1, 2, \ldots$, carry out the following steps.

1. Calculate $\mathbf{z}_{n+1}$ by solving the equation $\mathbf{A}\mathbf{z}_{n+1} = \mathbf{e}_n$.
2. Find α_{n+1}, the component of largest magnitude of $\mathbf{z}_{n+1}$.
3. Put $\mathbf{e}_{n+1} = \mathbf{z}_{n+1}/\alpha_{n+1}$.

For sufficiently large n, $\mathbf{e}_n$ will be a good approximation to an eigenvector corresponding to the eigenvalue of smallest magnitude, provided that $\mathbf{e}_0$ has a non-zero component of the required eigenvector. If the sequence α_n converges, then it converges to $1/\lambda_{\min}$.

Example 13

Given the matrix $\mathbf{A} = \begin{pmatrix} 3 & 2 \\ 3 & 4 \end{pmatrix}$, calculate $\mathbf{A}^{-1}$. Given $\mathbf{e}_0 = (1 \quad 1)^T$, use Procedure 5(a) to calculate $\mathbf{e}_1$, $\mathbf{e}_2$ and $\mathbf{e}_3$.

Solution

We have

$$\mathbf{A}^{-1} = \tfrac{1}{6} \begin{pmatrix} 4 & -2 \\ -3 & 3 \end{pmatrix}.$$

First iteration:

$$\mathbf{z}_1 = \mathbf{A}^{-1}\mathbf{e}_0 = \tfrac{1}{6} \begin{pmatrix} 4 & -2 \\ -3 & 3 \end{pmatrix} \begin{pmatrix} 1 \\ 1 \end{pmatrix} = \begin{pmatrix} \tfrac{1}{3} \\ 0 \end{pmatrix},$$

$$\alpha_1 = \tfrac{1}{3},$$

$$\mathbf{e}_1 = \frac{\mathbf{z}_1}{\alpha_1} = 3 \begin{pmatrix} \tfrac{1}{3} \\ 0 \end{pmatrix} = \begin{pmatrix} 1 \\ 0 \end{pmatrix}.$$

Second iteration:

$$\mathbf{z}_2 = \mathbf{A}^{-1}\mathbf{e}_1 = \tfrac{1}{6} \begin{pmatrix} 4 & -2 \\ -3 & 3 \end{pmatrix} \begin{pmatrix} 1 \\ 0 \end{pmatrix} = \begin{pmatrix} \tfrac{2}{3} \\ -\tfrac{1}{2} \end{pmatrix},$$

$$\alpha_2 = \tfrac{2}{3},$$

$$\mathbf{e}_2 = \frac{\mathbf{z}_2}{\alpha_2} = \tfrac{3}{2} \begin{pmatrix} \tfrac{2}{3} \\ -\tfrac{1}{2} \end{pmatrix} = \begin{pmatrix} 1 \\ -\tfrac{3}{4} \end{pmatrix}.$$

Third iteration:

$$\mathbf{z}_3 = \mathbf{A}^{-1}\mathbf{e}_2 = \tfrac{1}{6} \begin{pmatrix} 4 & -2 \\ -3 & 3 \end{pmatrix} \begin{pmatrix} 1 \\ -\tfrac{3}{4} \end{pmatrix} = \begin{pmatrix} \tfrac{11}{12} \\ -\tfrac{7}{8} \end{pmatrix},$$

$$\alpha_3 = \tfrac{11}{12},$$

$$\mathbf{e}_3 = \frac{\mathbf{z}_3}{\alpha_3} = \tfrac{12}{11} \begin{pmatrix} \tfrac{11}{12} \\ -\tfrac{7}{8} \end{pmatrix} = \begin{pmatrix} 1 \\ -\tfrac{21}{22} \end{pmatrix}.$$

If we were to continue the process in Example 13, we would find that the sequence of vectors $\mathbf{e}_n$ converges to the eigenvector $(1 \quad -1)^T$, and the sequence α_n converges to 1, corresponding to the eigenvalue $1/1 = 1$.

Exercise 36

Use Procedure 5(a) with $\mathbf{A} = \begin{pmatrix} 7 & 3 \\ 8 & 5 \end{pmatrix}$ and $\mathbf{e}_0 = \begin{pmatrix} 1 \\ 1 \end{pmatrix}$ to obtain $\mathbf{e}_1$, $\mathbf{e}_2$ and $\mathbf{e}_3$. Hence find an approximation to the eigenvalue of $\mathbf{A}$ of smallest magnitude, and a corresponding eigenvector.

Specific eigenvalues: modified inverse iteration

Procedures 4 and 5 are restricted to calculating the eigenvalue of largest or smallest magnitude. Sometimes we do not need either of these, but rather we need the eigenvalue closest to a given value. The following method will allow us to find it. We assume that there is just one eigenvalue of $\mathbf{A}$ closest to the given value p.

If λ is an eigenvalue of a matrix $\mathbf{A}$ (and p is not an eigenvalue of $\mathbf{A}$), then $(\lambda - p)^{-1}$ is an eigenvalue of the matrix $(\mathbf{A} - p\mathbf{I})^{-1}$, and the corresponding eigenvectors are unchanged. Suppose that λ_1 is the real eigenvalue closest to p. In other words, $|\lambda_1 - p|$ is the smallest of all possible choices of $|\lambda - p|$, thus $1/|\lambda_1 - p|$ is the largest of all possible choices of $1/|\lambda - p|$. It follows that repeatedly applying the matrix $(\mathbf{A} - p\mathbf{I})^{-1}$ to a chosen vector $\mathbf{e}_0$ produces an eigenvector corresponding to the eigenvalue closest to p. Thus the sequence $\mathbf{e}_{n+1} = (\mathbf{A} - p\mathbf{I})^{-1}\mathbf{e}_n$ $(n = 0, 1, 2, \ldots)$ should produce a sequence of approximations to the eigenvector.

See Subsection 2.4.

This method suffers from the deficiencies mentioned for inverse iteration, so we make similar refinements.

> ### Procedure 6 Modified inverse iteration
>
> Suppose that $\mathbf{A}$ is a square matrix for which one distinct real eigenvalue λ_1 is closest to a given real number p. To find an eigenvector corresponding to the eigenvalue closest to p, choose any vector $\mathbf{e}_0$.
>
> *The procedure breaks down if p is an eigenvalue.*
>
> (a) For $n = 0, 1, 2, \ldots$, carry out the following steps.
>
>   1. Calculate $\mathbf{z}_{n+1} = (\mathbf{A} - p\mathbf{I})^{-1}\mathbf{e}_n$.
>
>   2. Find α_{n+1}, the component of largest magnitude of $\mathbf{z}_{n+1}$.
>
>   3. Put $\mathbf{e}_{n+1} = \mathbf{z}_{n+1}/\alpha_{n+1}$.
>
> (b) The above method is inefficient for large matrices due to the difficulty of calculating $(\mathbf{A} - p\mathbf{I})^{-1}$. In such cases, for $n = 0, 1, 2, \ldots$, carry out the following steps.
>
>   1. Calculate $\mathbf{z}_{n+1}$ by solving the equation $(\mathbf{A} - p\mathbf{I})\mathbf{z}_{n+1} = \mathbf{e}_n$.
>
>   2. Find α_{n+1}, the component of largest magnitude of $\mathbf{z}_{n+1}$.
>
>   3. Put $\mathbf{e}_{n+1} = \mathbf{z}_{n+1}/\alpha_{n+1}$.
>
> For sufficiently large n, $\mathbf{e}_n$ will be a good approximation to an eigenvector corresponding to the eigenvalue closest to p, provided that $\mathbf{e}_0$ has a non-zero component of the required eigenvector. If the sequence α_n converges, then it converges to $1/(\lambda_1 - p)$.

In the following exercise, much of the work has been done for you.

Exercise 37

We wish to obtain an approximation to an eigenvector corresponding to the eigenvalue closest to $p = -1$ for the matrix

$$\mathbf{A} = \begin{pmatrix} 1 & 2 & 3 \\ 2 & 3 & 4 \\ 3 & 4 & 6 \end{pmatrix}.$$

This inverse could most easily be found using a computer algebra package. Alternatively, Gaussian elimination, as described in Unit 4, could be used.

We have

$$(\mathbf{A} - p\mathbf{I})^{-1} = (\mathbf{A} + \mathbf{I})^{-1} = \begin{pmatrix} \frac{3}{2} & -\frac{1}{4} & -\frac{1}{2} \\ -\frac{1}{4} & \frac{5}{8} & -\frac{1}{4} \\ -\frac{1}{2} & -\frac{1}{4} & \frac{1}{2} \end{pmatrix}.$$

Applying Procedure 6(a) with $\mathbf{e}_0 = (1 \quad 0 \quad 0)^T$ gives $\alpha_{20} \simeq 1.724\,96$ and $\mathbf{e}_{20} \simeq (1 \quad -0.141\,05 \quad -0.379\,39)^T$.

Calculate $\mathbf{e}_{21}$ with the components given to five decimal places so as to check convergence to three decimal places, and obtain an estimate for the corresponding eigenvalue to three decimal places.

Note that Procedure 5 is essentially the same as Procedure 4, but with $\mathbf{A}^{-1}$ in place of $\mathbf{A}$, and Procedure 6 is also essentially the same as Procedure 4, but with $(\mathbf{A} - p\mathbf{I})^{-1}$ in place of $\mathbf{A}$.

Procedures 4, 5 and 6 can be used to find individual eigenvalues and eigenvectors of a matrix. If we require *all* the eigenvalues and/or eigenvectors, then there are more efficient methods that can be used, though we do not discuss them here.

The rate of convergence of each of the methods depends on the relative closeness in magnitude of the other eigenvalues of $\mathbf{A}$ (or $\mathbf{A}^{-1}$, or $(\mathbf{A} - p\mathbf{I})^{-1}$) to the required eigenvalue. For example, in Exercise 37 the eigenvalues are 10.187, -0.420 and 0.234, to three decimal places. The direct iteration method applied to this problem would converge very rapidly since the largest eigenvalue, 10.187, is much larger in magnitude than the other two. On the other hand, inverse iteration would be slower, since the eigenvalues of $\mathbf{A}^{-1}$ are 4.281, -2.379 and 0.098 (to three decimal places), and the second largest eigenvalue in magnitude, -2.379, is just over half the magnitude of the largest eigenvalue.

A judicious choice of p for the modified inverse iteration method can significantly increase the rate of convergence. For example, choosing $p = 0.2$ for the matrix in Exercise 37 gives the eigenvalues of $\mathbf{A} - p\mathbf{I}$ as 9.987, -0.620 and 0.034, so the eigenvalues of $(\mathbf{A} - p\mathbf{I})^{-1}$ are 29.781, -1.612 and 0.100. We expect that the modified inverse iteration method with this value of p would converge very rapidly to the eigenvalue 0.234 of the matrix $\mathbf{A}$.

Procedures 4 and 5 cannot be used to determine complex eigenvalues, since complex eigenvalues of real matrices occur in complex conjugate pairs, and a complex eigenvalue and its complex conjugate have the same magnitude. Both procedures fail to find the required eigenvalue when there is a second distinct eigenvalue of the same magnitude.

However, it is possible to use Procedure 6 to find complex eigenvalues, provided that a complex value for p is chosen so that p is closer in magnitude to one of the complex eigenvalues than to any of the others.

Exercise 38

In this exercise, $\mathbf{A} = \begin{pmatrix} 0.5 & 0.6 \\ 1.4 & -0.3 \end{pmatrix}$.

These calculations are intended to be done by hand (with the aid of a scientific calculator).

(a) Given $\mathbf{e}_0 = (1 \quad 0)^T$, use direct iteration to calculate $\mathbf{e}_1$, $\mathbf{e}_2$ and $\mathbf{e}_3$.

(b) Use the methods of Section 2 to find the eigenvalues and corresponding eigenvectors of $\mathbf{A}$.

(c) To which eigenvector would you expect the sequence $\mathbf{e}_n$ of part (a) to converge?

(d) If $\mathbf{v}$ is an eigenvector of $\mathbf{A}$ corresponding to the eigenvalue λ, express $\mathbf{A}^8\mathbf{v}$ in terms of λ and $\mathbf{v}$.

(e) Designate the eigenvectors found in part (b) as $\mathbf{v}_1$ and $\mathbf{v}_2$. Express $\mathbf{e}_0$ in terms of $\mathbf{v}_1$ and $\mathbf{v}_2$, then calculate $\mathbf{e}_8$. (If this seems like hard work, then look for an easier method.)

(f) Find $\mathbf{A}^{-1}$, then use inverse iteration to calculate $\mathbf{e}_1$, $\mathbf{e}_2$ and $\mathbf{e}_3$, given $\mathbf{e}_0 = (-0.4 \quad 1)^T$. To which eigenvector would you expect this sequence to converge?

(g) Comment on the rates of convergence for direct iteration and inverse iteration applied to this problem.

Exercise 39

Suppose that you wish to find all the eigenvalues of the matrix

$$\mathbf{A} = \begin{pmatrix} 1 & 2 & 3 \\ 2 & 3 & 4 \\ 3 & 4 & 6 \end{pmatrix}.$$

Before you start this exercise, consider how the third eigenvalue can be obtained from the other two eigenvalues. Applying this method will reduce the work.

Further, suppose that you have used direct iteration to find an eigenvector

$$\mathbf{v}_1 \simeq (0.477 \quad 0.689 \quad 1)^T,$$

and inverse iteration to find another eigenvector

$$\mathbf{v}_2 \simeq (-0.102 \quad 1 \quad -0.641)^T.$$

Use this information to find approximations to all three eigenvalues.

Learning outcomes

After studying this unit, you should be able to:

- explain the meaning of the terms eigenvalue, eigenvector and characteristic equation
- calculate the eigenvalues of a given 2×2 matrix, and find the corresponding eigenvectors
- calculate the eigenvalues and corresponding eigenvectors of a 3×3 matrix, where one of the eigenvalues is 'obvious'
- appreciate that an $n \times n$ matrix with n distinct eigenvalues gives rise to n linearly independent eigenvectors
- appreciate that the eigenvalues of a matrix may be real and distinct, real and repeated, or complex
- recall that the sum of the eigenvalues of an $n \times n$ matrix $\mathbf{A}$ is $\operatorname{tr} \mathbf{A}$, and that the product of the eigenvalues of $\mathbf{A}$ is $\det \mathbf{A}$, and use these properties as a check in hand calculations
- write down the eigenvalues of a triangular matrix
- write down the eigenvalues of the matrices $\mathbf{A}^k$, $\mathbf{A}^{-1}$, $\mathbf{A} + p\mathbf{I}$, $(\mathbf{A} - p\mathbf{I})^{-1}$ and $p\mathbf{A}$, given the eigenvalues of $\mathbf{A}$;
- appreciate that the eigenvalues of a real symmetric matrix are real and the corresponding eigenvectors are orthogonal, and in the case of repeated eigenvalues, the corresponding eigenvectors can be chosen to be orthogonal
- appreciate the use of direct, inverse and modified inverse iteration in approximating individual eigenvalues and corresponding eigenvectors of a square matrix
- use iterative methods and hand calculation to estimate an eigenvalue and corresponding eigenvector in simple cases.

Solutions to exercises

Solution to Exercise 1

$$\mathbf{Aw} = \begin{pmatrix} 3 & 2 \\ 1 & 4 \end{pmatrix} \begin{pmatrix} 3 \\ -1 \end{pmatrix} = \begin{pmatrix} 7 \\ -1 \end{pmatrix},$$

$$\mathbf{Ax} = \begin{pmatrix} 3 & 2 \\ 1 & 4 \end{pmatrix} \begin{pmatrix} 1 \\ 1 \end{pmatrix} = \begin{pmatrix} 5 \\ 5 \end{pmatrix},$$

$$\mathbf{Ay} = \begin{pmatrix} 3 & 2 \\ 1 & 4 \end{pmatrix} \begin{pmatrix} -2 \\ 1 \end{pmatrix} = \begin{pmatrix} -4 \\ 2 \end{pmatrix},$$

$$\mathbf{Az} = \begin{pmatrix} 3 & 2 \\ 1 & 4 \end{pmatrix} \begin{pmatrix} 0 \\ 0 \end{pmatrix} = \begin{pmatrix} 0 \\ 0 \end{pmatrix}.$$

Solution to Exercise 2

If $(x \quad y)^T = \alpha(1 \quad 1)^T + \beta(-2 \quad 1)^T$, then

$$\alpha - 2\beta = x,$$
$$\alpha + \beta = y.$$

Solving these equations, we obtain $\alpha = (2y + x)/3$ and $\beta = (y - x)/3$.

Solution to Exercise 3

(a) $$\begin{pmatrix} 2 & 3 \\ 2 & 1 \end{pmatrix} \begin{pmatrix} 3 \\ 2 \end{pmatrix} = \begin{pmatrix} 12 \\ 8 \end{pmatrix} = 4 \begin{pmatrix} 3 \\ 2 \end{pmatrix},$$

so $(3 \quad 2)^T$ is an eigenvector with eigenvalue 4.

(b) $$\begin{pmatrix} 2 & 3 \\ 2 & 1 \end{pmatrix} \begin{pmatrix} 1 \\ -1 \end{pmatrix} = \begin{pmatrix} -1 \\ 1 \end{pmatrix} = (-1) \begin{pmatrix} 1 \\ -1 \end{pmatrix},$$

so $(1 \quad -1)^T$ is an eigenvector with eigenvalue -1.

(c) $$\begin{pmatrix} 2 & 0 \\ 1 & 2 \end{pmatrix} \begin{pmatrix} 0 \\ 6 \end{pmatrix} = \begin{pmatrix} 0 \\ 12 \end{pmatrix} = 2 \begin{pmatrix} 0 \\ 6 \end{pmatrix},$$

so $(0 \quad 6)^T$ is an eigenvector with eigenvalue 2.

(d) $$\begin{pmatrix} 12 & 3 \\ -8 & -2 \end{pmatrix} \begin{pmatrix} 1 \\ -4 \end{pmatrix} = \begin{pmatrix} 0 \\ 0 \end{pmatrix} = 0 \begin{pmatrix} 1 \\ -4 \end{pmatrix},$$

so $(1 \quad -4)^T$ is an eigenvector with eigenvalue 0.

Solution to Exercise 4

Since $\mathbf{v} = (12\,000 \quad 6000)^T$ is transformed to itself, this is an eigenvector with eigenvalue 1.

You may have noticed that there are many other eigenvectors with the same eigenvalue, for example $(12 \quad 6)^T$ and $(2 \quad 1)^T$.

There is another eigenvector $(1 \quad -1)^T$, with corresponding eigenvalue 0.7 (although we do not expect you to have found it).

Solution to Exercise 5

$$\begin{pmatrix} 1 & 4 \\ 9 & 1 \end{pmatrix} \begin{pmatrix} 2 \\ -3 \end{pmatrix} = \begin{pmatrix} -10 \\ 15 \end{pmatrix} = -5 \begin{pmatrix} 2 \\ -3 \end{pmatrix},$$

so $(2 \quad -3)^T$ is an eigenvector with eigenvalue -5. Also,

$$\begin{pmatrix} 1 & 4 \\ 9 & 1 \end{pmatrix} \begin{pmatrix} 2 \\ 3 \end{pmatrix} = \begin{pmatrix} 14 \\ 21 \end{pmatrix} = 7 \begin{pmatrix} 2 \\ 3 \end{pmatrix},$$

so $(2 \quad 3)^T$ is an eigenvector with eigenvalue 7.

Solution to Exercise 6

The eigenvectors act along the line of reflection $y = x$ and perpendicular to it, so they are the scalar multiples of $(1 \quad 1)^T$ and $(1 \quad -1)^T$. The vector $(1 \quad 1)^T$ is scaled by a factor of 1 by the transformation, while for $(1 \quad -1)^T$ the scale factor is -1; these scale factors are the corresponding eigenvalues.

We may check our conclusion by evaluating

$$\begin{pmatrix} 0 & 1 \\ 1 & 0 \end{pmatrix} \begin{pmatrix} 1 \\ 1 \end{pmatrix} = \begin{pmatrix} 1 \\ 1 \end{pmatrix},$$

so $(1 \quad 1)^T$ corresponds to the eigenvalue 1, and

$$\begin{pmatrix} 0 & 1 \\ 1 & 0 \end{pmatrix} \begin{pmatrix} 1 \\ -1 \end{pmatrix} = \begin{pmatrix} -1 \\ 1 \end{pmatrix} = -1 \begin{pmatrix} 1 \\ -1 \end{pmatrix},$$

so $(1 \quad -1)^T$ corresponds to the eigenvalue -1.

Solution to Exercise 7

$(0 \quad 1)^T$ is an eigenvector of $\mathbf{A}$ corresponding to the eigenvalue 1, and $(1 \quad 0)^T$ is an eigenvalue of $\mathbf{A}$ corresponding to the eigenvalue -1.

Solution to Exercise 8

The equation $\mathbf{A}\mathbf{v} = \lambda\mathbf{v}$ becomes

$$\begin{pmatrix} 5 & 2 \\ 2 & 5 \end{pmatrix} \begin{pmatrix} x \\ y \end{pmatrix} = \lambda \begin{pmatrix} x \\ y \end{pmatrix}.$$

Thus x and y satisfy the simultaneous equations

$$5x + 2y = \lambda x,$$
$$2x + 5y = \lambda y,$$

which can be rewritten as the eigenvector equations

$$(5 - \lambda)x + \qquad 2y = 0,$$
$$2x + (5 - \lambda)y = 0.$$

These equations have a non-zero solution only if

$$\begin{vmatrix} 5 - \lambda & 2 \\ 2 & 5 - \lambda \end{vmatrix} = 0.$$

So $(5 - \lambda)(5 - \lambda) - 4 = 0$, that is, $5 - \lambda = \pm 2$, so the eigenvalues are $\lambda = 7$ and $\lambda = 3$.

- For $\lambda = 7$, the eigenvector equations become

$$-2x + 2y = 0,$$
$$2x - 2y = 0.$$

These equations reduce to the single equation $y = x$, so an eigenvector corresponding to $\lambda = 7$ is $(1 \quad 1)^T$.

- For $\lambda = 3$, the eigenvector equations become

$$2x + 2y = 0,$$
$$2x + 2y = 0.$$

These equations reduce to the single equation $y = -x$, so an eigenvector corresponding to $\lambda = 3$ is $(1 \quad -1)^T$.

Solution to Exercise 9

(a) The characteristic equation is

$$\begin{vmatrix} 1 - \lambda & 4 \\ 1 & -2 - \lambda \end{vmatrix} = 0.$$

Expanding gives $(1 - \lambda)(-2 - \lambda) - 4 = 0$, which simplifies to $\lambda^2 + \lambda - 6 = (\lambda - 2)(\lambda + 3) = 0$. (Alternatively, you could have calculated $a + d = -1$ and $ad - bc = -6$, and so obtained this equation directly.) So the eigenvalues are $\lambda = 2$ and $\lambda = -3$.

The eigenvector equations are

$$(1 - \lambda)x + 4y = 0,$$
$$x + (-2 - \lambda)y = 0.$$

- For $\lambda = 2$, the eigenvector equations become

$$-x + 4y = 0 \quad \text{and} \quad x - 4y = 0,$$

which reduce to the single equation $4y = x$. So an eigenvector corresponding to $\lambda = 2$ is $(4 \quad 1)^T$.

- For $\lambda = -3$, the eigenvector equations become

$$4x + 4y = 0 \quad \text{and} \quad x + y = 0,$$

which reduce to the single equation $y = -x$. So an eigenvector corresponding to $\lambda = -3$ is $(1 \quad -1)^T$.

(b) The characteristic equation is

$$\begin{vmatrix} 8 - \lambda & -5 \\ 10 & -7 - \lambda \end{vmatrix} = 0.$$

Expanding gives $(8 - \lambda)(-7 - \lambda) + 50 = 0$, which simplifies to $\lambda^2 - \lambda - 6 = (\lambda - 3)(\lambda + 2) = 0$. (Alternatively, you could have calculated $a + d = 1$ and $ad - bc = -6$, and so obtained this equation directly.) So the eigenvalues are $\lambda = 3$ and $\lambda = -2$.

The eigenvector equations are

$$(8 - \lambda)x - 5y = 0,$$
$$10x - (7 + \lambda)y = 0.$$

- For $\lambda = 3$, the eigenvector equations become

$$5x - 5y = 0 \quad \text{and} \quad 10x - 10y = 0,$$

which reduce to the single equation $y = x$. So an eigenvector corresponding to $\lambda = 3$ is $(1 \quad 1)^T$.

- For $\lambda = -2$, the eigenvector equations become

$$10x - 5y = 0 \quad \text{and} \quad 10x - 5y = 0,$$

which reduce to the single equation $y = 2x$. So an eigenvector corresponding to $\lambda = -2$ is $(1 \quad 2)^T$.

(c) The characteristic equation is

$$\begin{vmatrix} -1 - \lambda & 0 \\ 9 & 2 - \lambda \end{vmatrix} = 0.$$

Expanding gives $(-1 - \lambda)(2 - \lambda) = 0$, so the eigenvalues are $\lambda = -1$ and $\lambda = 2$.

The eigenvector equations are

$$(-1 - \lambda)x + 0y = 0,$$
$$9x + (2 - \lambda)y = 0.$$

- For $\lambda = -1$, the eigenvector equations become

$$0x + 0y = 0 \quad \text{and} \quad 9x + 3y = 0,$$

which reduce to the single equation $y = -3x$. So an eigenvector corresponding to $\lambda = -1$ is $(1 \quad -3)^T$.

- For $\lambda = 2$, the eigenvector equations become

$$-3x + 0y = 0 \quad \text{and} \quad 9x + 0y = 0,$$

which reduce to the single equation $x = 0$. So an eigenvector corresponding to $\lambda = 2$ is $(0 \quad 1)^T$.

Solution to Exercise 10

(a) Sum of eigenvalues $= 5 + 2 = 7$, and $\operatorname{tr} \mathbf{A} = 3 + 4 = 7$.

Product of eigenvalues $= 5 \times 2 = 10$, and $\det \mathbf{A} = (3 \times 4) - (2 \times 1) = 10$.

(b) Sum of eigenvalues $= 7 + 3 = 10$, and $\operatorname{tr} \mathbf{A} = 5 + 5 = 10$.

Product of eigenvalues $= 7 \times 3 = 21$, and $\det \mathbf{A} = (5 \times 5) - (2 \times 2) = 21$.

(c) For part (a):

Sum of eigenvalues $= 2 + (-3) = -1$, and $\operatorname{tr} \mathbf{A} = 1 + (-2) = -1$.

Product of eigenvalues $= 2 \times (-3) = -6$, and $\det \mathbf{A} = (1 \times (-2)) - (4 \times 1) = -6$.

For part (b):

Sum of eigenvalues $= 3 + (-2) = 1$, and $\operatorname{tr} \mathbf{A} = 8 + (-7) = 1$.

Product of eigenvalues $= 3 \times (-2) = -6$, and
$\det \mathbf{A} = (8 \times (-7)) - ((-5) \times 10) = -6$.

For part (c):

Sum of eigenvalues $= -1 + 2 = 1$, and $\operatorname{tr} \mathbf{A} = -1 + 2 = 1$.

Product of eigenvalues $= (-1) \times 2 = -2$, and
$\det \mathbf{A} = ((-1) \times 2) - (0 \times 9) = -2$.

Solution to Exercise 11

The characteristic equation is

$$\begin{vmatrix} p - \lambda & 0 \\ 0 & q - \lambda \end{vmatrix} = (p - \lambda)(q - \lambda) = 0.$$

Thus the eigenvalues are $\lambda = p$ and $\lambda = q$.

The eigenvector equations are

$$(p - \lambda)x \qquad = 0,$$
$$(q - \lambda)y = 0.$$

- For $\lambda = p$, the eigenvector equations become

  $$0 = 0 \quad \text{and} \quad (q - p)y = 0,$$

  which reduce to the single equation $y = 0$ (since $p \neq q$), so a corresponding eigenvector is $(1 \quad 0)^T$.

- For $\lambda = q$, the eigenvector equations become

  $$(p - q)x = 0 \quad \text{and} \quad 0 = 0,$$

  which reduce to the single equation $x = 0$ (since $p \neq q$), so a corresponding eigenvector is $(0 \quad 1)^T$.

These results agree with the eigenvalues and eigenvectors in Figure 5.

Solution to Exercise 12

The characteristic equation is

$$\lambda^2 - 1.7\lambda + 0.7 = 0.$$

The eigenvalues are $\lambda = 1$ and $\lambda = 0.7$.

The eigenvector equations are

$$(0.9 - \lambda)x + \qquad 0.2y = 0,$$
$$0.1x + (0.8 - \lambda)y = 0.$$

- For $\lambda = 1$, the eigenvector equations become

  $$-0.1x + 0.2y = 0 \quad \text{and} \quad 0.1x - 0.2y = 0,$$

  which reduce to the single equation $2y = x$, so a corresponding eigenvector is $(2 \quad 1)^T$.

(In the migration problem, where the total population was 18 000, an eigenvector corresponding to $\lambda = 1$ was found to be $(12\,000 \quad 6000)^T$. This is a multiple of $(2 \quad 1)^T$, as expected, giving stable populations of 12 000 in Exton and 6000 in Wyeville.)

- For $\lambda = 0.7$, the eigenvector equations become

$$0.2x + 0.2y = 0 \quad \text{and} \quad 0.1x + 0.1y = 0,$$

which reduce to the single equation $y = -x$, so a corresponding eigenvector is $(1 \quad -1)^T$.

(Since populations cannot be negative, this solution has no relevance for the migration problem.)

Solution to Exercise 13

(a) The characteristic equation is

$$\begin{vmatrix} a - \lambda & 0 \\ 0 & a - \lambda \end{vmatrix} = (a - \lambda)^2 = 0,$$

for which $\lambda = a$ is a repeated root.

The eigenvector equations are

$$(a - \lambda)x \qquad\qquad = 0,$$
$$(a - \lambda)y = 0,$$

which for $\lambda = a$ become

$$0 = 0 \quad \text{and} \quad 0 = 0,$$

which are satisfied by all values of x and y, so the eigenvectors are all the non-zero vectors of the form $(k \quad l)^T$.

(Any non-zero vector is an eigenvector, but it is possible to choose two eigenvectors that are linearly independent, for example $(1 \quad 0)^T$ and $(0 \quad 1)^T$.)

(b) The characteristic equation is

$$\begin{vmatrix} a - \lambda & 1 \\ 0 & a - \lambda \end{vmatrix} = (a - \lambda)^2 = 0,$$

for which $\lambda = a$ is a repeated root.

The eigenvector equations are

$$(a - \lambda)x + \qquad y = 0,$$
$$(a - \lambda)y = 0,$$

which for $\lambda = a$ reduce to a single equation $y = 0$, and a corresponding eigenvector is $(1 \quad 0)^T$.

(In this case, there is only one linearly independent eigenvector.)

Solution to Exercise 14

The characteristic equation is $\lambda^2 - 4\lambda + 5 = 0$. The eigenvalues are

$$\lambda = \tfrac{1}{2}\left(4 \pm \sqrt{16-20}\right) = \tfrac{1}{2}(4 \pm 2i) = 2 \pm i,$$

that is, $\lambda = 2+i$ and $\lambda = 2-i$.

The eigenvector equations are

$$(3-\lambda)x - \quad\quad y = 0,$$
$$2x + (1-\lambda)y = 0.$$

- For $\lambda = 2+i$, the eigenvector equations become

  $$(1-i)x - y = 0 \quad \text{and} \quad 2x - (1+i)y = 0,$$

  which reduce to the single equation $y = (1-i)x$ (as can be seen by multiplying the second equation by $(1-i)/2$ and noting that $(1-i)(1+i) = 2$), so a corresponding eigenvector is $(1 \quad 1-i)^T$.

- For $\lambda = 2-i$, the eigenvector equations become

  $$(1+i)x - y = 0 \quad \text{and} \quad 2x - (1-i)y = 0,$$

  which reduce to the single equation $y = (1+i)x$ (as can be seen by multiplying the second equation by $(1+i)/2$ and noting that $(1+i)(1-i) = 2$), so a corresponding eigenvector is $(1 \quad 1+i)^T$.

Solution to Exercise 15

The eigenvalues are 1 and 2.

- For $\lambda = 1$, the eigenvector equations become

  $$3y = 0 \quad \text{and} \quad y = 0,$$

  which reduce to the single equation $y = 0$, so $(1 \quad 0)^T$ is a corresponding eigenvector.

- For $\lambda = 2$, the eigenvector equations become

  $$-x + 3y = 0 \quad \text{and} \quad 0 = 0,$$

  which reduce to the single equation $3y = x$, so $(3 \quad 1)^T$ is a corresponding eigenvector.

Solution to Exercise 16

For the eigenvalue to be repeated, we require $\sqrt{(a+d)^2 - 4(ad - b^2)} = 0$, that is, $(a-d)^2 + 4b^2 = 0$. This is true only if $a = d$ and $b = 0$, so the only symmetric 2×2 matrices with a repeated eigenvalue are of the form $\begin{pmatrix} a & 0 \\ 0 & a \end{pmatrix}$.

Solution to Exercise 17

(a) The eigenvalues are real, since $\mathbf{A}$ is real and symmetric. One is positive and the other negative, since $\lambda_1 \lambda_2 = \det \mathbf{A} < 0$. Also, $\lambda_1 + \lambda_2 = \operatorname{tr} \mathbf{A} = 50$.

(b) The eigenvalues are the diagonal entries 67 and -17, since $\mathbf{A}$ is triangular.

(c) The eigenvalues are real, since $\mathbf{A}$ is real and symmetric. In fact, $\mathbf{A}$ is non-invertible, since $\det \mathbf{A} = 0$. Thus one eigenvalue is 0. Hence the other is 306, since $0 + \lambda_2 = \operatorname{tr} \mathbf{A} = 306$.

Solution to Exercise 18

(a) (i) $\mathbf{A}^2 = \begin{pmatrix} 3 & 2 \\ 1 & 4 \end{pmatrix} \begin{pmatrix} 3 & 2 \\ 1 & 4 \end{pmatrix} = \begin{pmatrix} 11 & 14 \\ 7 & 18 \end{pmatrix}.$

The characteristic equation of $\mathbf{A}^2$ is

$$\lambda^2 - 29\lambda + 100 = 0.$$

So the eigenvalues of $\mathbf{A}^2$ are $\lambda = 25$ and $\lambda = 4$. These are the squares of the eigenvalues of $\mathbf{A}$.

(ii) $\mathbf{A}^{-1} = \tfrac{1}{10} \begin{pmatrix} 4 & -2 \\ -1 & 3 \end{pmatrix} = \begin{pmatrix} 0.4 & -0.2 \\ -0.1 & 0.3 \end{pmatrix}.$

The characteristic equation of $\mathbf{A}^{-1}$ is

$$\lambda^2 - 0.7\lambda + 0.1 = 0.$$

So the eigenvalues of $\mathbf{A}^{-1}$ are $\lambda = 0.5$ and $\lambda = 0.2$. These are the reciprocals of the eigenvalues of $\mathbf{A}$.

(iii) $\mathbf{A} + 2\mathbf{I} = \begin{pmatrix} 3 & 2 \\ 1 & 4 \end{pmatrix} + \begin{pmatrix} 2 & 0 \\ 0 & 2 \end{pmatrix} = \begin{pmatrix} 5 & 2 \\ 1 & 6 \end{pmatrix}.$

The characteristic equation of $\mathbf{A} + 2\mathbf{I}$ is

$$\lambda^2 - 11\lambda + 28 = 0.$$

So the eigenvalues of $\mathbf{A} + 2\mathbf{I}$ are $\lambda = 7$ and $\lambda = 4$. These can be obtained by adding 2 to the eigenvalues of $\mathbf{A}$.

(iv) $(\mathbf{A} - 4\mathbf{I})^{-1} = \begin{pmatrix} -1 & 2 \\ 1 & 0 \end{pmatrix}^{-1} = \frac{1}{(-2)} \begin{pmatrix} 0 & -2 \\ -1 & -1 \end{pmatrix} = \begin{pmatrix} 0 & 1 \\ 0.5 & 0.5 \end{pmatrix}.$

The characteristic equation of $(\mathbf{A} - 4\mathbf{I})^{-1}$ is

$$\lambda^2 - 0.5\lambda - 0.5 = 0.$$

So the eigenvalues of $(\mathbf{A} - 4\mathbf{I})^{-1}$ are $\lambda = 1$ and $\lambda = -0.5$. These can be obtained by subtracting 4 from the eigenvalues of $\mathbf{A}$ and then finding the reciprocals.

(v) $3\mathbf{A} = \begin{pmatrix} 9 & 6 \\ 3 & 12 \end{pmatrix}.$

The characteristic equation of $3\mathbf{A}$ is

$$\lambda^2 - 21\lambda + 90 = 0.$$

So the eigenvalues of $3\mathbf{A}$ are $\lambda = 15$ and $\lambda = 6$, which are three times those of $\mathbf{A}$.

(b) (i) $\mathbf{A}^2 \begin{pmatrix} 1 \\ 1 \end{pmatrix} = \begin{pmatrix} 11 & 14 \\ 7 & 18 \end{pmatrix} \begin{pmatrix} 1 \\ 1 \end{pmatrix} = \begin{pmatrix} 25 \\ 25 \end{pmatrix} = 25 \begin{pmatrix} 1 \\ 1 \end{pmatrix},$

       $\mathbf{A}^2 \begin{pmatrix} -2 \\ 1 \end{pmatrix} = \begin{pmatrix} 11 & 14 \\ 7 & 18 \end{pmatrix} \begin{pmatrix} -2 \\ 1 \end{pmatrix} = \begin{pmatrix} -8 \\ 4 \end{pmatrix} = 4 \begin{pmatrix} -2 \\ 1 \end{pmatrix},$

so the eigenvectors of $\mathbf{A}$ are also eigenvectors of $\mathbf{A}^2$.

(ii) $\mathbf{A}^{-1} \begin{pmatrix} 1 \\ 1 \end{pmatrix} = \begin{pmatrix} 0.4 & -0.2 \\ -0.1 & 0.3 \end{pmatrix} \begin{pmatrix} 1 \\ 1 \end{pmatrix} = \begin{pmatrix} 0.2 \\ 0.2 \end{pmatrix} = 0.2 \begin{pmatrix} 1 \\ 1 \end{pmatrix},$

       $\mathbf{A}^{-1} \begin{pmatrix} -2 \\ 1 \end{pmatrix} = \begin{pmatrix} 0.4 & -0.2 \\ -0.1 & 0.3 \end{pmatrix} \begin{pmatrix} -2 \\ 1 \end{pmatrix} = \begin{pmatrix} -1 \\ 0.5 \end{pmatrix} = 0.5 \begin{pmatrix} -2 \\ 1 \end{pmatrix},$

so the eigenvectors of $\mathbf{A}$ are also eigenvectors of $\mathbf{A}^{-1}$.

(iii) $(\mathbf{A} + 2\mathbf{I}) \begin{pmatrix} 1 \\ 1 \end{pmatrix} = \begin{pmatrix} 5 & 2 \\ 1 & 6 \end{pmatrix} \begin{pmatrix} 1 \\ 1 \end{pmatrix} = \begin{pmatrix} 7 \\ 7 \end{pmatrix} = 7 \begin{pmatrix} 1 \\ 1 \end{pmatrix},$

       $(\mathbf{A} + 2\mathbf{I}) \begin{pmatrix} -2 \\ 1 \end{pmatrix} = \begin{pmatrix} 5 & 2 \\ 1 & 6 \end{pmatrix} \begin{pmatrix} -2 \\ 1 \end{pmatrix} = \begin{pmatrix} -8 \\ 4 \end{pmatrix} = 4 \begin{pmatrix} -2 \\ 1 \end{pmatrix},$

so the eigenvectors of $\mathbf{A}$ are also eigenvectors of $\mathbf{A} + 2\mathbf{I}$.

(iv) $(\mathbf{A} - 4\mathbf{I})^{-1} \begin{pmatrix} 1 \\ 1 \end{pmatrix} = \begin{pmatrix} 0 & 1 \\ 0.5 & 0.5 \end{pmatrix} \begin{pmatrix} 1 \\ 1 \end{pmatrix} = \begin{pmatrix} 1 \\ 1 \end{pmatrix},$

       $(\mathbf{A} - 4\mathbf{I})^{-1} \begin{pmatrix} -2 \\ 1 \end{pmatrix} = \begin{pmatrix} 0 & 1 \\ 0.5 & 0.5 \end{pmatrix} \begin{pmatrix} -2 \\ 1 \end{pmatrix}$

                    $= \begin{pmatrix} 1 \\ -0.5 \end{pmatrix}$

                    $= -0.5 \begin{pmatrix} -2 \\ 1 \end{pmatrix},$

so the eigenvectors of $\mathbf{A}$ are also eigenvectors of $(\mathbf{A} - 4\mathbf{I})^{-1}$.

(v) $3\mathbf{A} \begin{pmatrix} 1 \\ 1 \end{pmatrix} = \begin{pmatrix} 9 & 6 \\ 3 & 12 \end{pmatrix} \begin{pmatrix} 1 \\ 1 \end{pmatrix} = \begin{pmatrix} 15 \\ 15 \end{pmatrix} = 15 \begin{pmatrix} 1 \\ 1 \end{pmatrix},$

       $3\mathbf{A} \begin{pmatrix} -2 \\ 1 \end{pmatrix} = \begin{pmatrix} 9 & 6 \\ 3 & 12 \end{pmatrix} \begin{pmatrix} -2 \\ 1 \end{pmatrix} = \begin{pmatrix} -12 \\ 6 \end{pmatrix} = 6 \begin{pmatrix} -2 \\ 1 \end{pmatrix},$

so the eigenvectors of $\mathbf{A}$ are also eigenvectors of $3\mathbf{A}$.

Solution to Exercise 19

(a) (i)   The eigenvalues are 4^3 and $(-1)^3$, i.e. 64 and -1.

   (ii)   The eigenvalues are 4^{-1} and $(-1)^{-1}$, i.e. $\frac{1}{4}$ and -1.

   (iii)   The eigenvalues are $4 - 6$ and $(-1) - 6$, i.e. -2 and -7.

   (iv)   The eigenvalues are $(4 + 3)^{-1}$ and $((-1) + 3)^{-1}$, i.e. $\frac{1}{7}$ and $\frac{1}{2}$.

(b) The eigenvalues of $\mathbf{A} - 4\mathbf{I}$ are $4 - 4 = 0$ and $-1 - 4 = -5$.

   The matrix $\mathbf{A} - 4\mathbf{I}$ is non-invertible because one of the eigenvalues is 0, so the inverse does not exist.

Solution to Exercise 20

(a) Using Procedure 1, we solve the characteristic equation $\det(\mathbf{A} - \lambda\mathbf{I}) = 0$, which can be written as

$$\begin{vmatrix} 1 - \lambda & 2 \\ 3 & -4 - \lambda \end{vmatrix} = \lambda^2 + 3\lambda - 10 = 0.$$

The eigenvalues are $\lambda = -5$ and $\lambda = 2$. Solving the eigenvector equations for each eigenvalue, we obtain corresponding eigenvectors $(1 \quad -3)^T$ and $(2 \quad 1)^T$, respectively.

The eigenvalues of $\mathbf{A}^{10}$ are $(-5)^{10}$ and 2^{10}, corresponding to eigenvectors $(1 \quad -3)^T$ and $(2 \quad 1)^T$, respectively.

(b) $\begin{pmatrix} 3 & 2 \\ 3 & -2 \end{pmatrix} = \mathbf{A} + 2\mathbf{I}$, where $\mathbf{A}$ is the matrix of part (a).

So the eigenvalues are $-5 + 2 = -3$ and $2 + 2 = 4$, with corresponding eigenvectors $(1 \quad -3)^T$ and $(2 \quad 1)^T$, respectively.

Solution to Exercise 21

(a) The characteristic equation is

$$\lambda^2 - (2\cos\theta)\lambda + 1 = 0,$$

since $\sin^2\theta + \cos^2\theta = 1$. Using the quadratic equation formula, the eigenvalues are

$$\lambda = \tfrac{1}{2}\left(2\cos\theta \pm \sqrt{4\cos^2\theta - 4}\right)$$
$$= \tfrac{1}{2}\left(2\cos\theta \pm \sqrt{-4\sin^2\theta}\right) = \cos\theta \pm i\sin\theta.$$

So the eigenvalues are $\cos\theta + i\sin\theta$ and $\cos\theta - i\sin\theta$.

The eigenvector equations are

$$(\cos\theta - \lambda)x - \quad (\sin\theta)y = 0,$$
$$(\sin\theta)x + (\cos\theta - \lambda)y = 0.$$

- For $\lambda = \cos\theta + i\sin\theta$, the eigenvector equations become $-(i\sin\theta)x - (\sin\theta)y = 0$ and $(\sin\theta)x - (i\sin\theta)y = 0$, which reduce to the single equation $iy = x$ (since $\sin\theta \neq 0$ as θ is not an integer multiple of π), so a corresponding eigenvector is $(i \quad 1)^T$.

- For $\lambda = \cos\theta - i\sin\theta$, the eigenvector equations become $(i\sin\theta)x - (\sin\theta)y = 0$ and $(\sin\theta)x + (i\sin\theta)y = 0$, which reduce to the single equation $-iy = x$ (since $\sin\theta \neq 0$), so a corresponding eigenvector is $(-i \quad 1)^T$.

(b) If $\theta = n\pi$, where n is an integer, then $\sin\theta = 0$ and $\cos\theta = (-1)^n$, so **A** is the diagonal matrix

$$\mathbf{A} = \begin{pmatrix} (-1)^n & 0 \\ 0 & (-1)^n \end{pmatrix},$$

with equal diagonal elements. Thus **A** has a repeated eigenvalue given by $(-1)^n$. As was found in Exercise 13(a), any non-zero vector is an eigenvector and we are free to select any two linearly independent vectors as eigenvectors.

Solution to Exercise 22

$$\begin{pmatrix} 5 & 0 & 0 \\ 1 & 2 & 1 \\ 1 & 1 & 2 \end{pmatrix} \begin{pmatrix} 0 \\ 1 \\ 1 \end{pmatrix} = \begin{pmatrix} 0 \\ 3 \\ 3 \end{pmatrix} = 3 \begin{pmatrix} 0 \\ 1 \\ 1 \end{pmatrix},$$

and the corresponding eigenvalue is 3.

$$\begin{pmatrix} 5 & 0 & 0 \\ 1 & 2 & 1 \\ 1 & 1 & 2 \end{pmatrix} \begin{pmatrix} 0 \\ 1 \\ -1 \end{pmatrix} = \begin{pmatrix} 0 \\ 1 \\ -1 \end{pmatrix},$$

and the corresponding eigenvalue is 1.

Solution to Exercise 23

The eigenvector equations are

$$\begin{aligned}
(1-\lambda)x_1 && - && x_3 &= 0, \\
x_1 + (2-\lambda)x_2 + && x_3 &= 0, \\
2x_1 + && 2x_2 + (3-\lambda)x_3 &= 0.
\end{aligned}$$

- For $\lambda = 1$, the eigenvector equations become

$$-x_3 = 0, \quad x_1 + x_2 + x_3 = 0, \quad 2x_1 + 2x_2 + 2x_3 = 0,$$

which reduce to the equations $x_3 = 0$ and $x_2 = -x_1$, so a corresponding eigenvector is $(1 \quad -1 \quad 0)^T$.

- For $\lambda = 2$, the eigenvector equations become

$$-x_1 - x_3 = 0, \quad x_1 + x_3 = 0, \quad 2x_1 + 2x_2 + x_3 = 0,$$

which reduce to the equations $-x_3 = x_1$ and $-2x_2 = x_1$, so a corresponding eigenvector is $(-2 \quad 1 \quad 2)^T$.

- For $\lambda = 3$, the eigenvector equations become

$$-2x_1 - x_3 = 0, \quad x_1 - x_2 + x_3 = 0, \quad 2x_1 + 2x_2 = 0,$$

which reduce to the equations $x_3 = -2x_1$ and $x_2 = -x_1$, so a corresponding eigenvector is $(1 \quad -1 \quad -2)^T$.

Solution to Exercise 24

The characteristic equation is

$$\begin{vmatrix} -\lambda & 0 & 6 \\ \frac{1}{2} & -\lambda & 0 \\ 0 & \frac{1}{3} & -\lambda \end{vmatrix} = 0.$$

Expanding the determinant by the top row gives

$$-\lambda \begin{vmatrix} -\lambda & 0 \\ \frac{1}{3} & -\lambda \end{vmatrix} + 6 \begin{vmatrix} \frac{1}{2} & -\lambda \\ 0 & \frac{1}{3} \end{vmatrix} = 0,$$

which simplifies to $\lambda^3 - 1 = 0$. Since $\lambda = 1$ satisfies this equation, it is an eigenvalue of $\mathbf{A}$. (The other two eigenvalues are complex numbers.)

For $\lambda = 1$, the eigenvector equations become

$$-x_1 + 6x_3 = 0, \quad \tfrac{1}{2}x_1 - x_2 = 0, \quad \tfrac{1}{3}x_2 - x_3 = 0,$$

which reduce to the equations $x_1 = 6x_3$ and $x_2 = 3x_3$, so an eigenvector is $(6 \quad 3 \quad 1)^T$.

Solution to Exercise 25

(a) The characteristic equation is

$$\begin{vmatrix} -\lambda & 0 & 1 \\ 0 & -\lambda & 0 \\ 1 & 0 & -\lambda \end{vmatrix} = 0.$$

Expanding the determinant by the middle row (where there are two zeros) gives

$$-\lambda \begin{vmatrix} -\lambda & 1 \\ 1 & -\lambda \end{vmatrix} = 0,$$

which simplifies to $\lambda(\lambda^2 - 1) = 0$, so the eigenvalues are $\lambda = 0$, $\lambda = -1$ and $\lambda = 1$.

(b) The matrix is triangular, so from Subsection 2.3, the eigenvalues are $\lambda = 1$, $\lambda = 2$ and $\lambda = 3$.

Solution to Exercise 26

The characteristic equation is

$$\begin{vmatrix} 8 - \lambda & 0 & -5 \\ 9 & 3 - \lambda & -6 \\ 10 & 0 & -7 - \lambda \end{vmatrix} = 0.$$

Expanding by the middle column gives

$$(3 - \lambda) \begin{vmatrix} 8 - \lambda & -5 \\ 10 & -7 - \lambda \end{vmatrix} = 0,$$

so $\lambda = 3$ or $(8 - \lambda)(-7 - \lambda) + 50 = 0$. This quadratic equation simplifies to $\lambda^2 - \lambda - 6 = 0$, which has roots $\lambda = 3$ and $\lambda = -2$.

Thus the eigenvalues are $\lambda = 3$ (repeated) and $\lambda = -2$.

Solution to Exercise 27

The characteristic equation of the first matrix is

$$\begin{vmatrix} a - \lambda & 0 & 0 \\ d & b - \lambda & 0 \\ e & f & c - \lambda \end{vmatrix} = 0.$$

Expanding by the top row gives

$$(a - \lambda) \begin{vmatrix} b - \lambda & 0 \\ f & c - \lambda \end{vmatrix} = 0,$$

so $(a - \lambda)(b - \lambda)(c - \lambda) = 0$.

Thus the eigenvalues are $\lambda = a$, $\lambda = b$ and $\lambda = c$.

The second matrix is the transpose of the first, so it has the same eigenvalues.

Solution to Exercise 28

(a) Sum of eigenvalues $= 5 + 3 + 1 = 9$, and $\operatorname{tr} \mathbf{A} = 5 + 2 + 2 = 9$.

Also, $\det \mathbf{A} = 5 \times (4 - 1) = 15$, and product of eigenvalues $= 5 \times 3 \times 1 = 15$.

(b) Sum of eigenvalues $= 6 + 7 + 3 = 16$, and $\operatorname{tr} \mathbf{A} = 5 + 5 + 6 = 16$.

Also, $\det \mathbf{A} = 6 \times (25 - 4) = 126$, and product of eigenvalues $= 6 \times 7 \times 3 = 126$.

(c) Sum of eigenvalues $= 1 + 2 + 3 = 6$, and $\operatorname{tr} \mathbf{A} = 1 + 2 + 3 = 6$.

Also, $\det \mathbf{A} = 1 \times (6 - 2) + (-1) \times (2 - 4) = 6$, and product of eigenvalues $= 1 \times 2 \times 3 = 6$.

(d) For part (a):

Sum of eigenvalues $= 0 + (-1) + 1 = 0$, and $\operatorname{tr} \mathbf{A} = 0 + 0 + 0 = 0$.

Also, $\det \mathbf{A} = 1 \times (0 - 0) = 0$, and product of eigenvalues $= 0 \times (-1) \times 1 = 0$.

For part (b):

Sum of eigenvalues $= 1 + 2 + 3 = 6$, and $\operatorname{tr} \mathbf{A} = 1 + 2 + 3 = 6$.

Also, $\det \mathbf{A} = 1 \times (6 - 0) = 6$, and product of eigenvalues $= 1 \times 2 \times 3 = 6$.

(e) Sum of eigenvalues $= 3 + 3 + (-2) = 4$, and $\operatorname{tr} \mathbf{A} = 8 + 3 + (-7) = 4$.

Also, $\det \mathbf{A} = 8 \times (-21 - 0) - 5 \times (0 - 30) = -18$, and product of eigenvalues $= 3 \times 3 \times (-2) = -18$.

Solution to Exercise 29

(a) The characteristic equation is

$$\begin{vmatrix} -\lambda & 0 & 1 \\ 0 & 1-\lambda & 0 \\ 1 & 0 & -\lambda \end{vmatrix} = 0.$$

Expanding by the middle row gives

$$(1-\lambda)\begin{vmatrix} -\lambda & 1 \\ 1 & -\lambda \end{vmatrix} = 0,$$

so $\lambda = 1$ or $\lambda^2 - 1 = 0$.

Since $\lambda^2 - 1 = (\lambda - 1)(\lambda + 1)$, the eigenvalues are $\lambda = 1$ (repeated) and $\lambda = -1$.

The eigenvector equations are

$$\begin{aligned} -\lambda x_1 \qquad\qquad + \quad x_3 &= 0, \\ (1-\lambda)x_2 \qquad\quad &= 0, \\ x_1 \qquad\qquad - \lambda x_3 &= 0. \end{aligned}$$

- For $\lambda = 1$, the eigenvector equations become

$$-x_1 + x_3 = 0, \quad 0 = 0, \quad x_1 - x_3 = 0,$$

which reduce to the single equation $x_3 = x_1$.

Since x_2 can take any value, two linearly independent eigenvectors are $(0 \quad 1 \quad 0)^T$ and $(1 \quad 0 \quad 1)^T$.

- For $\lambda = -1$, the eigenvector equations become

$$x_1 + x_3 = 0, \quad 2x_2 = 0, \quad x_1 + x_3 = 0,$$

which reduce to the equations $x_3 = -x_1$ and $x_2 = 0$, so an eigenvector is $(1 \quad 0 \quad -1)^T$.

(b) The characteristic equation is

$$\begin{vmatrix} \frac{1}{\sqrt{2}} - \lambda & 0 & \frac{1}{\sqrt{2}} \\ 0 & 1-\lambda & 0 \\ -\frac{1}{\sqrt{2}} & 0 & \frac{1}{\sqrt{2}} - \lambda \end{vmatrix} = 0,$$

which, after expanding by the middle row, simplifies to

$$(1-\lambda)(\lambda^2 - \sqrt{2}\lambda + 1) = 0.$$

The quadratic equation $\lambda^2 - \sqrt{2}\lambda + 1 = 0$ has roots

$$\lambda = \tfrac{1}{\sqrt{2}}(1+i) \quad \text{and} \quad \lambda = \tfrac{1}{\sqrt{2}}(1-i).$$

Thus the eigenvalues are $\lambda = 1$, $\lambda = \tfrac{1}{\sqrt{2}}(1+i)$ and $\lambda = \tfrac{1}{\sqrt{2}}(1-i)$.

The eigenvector equations are

$$\begin{aligned} \left(\tfrac{1}{\sqrt{2}} - \lambda\right) x_1 \qquad\qquad + \qquad\quad \tfrac{1}{\sqrt{2}}x_3 &= 0, \\ (1-\lambda)x_2 \qquad\qquad\qquad &= 0, \\ -\tfrac{1}{\sqrt{2}}x_1 \qquad\qquad + \left(\tfrac{1}{\sqrt{2}} - \lambda\right) x_3 &= 0. \end{aligned}$$

- For $\lambda = 1$, the eigenvector equations become

$$\left(\tfrac{1}{\sqrt{2}} - 1\right) x_1 + \tfrac{1}{\sqrt{2}} x_3 = 0, \quad 0 = 0, \quad -\tfrac{1}{\sqrt{2}} x_1 + \left(\tfrac{1}{\sqrt{2}} - 1\right) x_3 = 0,$$

  which reduce to the equations $x_1 = 0$ and $x_3 = 0$, so a corresponding eigenvector is $(0 \quad 1 \quad 0)^T$.

- For $\lambda = \tfrac{1}{\sqrt{2}}(1 + i)$, the eigenvector equations become

$$-\tfrac{1}{\sqrt{2}} i x_1 + \tfrac{1}{\sqrt{2}} x_3 = 0, \quad \tfrac{1}{\sqrt{2}}(\sqrt{2} - 1 - i) x_2 = 0,$$
$$-\tfrac{1}{\sqrt{2}} x_1 - \tfrac{1}{\sqrt{2}} i x_3 = 0,$$

  which reduce to the equations $x_3 = i x_1$ and $x_2 = 0$, so a corresponding eigenvector is $(1 \quad 0 \quad i)^T$.

- For $\lambda = \tfrac{1}{\sqrt{2}}(1 - i)$, the eigenvector equations become

$$\tfrac{1}{\sqrt{2}} i x_1 + \tfrac{1}{\sqrt{2}} x_3 = 0, \quad \tfrac{1}{\sqrt{2}}(\sqrt{2} - 1 + i) x_2 = 0,$$
$$-\tfrac{1}{\sqrt{2}} x_1 + \tfrac{1}{\sqrt{2}} i x_3 = 0,$$

  which reduce to the equations $x_3 = -i x_1$ and $x_2 = 0$, so a corresponding eigenvector is $(1 \quad 0 \quad -i)^T$.

(The eigenvalue $\tfrac{1}{\sqrt{2}}(1 - i)$ and eigenvector $(1 \quad 0 \quad -i)^T$ can be obtained from $\tfrac{1}{\sqrt{2}}(1 + i)$ and $(1 \quad 0 \quad i)^T$, respectively, by replacing i by $-i$. That is, the second complex eigenvalue and corresponding eigenvector are the complex conjugates of the first complex eigenvalue and corresponding eigenvector.)

(c) The matrix is upper triangular, so the eigenvalues are 2, -3 and 4.

- For $\lambda = 2$, the eigenvector equations become

$$x_2 - x_3 = 0, \quad -5x_2 + 2x_3 = 0, \quad 2x_3 = 0,$$

  which reduce to $x_2 = x_3 = 0$, so a corresponding eigenvector is $(1 \quad 0 \quad 0)^T$.

- For $\lambda = -3$, the eigenvector equations become

$$5x_1 + x_2 - x_3 = 0, \quad 2x_3 = 0, \quad 7x_3 = 0,$$

  which reduce to $5x_1 + x_2 = 0$ and $x_3 = 0$, so a corresponding eigenvector is $(1 \quad -5 \quad 0)^T$.

- For $\lambda = 4$, the eigenvector equations become

$$-2x_1 + x_2 - x_3 = 0, \quad -7x_2 + 2x_3 = 0, \quad 0 = 0.$$

  Choosing $x_3 = 14$ keeps the numbers simple, and a corresponding eigenvector is $(-5 \quad 4 \quad 14)^T$.

(d) The characteristic equation is

$$\begin{vmatrix} -\lambda & 2 & 0 \\ -2 & -\lambda & 0 \\ 0 & 0 & 1 - \lambda \end{vmatrix} = 0,$$

and (after expanding the determinant by the third row) this gives $(1 - \lambda)(\lambda^2 + 4) = 0$, so the eigenvalues are 1, $2i$ and $-2i$.

- For $\lambda = 1$, the eigenvector equations become
  $$-x_1 + 2x_2 = 0, \quad -2x_1 - x_2 = 0, \quad 0 = 0,$$
  so a corresponding eigenvector is $(0 \quad 0 \quad 1)^T$.

- For $\lambda = 2i$, the eigenvector equations become
  $$-2ix_1 + 2x_2 = 0, \quad -2x_1 - 2ix_2 = 0, \quad (1 - 2i)x_3 = 0,$$
  which reduce to $x_2 = ix_1$ and $x_3 = 0$, so a corresponding eigenvector is $(1 \quad i \quad 0)^T$.

- For $\lambda = -2i$, similarly, an eigenvector corresponding to $\lambda = -2i$ is $(1 \quad -i \quad 0)^T$.

(e) The characteristic equation is
$$\begin{vmatrix} 1-\lambda & 0 & 0 \\ 0 & 1-\lambda & 2 \\ 0 & -2 & 5-\lambda \end{vmatrix} = 0,$$
which gives $(1 - \lambda)((1 - \lambda)(5 - \lambda) + 4) = 0$. This simplifies to $(1 - \lambda)(\lambda - 3)^2 = 0$, so the eigenvalues are $\lambda = 1$ and $\lambda = 3$ (repeated).

- For $\lambda = 1$, the eigenvector equations become
  $$0 = 0, \quad 2x_3 = 0, \quad -2x_2 + 4x_3 = 0,$$
  which reduce to $x_2 = x_3 = 0$, so $(1 \quad 0 \quad 0)^T$ is a corresponding eigenvector.

- For $\lambda = 3$, the eigenvector equations become
  $$-2x_1 = 0, \quad -2x_2 + 2x_3 = 0, \quad -2x_2 + 2x_3 = 0,$$
  which reduce to $x_1 = 0$ and $x_2 = x_3$, so a corresponding eigenvector is $(0 \quad 1 \quad 1)^T$. In this case, the repeated eigenvalue $\lambda = 3$ has only one linearly independent eigenvector.

(f) The matrix is lower triangular, so the eigenvalues are -2 and 1 (repeated).

- For $\lambda = -2$, the eigenvector equations become
  $$3x_1 = 0, \quad 3x_2 = 0, \quad x_1 + x_2 = 0,$$
  which reduce to $x_1 = x_2 = 0$, so $(0 \quad 0 \quad 1)^T$ is a corresponding eigenvector.

- For $\lambda = 1$, the eigenvector equations become
  $$0 = 0, \quad 0 = 0, \quad x_1 + x_2 - 3x_3 = 0.$$
  These equations are satisfied if $x_1 = 3x_3 - x_2$ (whatever values we choose for x_2 and x_3). Two linearly independent eigenvectors can be found. For example, setting $x_2 = 1$ and $x_3 = 0$ gives $(-1 \quad 1 \quad 0)^T$, and setting $x_2 = 0$ and $x_3 = 1$ gives $(3 \quad 0 \quad 1)^T$.

Solution to Exercise 30

(a) The characteristic equation is

$$\begin{vmatrix} 1 - \lambda & 2 \\ 2 & 1 - \lambda \end{vmatrix} = 0.$$

Expanding gives $(1 - \lambda)^2 - 4 = 0$, so $1 - \lambda = \pm 2$. Hence the eigenvalues are $\lambda = 3$ and $\lambda = -1$, and these are both real. (Alternatively, you could have calculated $\operatorname{tr} \mathbf{A} = 2$ and $\det \mathbf{A} = -3$, and so obtained the equation $\lambda^2 - 2\lambda - 3 = (\lambda - 3)(\lambda + 1) = 0$.) The eigenvector equations are

$$(1 - \lambda)x + 2y = 0,$$
$$2x + (1 - \lambda)y = 0.$$

- For $\lambda = 3$, the eigenvector equations become

  $$-2x + 2y = 0 \quad \text{and} \quad 2x - 2y = 0,$$

  which reduce to the single equation $y = x$. So an eigenvector corresponding to $\lambda = 3$ is $\mathbf{v}_1 = (1 \quad 1)^T$.

- For $\lambda = -1$, the eigenvector equations become

  $$2x + 2y = 0 \quad \text{and} \quad 2x + 2y = 0,$$

  which reduce to the single equation $y = -x$. So an eigenvector corresponding to $\lambda = -1$ is $\mathbf{v}_2 = (1 \quad -1)^T$.

The two eigenvectors are orthogonal since

$$\mathbf{v}_1^T \mathbf{v}_2 = (1)(1) + (1)(-1) = 0.$$

(b) The characteristic equation is

$$\begin{vmatrix} 4 - \lambda & -2 \\ -2 & 1 - \lambda \end{vmatrix} = 0.$$

Expanding this gives $(4 - \lambda)(1 - \lambda) - 4 = 0$, which simplifies to $\lambda^2 - 5\lambda = 0$. (Alternatively, note that $\operatorname{tr} \mathbf{A} = 5$ and $\det \mathbf{A} = 0$, from which it immediately follows that $\lambda = 0$ and $\lambda = 5$.) So the eigenvalues are $\lambda = 0$ and $\lambda = 5$, which are real.

- For $\lambda = 0$, the eigenvector equations become

  $$4x - 2y = 0 \quad \text{and} \quad -2x + y = 0,$$

  which reduce to the single equation $y = 2x$. So an eigenvector corresponding to $\lambda = 0$ is $\mathbf{v}_1 = (1 \quad 2)^T$.

- For $\lambda = 5$, the eigenvector equations become

  $$-x - 2y = 0 \quad \text{and} \quad -2x - 4y = 0,$$

  which reduce to the single equation $x = -2y$. So an eigenvector corresponding to $\lambda = 5$ is $\mathbf{v}_2 = (-2 \quad 1)^T$.

The two eigenvectors are orthogonal since

$$\mathbf{v}_1^T \mathbf{v}_2 = (1)(-2) + (2)(1) = 0.$$

(c) The characteristic equation is

$$\begin{vmatrix} 2-\lambda & 0 & 0 \\ 0 & -\lambda & 1 \\ 0 & 1 & -\lambda \end{vmatrix} = 0,$$

and this gives $(2-\lambda)(\lambda^2 - 1) = 0$, so the eigenvalues are $\lambda = 2$, $\lambda = 1$ and $\lambda = -1$, which are all real.

- For $\lambda = 2$, the eigenvector equations become

$$0 = 0, \quad -2x_2 + x_3 = 0, \quad x_2 - 2x_3 = 0,$$

so a corresponding eigenvector is $\mathbf{v}_1 = (1 \quad 0 \quad 0)^T$.

- For $\lambda = 1$, the eigenvector equations become

$$x_1 = 0, \quad -x_2 + x_3 = 0, \quad x_2 - x_3 = 0,$$

so a corresponding eigenvector is $\mathbf{v}_2 = (0 \quad 1 \quad 1)^T$.

- For $\lambda = -1$, the eigenvector equations become

$$3x_1 = 0, \quad x_2 + x_3 = 0, \quad x_2 + x_3 = 0,$$

so a corresponding eigenvector is $\mathbf{v}_3 = (0 \quad 1 \quad -1)^T$.

Note that

$$\mathbf{v}_1^T \mathbf{v}_2 = (1)(0) + (0)(1) + (0)(1) = 0,$$
$$\mathbf{v}_1^T \mathbf{v}_3 = (1)(0) + (0)(1) + (0)(-1) = 0,$$
$$\mathbf{v}_2^T \mathbf{v}_3 = (0)(0) + (1)(1) + (1)(-1) = 0,$$

so all the eigenvectors are mutually orthogonal.

Solution to Exercise 31

The characteristic equation is

$$\begin{vmatrix} 2-\lambda & 0 & 1 \\ 0 & 3-\lambda & 0 \\ 1 & 0 & 2-\lambda \end{vmatrix} = 0,$$

and expanding the determinant by the middle row gives

$$(3-\lambda)((2-\lambda)^2 - 1) = 0,$$

which simplifies to

$$(3-\lambda)^2(1-\lambda) = 0,$$

so the eigenvalues are $\lambda = 1$ and $\lambda = 3$ (repeated), which are real.

- For $\lambda = 1$, the eigenvector equations become

$$x_1 + x_3 = 0, \quad 2x_2 = 0, \quad x_1 + x_3 = 0,$$

so a corresponding eigenvector is $\mathbf{v}_1 = (1 \quad 0 \quad -1)^T$.

- For $\lambda = 3$, the eigenvector equations become

$$-x_1 + x_3 = 0, \quad 0 = 0, \quad x_1 - x_3 = 0,$$

with general solution $x_1 = x_3 = k$ and $x_2 = l$, giving the vector

$$\begin{pmatrix} k \\ l \\ k \end{pmatrix} = k \begin{pmatrix} 1 \\ 0 \\ 1 \end{pmatrix} + l \begin{pmatrix} 0 \\ 1 \\ 0 \end{pmatrix},$$

viewed as a linear combination of two linearly independent eigenvectors $\mathbf{v}_2 = (1 \quad 0 \quad 1)^T$ and $\mathbf{v}_3 = (0 \quad 1 \quad 0)^T$, which also happen to be orthogonal since

$$\mathbf{v}_2^T \mathbf{v}_3 = (1)(0) + (0)(1) + (1)(0) = 0.$$

Moreover, $\mathbf{v}_2$ and $\mathbf{v}_3$ are both orthogonal to $\mathbf{v}_1$ since

$$\mathbf{v}_1^T \mathbf{v}_2 = (1)(1) + (0)(0) + (-1)(1) = 0,$$
$$\mathbf{v}_1^T \mathbf{v}_3 = (1)(0) + (0)(1) + (-1)(0) = 0,$$

so it is possible to find three mutually orthogonal eigenvectors.

Solution to Exercise 32

$$\mathbf{e}_1 = \mathbf{A}\mathbf{e}_0 = \begin{pmatrix} 3 & 2 \\ 1 & 4 \end{pmatrix} \begin{pmatrix} 1 \\ 0 \end{pmatrix} = \begin{pmatrix} 3 \\ 1 \end{pmatrix},$$

$$\mathbf{e}_2 = \mathbf{A}\mathbf{e}_1 = \begin{pmatrix} 3 & 2 \\ 1 & 4 \end{pmatrix} \begin{pmatrix} 3 \\ 1 \end{pmatrix} = \begin{pmatrix} 11 \\ 7 \end{pmatrix},$$

$$\mathbf{e}_3 = \mathbf{A}\mathbf{e}_2 = \begin{pmatrix} 3 & 2 \\ 1 & 4 \end{pmatrix} \begin{pmatrix} 11 \\ 7 \end{pmatrix} = \begin{pmatrix} 47 \\ 39 \end{pmatrix},$$

$$\mathbf{e}_4 = \mathbf{A}\mathbf{e}_3 = \begin{pmatrix} 3 & 2 \\ 1 & 4 \end{pmatrix} \begin{pmatrix} 47 \\ 39 \end{pmatrix} = \begin{pmatrix} 219 \\ 203 \end{pmatrix}.$$

Solution to Exercise 33

(a) $\mathbf{e}_1 = \mathbf{A}\mathbf{e}_0 = \begin{pmatrix} 2 & 1 \\ 1 & 2 \end{pmatrix} \begin{pmatrix} 1 \\ 0 \end{pmatrix} = \begin{pmatrix} 2 \\ 1 \end{pmatrix},$

$\mathbf{e}_2 = \mathbf{A}\mathbf{e}_1 = \begin{pmatrix} 2 & 1 \\ 1 & 2 \end{pmatrix} \begin{pmatrix} 2 \\ 1 \end{pmatrix} = \begin{pmatrix} 5 \\ 4 \end{pmatrix},$

$\mathbf{e}_3 = \mathbf{A}\mathbf{e}_2 = \begin{pmatrix} 2 & 1 \\ 1 & 2 \end{pmatrix} \begin{pmatrix} 5 \\ 4 \end{pmatrix} = \begin{pmatrix} 14 \\ 13 \end{pmatrix}.$

(b) $\mathbf{e}_{11} = \mathbf{A}\mathbf{e}_{10} = (88\,574 \quad 88\,573)^T.$

(c) The characteristic equation is $(2 - \lambda)^2 - 1 = 0$, so $2 - \lambda = \pm 1$, thus $\lambda_1 = 3$ and $\lambda_2 = 1$. Corresponding eigenvectors are $\mathbf{v}_1 = (1 \quad 1)^T$ and $\mathbf{v}_2 = (1 \quad -1)^T.$

(d) We need to determine constants α and β so that $\mathbf{e}_0 = \alpha\mathbf{v}_1 + \beta\mathbf{v}_2$, that is,

$$\begin{pmatrix} 1 & 1 \\ 1 & -1 \end{pmatrix} \begin{pmatrix} \alpha \\ \beta \end{pmatrix} = \begin{pmatrix} 1 \\ 0 \end{pmatrix}.$$

Solving this equation for α and β gives $\alpha = \frac{1}{2}$ and $\beta = \frac{1}{2}$. Thus we have

$$\mathbf{e}_0 = \tfrac{1}{2}\mathbf{v}_1 + \tfrac{1}{2}\mathbf{v}_2.$$

(e) $\mathbf{e}_1 = \mathbf{A}\mathbf{e}_0 = \mathbf{A}(\tfrac{1}{2}\mathbf{v}_1 + \tfrac{1}{2}\mathbf{v}_2) = \tfrac{1}{2}\mathbf{A}\mathbf{v}_1 + \tfrac{1}{2}\mathbf{A}\mathbf{v}_2 = \tfrac{3}{2}\mathbf{v}_1 + \tfrac{1}{2}\mathbf{v}_2,$

$\mathbf{e}_2 = \mathbf{A}\mathbf{e}_1 = \mathbf{A}(\tfrac{3}{2}\mathbf{v}_1 + \tfrac{1}{2}\mathbf{v}_2) = \tfrac{3}{2}\mathbf{A}\mathbf{v}_1 + \tfrac{1}{2}\mathbf{A}\mathbf{v}_2 = \tfrac{9}{2}\mathbf{v}_1 + \tfrac{1}{2}\mathbf{v}_2.$

Similarly,

$$\mathbf{e}_n = \tfrac{1}{2}(3^n\mathbf{v}_1 + \mathbf{v}_2).$$

(f) The coefficient of $\mathbf{v}_1$, namely $\frac{1}{2} \times 3^n$, dominates the expression for $\mathbf{e}_n$, so we obtain an approximation to $\mathbf{v}_1$ (an eigenvector corresponding to the eigenvalue of larger magnitude).

Solution to Exercise 34

(a) If $\mathbf{e}_0 = \alpha\mathbf{v}_1 + \beta\mathbf{v}_2$, then

$$\begin{pmatrix} 10\,000 \\ 8\,000 \end{pmatrix} = \alpha \begin{pmatrix} 2 \\ 1 \end{pmatrix} + \beta \begin{pmatrix} 1 \\ -1 \end{pmatrix},$$

so α and β satisfy the simultaneous equations

$$2\alpha + \beta = 10\,000,$$
$$\alpha - \beta = 8000.$$

Solving these equations gives $\alpha = 6000$, $\beta = -2000$, so

$$\mathbf{e}_0 = 6000\mathbf{v}_1 - 2000\mathbf{v}_2.$$

(b) Since $\mathbf{A}\mathbf{v}_1 = \mathbf{v}_1$ and $\mathbf{A}\mathbf{v}_2 = 0.7\mathbf{v}_2$, we have

$$\mathbf{e}_1 = \mathbf{A}\mathbf{e}_0 = 6000\mathbf{A}\mathbf{v}_1 - 2000\mathbf{A}\mathbf{v}_2 = 6000\mathbf{v}_1 - 2000(0.7)\mathbf{v}_2,$$
$$\mathbf{e}_2 = \mathbf{A}\mathbf{e}_1 = 6000\mathbf{A}\mathbf{v}_1 - 2000(0.7)\mathbf{A}\mathbf{v}_2 = 6000\mathbf{v}_1 - 2000(0.7)^2\mathbf{v}_2.$$

Continuing in this way, we obtain

$$\mathbf{e}_n = 6000\mathbf{v}_1 - 2000(0.7)^n\mathbf{v}_2.$$

(c) As n becomes large, $(0.7)^n$ becomes small and the term involving $\mathbf{v}_2$ can be ignored in comparison with the term involving $\mathbf{v}_1$. Thus

$$\mathbf{e}_n \simeq 6000\mathbf{v}_1 = (12\,000 \quad 6000)^T,$$

which agrees with our observations in the Introduction.

Solution to Exercise 35

First iteration:
$$\mathbf{z}_1 = \begin{pmatrix} 3 & 6 \\ 4 & 8 \end{pmatrix} \begin{pmatrix} 1 \\ 0 \end{pmatrix} = \begin{pmatrix} 3 \\ 4 \end{pmatrix},$$
$$\alpha_1 = 4,$$
$$\mathbf{e}_1 = \frac{\mathbf{z}_1}{\alpha_1} = \tfrac{1}{4} \begin{pmatrix} 3 \\ 4 \end{pmatrix} = \begin{pmatrix} \frac{3}{4} \\ 1 \end{pmatrix}.$$

Second iteration:
$$\mathbf{z}_2 = \begin{pmatrix} 3 & 6 \\ 4 & 8 \end{pmatrix} \begin{pmatrix} \frac{3}{4} \\ 1 \end{pmatrix} = \begin{pmatrix} \frac{33}{4} \\ 11 \end{pmatrix},$$
$$\alpha_2 = 11,$$
$$\mathbf{e}_2 = \frac{\mathbf{z}_2}{\alpha_2} = \tfrac{1}{11} \begin{pmatrix} \frac{33}{4} \\ 11 \end{pmatrix} = \begin{pmatrix} \frac{3}{4} \\ 1 \end{pmatrix}.$$

Since $\mathbf{e}_2 = \mathbf{e}_1$, the third iteration will be identical to the second, and $\mathbf{e}_3$ is also $(\tfrac{3}{4} \quad 1)^T$.

So $(\tfrac{3}{4} \quad 1)^T$ is an eigenvector. We have
$$\begin{pmatrix} 3 & 6 \\ 4 & 8 \end{pmatrix} \begin{pmatrix} \frac{3}{4} \\ 1 \end{pmatrix} = \begin{pmatrix} \frac{33}{4} \\ 11 \end{pmatrix} = 11 \begin{pmatrix} \frac{3}{4} \\ 1 \end{pmatrix},$$

so the corresponding eigenvalue is 11. Since $\operatorname{tr} \mathbf{A} = 11$, the other eigenvalue is 0, which explains why the iteration converges so rapidly.

(This is a very special case; generally, we would not expect $\mathbf{e}_n$ to be *equal* to an eigenvector for any value of n, unless we start with an eigenvector.)

Solution to Exercise 36

We have
$$\mathbf{A}^{-1} = \tfrac{1}{11} \begin{pmatrix} 5 & -3 \\ -8 & 7 \end{pmatrix}.$$

First iteration:
$$\mathbf{z}_1 = \tfrac{1}{11} \begin{pmatrix} 5 & -3 \\ -8 & 7 \end{pmatrix} \begin{pmatrix} 1 \\ 1 \end{pmatrix} = \begin{pmatrix} \frac{2}{11} \\ -\frac{1}{11} \end{pmatrix},$$
therefore $\alpha_1 = \tfrac{2}{11}$ and $\mathbf{e}_1 = (1 \quad -\tfrac{1}{2})^T$.

Second iteration:
$$\mathbf{z}_2 = \tfrac{1}{11} \begin{pmatrix} 5 & -3 \\ -8 & 7 \end{pmatrix} \begin{pmatrix} 1 \\ -\frac{1}{2} \end{pmatrix} = \begin{pmatrix} \frac{13}{22} \\ -\frac{23}{22} \end{pmatrix},$$
therefore $\alpha_2 = -\tfrac{23}{22}$ and $\mathbf{e}_2 = (-\tfrac{13}{23} \quad 1)^T$.

Third iteration:

$$\mathbf{z}_3 = \frac{1}{11}\begin{pmatrix} 5 & -3 \\ -8 & 7 \end{pmatrix}\begin{pmatrix} -\frac{13}{23} \\ 1 \end{pmatrix} = \begin{pmatrix} -\frac{134}{253} \\ \frac{265}{253} \end{pmatrix},$$

therefore $\alpha_3 = \frac{265}{253}$ and $\mathbf{e}_3 = (-\frac{134}{265} \quad 1)^T$.

Taking $\mathbf{e}_3 = (-\frac{134}{265} \quad 1)^T \simeq (-0.506 \quad 1)^T$ as our approximation to the eigenvector, the estimate for the corresponding eigenvalue of $\mathbf{A}$ of smallest magnitude is $1/\alpha_3 = \frac{253}{265} \simeq 0.955$. (The exact eigenvector is $(-0.5 \quad 1)^T$, corresponding to the eigenvalue 1.)

Solution to Exercise 37

We follow Procedure 6(a).

Twenty-first iteration:

$$\mathbf{z}_{21} = (\mathbf{A} + \mathbf{I})^{-1}\mathbf{e}_{20}$$
$$= \begin{pmatrix} \frac{3}{2} & -\frac{1}{4} & -\frac{1}{2} \\ -\frac{1}{4} & \frac{5}{8} & -\frac{1}{4} \\ -\frac{1}{2} & -\frac{1}{4} & \frac{1}{2} \end{pmatrix}\begin{pmatrix} 1 \\ -0.141\,05 \\ -0.379\,39 \end{pmatrix} = \begin{pmatrix} 1.724\,96 \\ -0.243\,31 \\ -0.654\,43 \end{pmatrix},$$
$$\alpha_{21} = 1.724\,96,$$
$$\mathbf{e}_{21} = \frac{\mathbf{z}_{21}}{\alpha_{21}} \simeq (1 \quad -0.141\,05 \quad -0.379\,39)^T.$$

The sequence α_n appears to have converged to $1.724\,96$, and a corresponding eigenvector is approximately $(1 \quad -0.141 \quad -0.379)^T$ (here given to three decimal places).

Since α_n converges to $1/(\lambda_1 - p) = 1/(\lambda_1 + 1) = 1.724\,96$, we have

$$\lambda_1 = \frac{1}{1.724\,96} - 1 \simeq -0.420.$$

We can be confident of results quoted to three decimal places since convergence of the iteration appears to have occurred at five decimal places.

Solution to Exercise 38

(a) We follow Procedure 4.

First iteration:

$$\mathbf{z}_1 = \mathbf{A}\mathbf{e}_0 = \begin{pmatrix} 0.5 & 0.6 \\ 1.4 & -0.3 \end{pmatrix}\begin{pmatrix} 1 \\ 0 \end{pmatrix} = \begin{pmatrix} 0.5 \\ 1.4 \end{pmatrix},$$
$$\alpha_1 = 1.4,$$
$$\mathbf{e}_1 = \frac{\mathbf{z}_1}{\alpha_1} = \frac{1}{1.4}\begin{pmatrix} 0.5 \\ 1.4 \end{pmatrix} = \begin{pmatrix} 0.357\,143 \\ 1 \end{pmatrix}.$$

Second iteration: $\mathbf{e}_2 = (1 \quad 0.256\,881)^T$.

Third iteration: $\mathbf{e}_3 = (0.494\,452 \quad 1)^T$.

(b) We follow Procedure 1.

The characteristic equation is

$$\lambda^2 - 0.2\lambda - 0.99 = 0,$$

so the eigenvalues are $\lambda_1 = -0.9$ and $\lambda_2 = 1.1$.

- For $\lambda_1 = -0.9$, the eigenvector equations both become

$$1.4x + 0.6y = 0, \quad \text{i.e.} \quad 3y = -7x,$$

so a corresponding eigenvector is $(3 \quad -7)^T$.

- For $\lambda_2 = 1.1$, the eigenvector equations become

$$-0.6x + 0.6y = 0, \quad 1.4x - 1.4y = 0,$$

which reduce to $x = y$, so a corresponding eigenvector is $(1 \quad 1)^T$.

(c) The sequence $\mathbf{e}_n$ will converge to an eigenvector corresponding to the eigenvalue of largest magnitude, that is, to $(1 \quad 1)^T$.

(d) $\mathbf{A}^8\mathbf{v} = \lambda^8\mathbf{v}$.

(e) We express $\mathbf{e}_0$ in terms of the eigenvectors as $\mathbf{e}_0 = \alpha\mathbf{v}_1 + \beta\mathbf{v}_2$, so

$$\mathbf{e}_0 = \begin{pmatrix}1\\0\end{pmatrix} = \alpha\begin{pmatrix}3\\-7\end{pmatrix} + \beta\begin{pmatrix}1\\1\end{pmatrix},$$

giving $\alpha = 0.1$ and $\beta = 0.7$.

In general, $\mathbf{e}_n = \mathbf{A}^n\mathbf{e}_0$, so we calculate

$$\begin{aligned}\mathbf{A}^8\mathbf{e}_0 &= \mathbf{A}^8(0.1\mathbf{v}_1 + 0.7\mathbf{v}_2)\\ &= 0.1(\mathbf{A}^8\mathbf{v}_1) + 0.7(\mathbf{A}^8\mathbf{v}_2)\\ &= (0.1)(-0.9)^8\mathbf{v}_1 + (0.7)(1.1)^8\mathbf{v}_2\\ &\simeq 0.043\,047\mathbf{v}_1 + 1.500\,512\mathbf{v}_2\\ &= (0.129\,140 \quad -0.301\,327)^T + (1.500\,512 \quad 1.500\,512)^T\\ &= (1.629\,652 \quad 1.199\,185)^T.\end{aligned}$$

Dividing by $1.629\,652$, we obtain $\mathbf{e}_8 = (1 \quad 0.735\,853)^T$.

(f) $\mathbf{A}^{-1} = \begin{pmatrix}0.303\,030 & 0.606\,060\\1.414\,141 & -0.505\,050\end{pmatrix}.$

We follow Procedure 5(a).

First iteration:

$$\mathbf{z}_1 = \mathbf{A}^{-1}\mathbf{e}_0 = \begin{pmatrix}0.484\,848\\-1.070\,707\end{pmatrix},$$

$\alpha_1 = -1.070\,707,$

$$\mathbf{e}_1 = \frac{\mathbf{z}_1}{\alpha_1} = -\frac{1}{1.070\,707}\begin{pmatrix}0.484\,848\\-1.070\,707\end{pmatrix} = \begin{pmatrix}-0.452\,830\\1\end{pmatrix}.$$

Second iteration:

$$\alpha_2 = -1.145\,416, \quad \mathbf{e}_2 = (-0.409\,318 \quad 1)^T.$$

Third iteration:

$$\alpha_3 = -1.083\,884, \quad \mathbf{e}_3 = (-0.444\,720 \quad 1)^T.$$

This sequence of vectors is converging to

$$(-\tfrac{3}{7} \quad 1)^T \simeq (-0.428\,571 \quad 1)^T,$$

an eigenvector corresponding to the eigenvalue of smallest magnitude, $\lambda = -0.9$.

(g) Convergence is slow for direct iteration, since the two eigenvalues of $\mathbf{A}$ are -0.9 and 1.1, which are relatively close in magnitude. Similarly, inverse iteration is also slow to converge, since the eigenvalues of $\mathbf{A}^{-1}$ are -1.1111 and 0.9091, to four decimal places, and these are relatively close in magnitude.

Solution to Exercise 39

We could use Procedure 6 to find the third eigenvector, but without a computer this could be very hard work. Alternatively, we could find two of the eigenvalues from the given eigenvectors, and we could then find the third eigenvalue very easily because the sum of the eigenvalues is $\operatorname{tr} \mathbf{A}$.

We know that $\mathbf{v}_1$ is an eigenvector, so $\mathbf{A}\mathbf{v}_1 = \lambda_1 \mathbf{v}_1$. Calculating just the third components, we have

$$(3 \times 0.477) + (4 \times 0.689) + (6 \times 1) = \lambda_1 \times 1,$$

so $\lambda_1 \simeq 10.187$.

Similarly, using the second components of $\mathbf{A}\mathbf{v}_2 = \lambda_2 \mathbf{v}_2$, we have

$$(2 \times (-0.102)) + (3 \times 1) + (4 \times (-0.641)) = \lambda_2 \times 1,$$

so $\lambda_2 \simeq 0.232$.

Since $\operatorname{tr} \mathbf{A} = 1 + 3 + 6 = 10$,

$$\lambda_3 = 10 - \lambda_1 - \lambda_2 \simeq -0.419.$$

Unit 6

Systems of linear differential equations

Introduction

You have already met several types of linear differential equation in this module. For example, in Unit 1 you met linear first-order differential equations of the form

$$\frac{dx}{dt} + g(t)\,x = h(t),$$

where $x(t)$ is a function of the independent variable t, and $g(t)$ and $h(t)$ are given functions of t. Also in Unit 1 you met linear constant-coefficient second-order differential equations of the form

$$a\frac{d^2x}{dt^2} + b\frac{dx}{dt} + cx = f(t), \quad a \neq 0,$$

where a, b and c are constants, and $f(t)$ is a given function of the independent variable t.

However, the homogeneous case (i.e. setting $f(t) = 0$) of this second equation can be expressed as a pair of coupled linear first-order differential equations:

$$\dot{x} = y,$$
$$\dot{y} = -(cx + by)/a,$$

Recall that $\dot{x}$ means dx/dt and $\dot{y}$ means dy/dt.

where $y(t)$ is a another function of t. Systems of this type, that is, of linear differential equations relating two or more functions and their derivatives, are the subject of this unit. Another simple example of such a system is

$$\dot{x} = 3x + 2y,$$
$$\dot{y} = x + 4y,$$

where $x(t)$ and $y(t)$ are both functions of the independent variable t. You can think of the vector $(\dot{x} \quad \dot{y})^T = (\dot{x}(t) \quad \dot{y}(t))^T$ as the velocity at time t of a particle at position $(x, y) = (x(t), y(t))$. If we are given a system and an initial condition for the position of the particle at time $t = 0$, then solving the differential equations will give us the position $(x(t), y(t))$ of the particle at any subsequent time t.

In this unit we develop techniques for solving such systems of linear differential equations with constant coefficients. We will see that such systems can be written in matrix form, and that we can solve them by calculating the eigenvalues and eigenvectors of the resulting coefficient matrix.

We also examine systems of equations involving second derivatives, such as

$$\ddot{x} = x + 4y,$$
$$\ddot{y} = x - 2y,$$

where you can think of the vector $(\ddot{x} \quad \ddot{y})^T = (\ddot{x}(t) \quad \ddot{y}(t))^T$ as the acceleration at time t of a particle at position $(x, y) = (x(t), y(t))$.

In Section 1 we show how various situations can be modelled by a system of linear differential equations. In Section 2 we show how such a system can be written in matrix form, and use eigenvalues and eigenvectors to solve it when the equations are homogeneous with constant coefficients. This discussion spills over into Section 3, where we discuss the inhomogeneous case, and into Section 4, where we show how similar techniques can be used to solve certain systems of *second-order* differential equations.

Although many of the problems that we consider in this unit may appear to be rather restricted in scope, the type of system discussed here arises surprisingly often in practice. In particular, systems of linear constant-coefficient differential equations occur frequently in modelling situations, especially when we need to make simplifying assumptions about the situations involved. They also play an important role in understanding certain properties of the solutions of particular *non-linear* systems, as we will see in Unit 12.

1 Systems of differential equations as models

In this short motivational section, you will see how systems of linear differential equations arise in the process of modelling three rather different types of situation.

We do not give here full details of the modelling process that is required in each case, since the aim is to give a fairly rapid impression of where systems of differential equations might occur in practice. You should not spend too much time dwelling on the details.

1.1 Conflicts

Figure 1 Frederick William Lanchester (1868–1946)

Frederick William Lanchester

The model described in this subsection was first published by F.W. Lanchester (Figure 1) in 1914.

Lanchester was an English polymath and an engineer of outstanding ability. In addition to his mathematical work on conflicts, he also made significant contributions to aeronautics and automotive engineering, and played an important pioneering role in the early development of the British car industry, founding the Lanchester Engine Company in 1899.

Consider a situation in which two different groups are in direct competition for survival. In a military context, the individual members of these groups might be humans (soldiers, say) or they might be tanks, ships or aircraft. In the absence of any external means of stopping the conflict, a battle unfolds by a process of attrition, in which individual members of the two groups are in one way or another rendered inactive (in the case of humans, killed or severely wounded). The battle terminates when one side or the other has lost all of its active members.

What factors affect who will 'win' such a conflict? Other things being equal, we would expect a larger group to prevail over a smaller one, so the size of each group is important. However, it is often the case that one side is more effective per member than the other. Militarily, this effectiveness is determined by the choice and design of the weaponry used, and a recognised measure of this effectiveness is the abhorrent term *kill rate*, that is, the rate at which single members of one group can, on average, render members of the other group inactive.

For two groups of equal initial size, the more effective group will, on average, win a battle. But what will occur when group X is numerically larger than group Y but has inferior weaponry? We will describe a simple model that is capable of providing a first answer to this question.

The model is a continuous one: it approximates the actual situation, in which the active group size at any time is an integer, by assuming that the group size is capable of continuous variation. This is a very reasonable approximation if each group has a large number of members.

Let the active sizes of groups X and Y be denoted by x and y, respectively. These sizes vary with time t, so $x(t)$ represents the active size of group X at time t, and similarly for $y(t)$. Suppose that the constant kill rates of the two groups are α for group X, and β for group Y, where α and β are both positive.

We suppose that the rate of reduction of each group is proportional to the size of the other, so

$$\frac{dx}{dt} = -\beta y \quad \text{and} \quad \frac{dy}{dt} = -\alpha x.$$

This pair of equations can be written alternatively as

$$\begin{cases} \dot{x} = -\beta y, \\ \dot{y} = -\alpha x, \end{cases} \tag{1}$$

which is a system of two first-order differential equations. Neither of these equations is soluble directly by the methods of Unit 1, because they are *coupled*; that is, the equation that features the derivative of one of the variables, x say, also includes the other variable y on the right-hand side, and vice versa. In order to solve the first equation for x, we need to know explicitly what the function $y(t)$ is, and similarly for the second equation.

You will appreciate in Section 2 that this system of equations may be solved in terms of the eigenvalues and eigenvectors of the matrix

$$\begin{pmatrix} 0 & -\beta \\ -\alpha & 0 \end{pmatrix},$$

which arises from expressing equations (1) in the matrix form

$$\begin{pmatrix} \dot{x} \\ \dot{y} \end{pmatrix} = \begin{pmatrix} 0 & -\beta \\ -\alpha & 0 \end{pmatrix} \begin{pmatrix} x \\ y \end{pmatrix}.$$

Indeed, this approach is the central theme of this unit, and although there are also other methods of solution, these will not be discussed further in this unit. However, as a digression, it is worth noting that without solving the system of differential equations, it is possible to deduce an interesting conclusion about such conflicts. Suppose that we multiply both sides of the first equation of (1) by αx, then both sides of the second equation by βy, and finally subtract the resulting equations. This produces

$$\alpha x \dot{x} - \beta y \dot{y} = 0,$$

which, by the chain rule, can also be expressed as

$$\tfrac{1}{2}\alpha \frac{d}{dt}(x^2) - \tfrac{1}{2}\beta \frac{d}{dt}(y^2) = 0.$$

Integration with respect to time then gives

$$\alpha x^2 - \beta y^2 = c,$$

where c is a constant. If the initial sizes of the two groups (at time $t = 0$) are respectively x_0 and y_0, then the value of c is $\alpha x_0^2 - \beta y_0^2$, and we have

$$\alpha x^2 - \beta y^2 = \alpha x_0^2 - \beta y_0^2 \tag{2}$$

throughout the conflict.

This relationship allows us to predict when two sides are equally matched in a conflict. Neither side wins if both have their size reduced to zero at the same time, that is, if $x = 0$ when $y = 0$. In this case, we must have $\alpha x^2 - \beta y^2 = 0$ throughout the conflict, so at the start $\alpha x_0^2 = \beta y_0^2$. This reasoning led Lanchester to define the *fighting strength* of a force as 'the square of its size multiplied by the kill rate of its individual units'.

Lanchester applied this model to the situation at the Battle of Trafalgar (1805), and was able to demonstrate why Nelson's tactic of splitting the opposition fleet into two parts might have been expected to succeed, even though Nelson had a smaller total number of ships.

According to this definition, a force that outnumbers an adversarial force by only half as much again is more than twice as strong, assuming equal effectiveness on both sides. For any potential conflict, the initial fighting strengths of the two sides can be estimated, and according to equation (2), any difference in these strengths remains constant throughout the conflict. At the end, the size and therefore the strength of the loser is zero, so this difference is equal to the remaining strength of the winning side. From this, the number of survivors can be predicted.

This model is of course very simple, and will not be applicable in exact form for any particular conflict. Nevertheless, the rule of thumb that it provides is an informative one, and is taken into account by, for example, military strategists.

We again stress that the method leading to equation (2) will not be used further in this unit.

1.2 Two-compartment drug model

The administration of clinical drugs is a complex task. The doctor must ensure that the concentration of the drug in the patient's blood remains between certain upper and lower limits. One model that has been developed to assist in understanding the process is given by the following differential equation, in which $c(t)$ represents the concentration of drug in the patient's blood (as a function of time):

$$\frac{dc}{dt} = \frac{q}{V} - \lambda c.$$

We will not go into detail on how the concentration $c(t)$ is defined. A number of choices are possible.

Here the drug enters the bloodstream at a constant rate q, V is the 'apparent volume of distribution', and λ is a constant (which may be interpreted as the proportionate rate at which the kidneys excrete the drug). You are not expected to understand how this equation is derived.

Such a constant rate q of drug input to the bloodstream may be achieved by intravenous infusion, but this requires the patient to be connected to certain apparatus and is consequently inconvenient. A modern alternative is to use slow-release capsules that are taken orally. These capsules gradually dissolve within the stomach and by so doing raise the drug concentration there. The drug reaches the bloodstream from the stomach by a process that may be represented as passing through a membrane that separates the stomach 'compartment' from the bloodstream 'compartment'. Later, the drug is excreted from the kidneys, as before. The whole process is indicated diagrammatically in Figure 2.

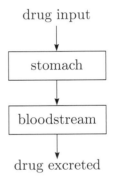

Figure 2 Schematic flow diagram showing how a drug passes through a patient

We will now indicate briefly how to model such a two-compartment situation. We make the following assumptions.

(a) The slow-release capsule has the effect of providing a constant rate of input of the drug to the stomach, until the capsule is completely dissolved.

(b) The concentrations of drug within the stomach compartment and within the bloodstream compartment are each uniform at any instant of time.

(c) The rate at which the drug passes from the stomach to the bloodstream is proportional to the difference in concentrations between them.

Assumption (c) is based on *Fick's law*, which is an empirical result stating that 'the amount of material passing through a membrane is proportional to the difference in concentration between the two sides of the membrane'.

(d) The rate of excretion from the bloodstream via the kidneys is (as in the earlier model) proportional to the concentration in the bloodstream.

Suppose that the drug concentrations in the stomach and bloodstream at time t are denoted by $x(t)$ and $y(t)$, respectively, and consider the period after the slow-release capsule has been swallowed but before it has completely dissolved.

The drug concentration in the stomach will be raised at a constant rate, k_1 say, by Assumption (a), but simultaneously lowered at a rate $k_2(x - y)$, where k_2 is a constant, by Assumption (c). Hence we have

$$\frac{dx}{dt} = k_1 - k_2(x - y).$$

Depending on how the concentrations are defined, we might expect that $k_2 = k_3$ if all the drug leaving the stomach enters the bloodstream, but this is not one of our assumptions.

The drug concentration in the blood will be raised at a rate $k_3(x - y)$, by Assumption (c), but also lowered at a rate $k_4 y$, by Assumption (d) (where k_3 and k_4 are constants). This gives

$$\frac{dy}{dt} = k_3(x - y) - k_4 y.$$

The drug concentrations in the two compartments are therefore governed within the model by the pair of differential equations

$$\begin{cases} \dot{x} = -k_2 x + k_2 y + k_1, \\ \dot{y} = k_3 x - (k_3 + k_4)y, \end{cases} \tag{3}$$

which can be written in matrix form as

$$\begin{pmatrix} \dot{x} \\ \dot{y} \end{pmatrix} = \begin{pmatrix} -k_2 & k_2 \\ k_3 & -(k_3 + k_4) \end{pmatrix} \begin{pmatrix} x \\ y \end{pmatrix} + \begin{pmatrix} k_1 \\ 0 \end{pmatrix}.$$

Figure 3 Plot of the drug concentration in the bloodstream, $y(t)$, against time t

Figure 3 sketches the type of behaviour that this model predicts for the drug concentration $y(t)$ in the bloodstream. It is characterised by an absorption phase followed by a steady decline as the drug is eliminated. The graph for the drug concentration $x(t)$ in the stomach is of similar shape. The drug concentrations do not approach zero for large values of t so long as k_1 is non-zero. In reality, a slow-release capsule will eventually dissolve completely, and then the patient must swallow another capsule in order to prevent the drug concentration from falling below some predetermined level.

The eigenvalues and eigenvectors of the matrix of coefficients

$$\begin{pmatrix} -k_2 & k_2 \\ k_3 & -(k_3 + k_4) \end{pmatrix}$$

You will study methods of solution in the following two sections.

However, system (3) becomes homogeneous when modelling the system after the slow-release capsule dissolves completely and is not replaced. This corresponds to putting $k_1 = 0$.

provide a starting point for solving the system of equations (3). However, the form of this system differs from the one derived in the previous subsection. The presence of the term k_1 on the right-hand side of the first equation, which is non-zero and does not depend on x or y, makes this system *inhomogeneous*, whereas system (1) in Subsection 1.1 is *homogeneous*, since it has no such term present. You will see shortly that, as with ordinary differential equations, the solution of an inhomogeneous system is related to, but slightly more complicated than, that of a homogeneous system.

1.3   Motion of a ball-bearing in a bowl

The previous examples each led to a system of two first-order linear differential equations, homogeneous in the case of the conflict model, and inhomogeneous for the two-compartment drug model.

We now look at an example where the system that arises involves *second-order* linear differential equations.

When a ball-bearing (that is, a small metallic ball) is placed in a bowl and set in motion, it tends to roll along the surface of the bowl for some considerable time before coming to rest. We will now indicate how this motion might be modelled for a generalised 'bowl'.

To simplify matters, we model the ball-bearing as a particle (so that the rolling aspect of the motion is ignored), and assume that the surface of the bowl is frictionless and that there is no air resistance. To describe the surface, suppose that a three-dimensional Cartesian coordinate system is chosen with the (x, y)-plane horizontal, the z-axis vertical, and the lowest point of the bowl's surface at the origin, $(0, 0, 0)$. We assume further that in the vicinity of the origin, the surface may be described by an equation of the form

$$z = \tfrac{1}{2}ax^2 + bxy + \tfrac{1}{2}cy^2, \tag{4}$$

where the constants a, b, c satisfy the conditions $ac - b^2 > 0$ and $a > 0$. The first condition here ensures that the surface under consideration is a *paraboloid*, for which any vertical cross-section through the origin is a parabola, while the second condition means that these cross-sectional parabolas are all concave upwards rather than downwards. The surface is sketched in Figure 4.

Figure 4 Surface of a bowl, inside which a ball-bearing is set in motion

It may seem restrictive to specify the particular form of surface given by equation (4). However, it turns out that many other functions $z = f(x, y)$ with a minimum value $z = 0$ at $(0, 0)$ can be approximated satisfactorily by a function of the form (4) near to the origin.

You will be able to appreciate this point more fully after studying the topic of two-variable Taylor polynomial approximations in Unit 7.

Since the surface is assumed to be frictionless and there is no air resistance, the only forces that act on the particle are its weight $\mathbf{W} = -mg\mathbf{k}$ (where m is its mass and g is the acceleration due to gravity) and the normal reaction $\mathbf{N}$ from the surface. In order to describe the latter, we need to be able to write down a vector that is normal to the surface given by equation (4) at any point (x, y, z) on the surface. One such vector, pointing inwards, is

$$-(ax + by)\mathbf{i} - (bx + cy)\mathbf{j} + \mathbf{k}.$$

We ask you to take this on trust.

Hence the normal reaction is

$$\mathbf{N} = C(-(ax + by)\mathbf{i} - (bx + cy)\mathbf{j} + \mathbf{k}),$$

where C is some positive quantity. Newton's second law then gives

Newton's second law is considered in Unit 3.

$$m\ddot{\mathbf{r}} = \mathbf{N} + \mathbf{W}$$
$$= -C(ax + by)\mathbf{i} - C(bx + cy)\mathbf{j} + (C - mg)\mathbf{k},$$

where $\mathbf{r} = x\mathbf{i} + y\mathbf{j} + z\mathbf{k}$ is the position vector of a point on the surface, relative to the origin. Resolving in the $\mathbf{i}$-, $\mathbf{j}$- and $\mathbf{k}$-directions, we obtain

$$m\ddot{x} = -C(ax + by),$$
$$m\ddot{y} = -C(bx + cy),$$
$$m\ddot{z} = C - mg.$$

On eliminating the quantity C between these equations, and dividing through by m, we have

$$\ddot{x} = -(ax + by)(g + \ddot{z}) \quad \text{and} \quad \ddot{y} = -(bx + cy)(g + \ddot{z}).$$

For motions that do not move too far from the lowest point of the bowl, the vertical component of acceleration, $\ddot{z}$, will be small in magnitude compared with g, so to a good approximation the horizontal motion of the particle is governed by the pair of equations

$$\ddot{x} = -g(ax + by),$$
$$\ddot{y} = -g(bx + cy).$$

This motion is what would be observed if you looked down onto the surface from some distance above it, as indicated in Figure 5.

For example, if the surface is given by

$$z = 0.25x^2 - 0.4xy + 0.25y^2,$$

then the corresponding equations for horizontal motion (taking $g \simeq 10\,\mathrm{m\,s^{-2}}$) are

$$\begin{cases} \ddot{x} = -5x + 4y, \\ \ddot{y} = 4x - 5y. \end{cases} \tag{5}$$

These differential equations are linear, constant-coefficient, homogeneous and second-order. You will see them solved, and the possible motions interpreted, in Subsection 4.2. As you will see, their solutions can be expressed in terms of the eigenvalues and eigenvectors of the matrix

$$\begin{pmatrix} -5 & 4 \\ 4 & -5 \end{pmatrix},$$

which arises from expressing the pair of equations (5) in matrix form as

$$\begin{pmatrix} \ddot{x} \\ \ddot{y} \end{pmatrix} = \begin{pmatrix} -5 & 4 \\ 4 & -5 \end{pmatrix} \begin{pmatrix} x \\ y \end{pmatrix}.$$

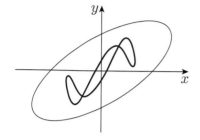

Figure 5   The projection of the ball-bearing's motion in the (x, y)-plane, showing an example of a path that might be observed

2 First-order homogeneous systems

In this unit we discuss systems of equations involving either two functions of time $x(t)$ and $y(t)$, or three functions of time $x(t)$, $y(t)$ and $z(t)$ (which we abbreviate to x, y and z). For larger systems it is often convenient to denote the functions by subscripts, for example $x_1, x_2, \ldots, x_n$, but we do not use this notation here because we wish to use subscripts later for another purpose. Throughout, we write

$$\mathbf{x} = \begin{pmatrix} x \\ y \end{pmatrix}, \quad \mathbf{x} = \begin{pmatrix} x \\ y \\ z \end{pmatrix} \quad \text{or} \quad \mathbf{x} = \begin{pmatrix} x_1 \\ x_2 \\ \vdots \\ x_n \end{pmatrix},$$

as appropriate.

In Unit 4 you saw that any system of linear equations can be written in matrix form. For example, the equations

$$3x + 2y = 5,$$
$$x + 4y = 5,$$

can be written in matrix form as

$$\begin{pmatrix} 3 & 2 \\ 1 & 4 \end{pmatrix} \begin{pmatrix} x \\ y \end{pmatrix} = \begin{pmatrix} 5 \\ 5 \end{pmatrix},$$

that is, as $\mathbf{Ax} = \mathbf{b}$, where

$$\mathbf{A} = \begin{pmatrix} 3 & 2 \\ 1 & 4 \end{pmatrix}, \quad \mathbf{x} = \begin{pmatrix} x \\ y \end{pmatrix} \quad \text{and} \quad \mathbf{b} = \begin{pmatrix} 5 \\ 5 \end{pmatrix}.$$

In a similar way, we can write systems of linear differential equations in matrix form. To see what is involved, consider the system

$$\begin{cases} \dot{x} = 3x + 2y + 5t, \\ \dot{y} = \ \ x + 4y + 5, \end{cases} \qquad (6)$$

Here x and y are functions of t.

which can be written in matrix form as

$$\begin{pmatrix} \dot{x} \\ \dot{y} \end{pmatrix} = \begin{pmatrix} 3 & 2 \\ 1 & 4 \end{pmatrix} \begin{pmatrix} x \\ y \end{pmatrix} + \begin{pmatrix} 5t \\ 5 \end{pmatrix},$$

that is, as $\dot{\mathbf{x}} = \mathbf{Ax} + \mathbf{h}$, where

Here $\mathbf{h}$ is generally a function of t, but $\mathbf{A}$ is constant.

$$\mathbf{A} = \begin{pmatrix} 3 & 2 \\ 1 & 4 \end{pmatrix}, \quad \mathbf{x} = \begin{pmatrix} x \\ y \end{pmatrix} \quad \text{and} \quad \mathbf{h} = \begin{pmatrix} 5t \\ 5 \end{pmatrix}.$$

Note that $\dot{\mathbf{x}} = (\dot{x} \ \ \dot{y})^T$.

We can similarly represent systems of three, or more, linear differential equations in matrix form. For example, the system

$$\dot{x} = 3x + 2y + 2z + \ \ e^t,$$
$$\dot{y} = 2x + 2y \ \ \ \ \ \ + 2e^t,$$
$$\dot{z} = 2x \ \ \ \ \ \ + 4z,$$

can be written in matrix form as $\dot{\mathbf{x}} = \mathbf{Ax} + \mathbf{h}$, where

Note that here $\dot{\mathbf{x}} = (\dot{x} \ \ \dot{y} \ \ \dot{z})^T$.

$$\mathbf{A} = \begin{pmatrix} 3 & 2 & 2 \\ 2 & 2 & 0 \\ 2 & 0 & 4 \end{pmatrix}, \quad \mathbf{x} = \begin{pmatrix} x \\ y \\ z \end{pmatrix} \quad \text{and} \quad \mathbf{h} = \begin{pmatrix} e^t \\ 2e^t \\ 0 \end{pmatrix} = \begin{pmatrix} 1 \\ 2 \\ 0 \end{pmatrix} e^t. \qquad (7)$$

Homogeneous and inhomogeneous equations

A matrix equation of the form $\dot{\mathbf{x}} = \mathbf{Ax} + \mathbf{h}$ is said to be **homogeneous** if $\mathbf{h} = \mathbf{0}$, and **inhomogeneous** otherwise.

Note that in an inhomogeneous equation, some, *but not all*, of the components of $\mathbf{h}$ may be 0.

For example, the matrix equation

$$\begin{pmatrix} \dot{x} \\ \dot{y} \end{pmatrix} = \begin{pmatrix} 2 & 3 \\ 2 & 1 \end{pmatrix} \begin{pmatrix} x \\ y \end{pmatrix}$$

is homogeneous, whereas the matrix equations represented by (6) and (7) are inhomogeneous.

Exercise 1

Write each of the following systems in matrix form, and classify it as homogeneous or inhomogeneous.

(a) $\begin{cases} \dot{x} = 2x + y + 1 \\ \dot{y} = x - 2 \end{cases}$
(b) $\begin{cases} \dot{x} = y \\ \dot{y} = t \end{cases}$
(c) $\begin{cases} \dot{x} = 5x \\ \dot{y} = x + 2y + z \\ \dot{z} = x + y + 2z \end{cases}$

In this section we present an algebraic method for solving homogeneous systems of linear first-order differential equations with constant coefficients. In Section 3 we show how this method can be adapted to inhomogeneous systems.

2.1   Eigenvalue method

Our intention is to develop a method for finding the general solution of any homogeneous system $\dot{\mathbf{x}} = \mathbf{A}\mathbf{x}$, however large, but we start with a 2×2 matrix $\mathbf{A}$. We begin by solving a system of differential equations using a non-matrix method, then we look at the same example again, but this time the emphasis is on the links to matrices.

Suppose that we wish to find a solution of the system

$$\dot{x} = 3x + 2y, \tag{8}$$
$$\dot{y} = x + 4y. \tag{9}$$

Equation (9) gives $x = \dot{y} - 4y$, so $\dot{x} = \ddot{y} - 4\dot{y}$. Substituting into equation (8), we obtain

$$\ddot{y} - 4\dot{y} = 3(\dot{y} - 4y) + 2y,$$

which simplifies to give

$$\ddot{y} - 7\dot{y} + 10y = 0.$$

Using the methods of Unit 1, we see that the auxiliary equation is

$$\lambda^2 - 7\lambda + 10 = 0,$$

with roots $\lambda = 5$ and $\lambda = 2$, from which we have $y = \alpha e^{5t} + \beta e^{2t}$ (for arbitrary constants α and β). Having found y, we can substitute for y and $\dot{y}$ in equation (9) and obtain $x = \alpha e^{5t} - 2\beta e^{2t}$, so the solution is

$$x = \alpha e^{5t} - 2\beta e^{2t} \quad \text{and} \quad y = \alpha e^{5t} + \beta e^{2t}. \tag{10}$$

Thus we have found the general solution of our original system of two equations, and this solution contains two arbitrary constants, as expected (one for each derivative).

General and particular solutions

The **general solution** of a system of n linear constant-coefficient first-order differential equations is a collection of all possible solutions of the system of equations.

A **particular solution** of a system of n linear constant-coefficient first-order differential equations is a solution containing no arbitrary constants and satisfying given conditions.

Compare the definitions for the single equation cases in Unit 1, Subsection 1.1.

Usually, the general solution of a system of n first-order differential equations contains n arbitrary constants.

The above method does not extend very well to larger systems and will no longer be used in what follows. However, notice that the above general solution is a linear combination of exponential terms of the form $e^{\lambda_1 t}$ and $e^{\lambda_2 t}$ (where in the above case $\lambda_1 = 5$ and $\lambda_2 = 2$). This suggests an alternative approach to solving such systems of equations, and this will turn out to be the method forming the subject of this unit. In the above case we have a solution $x = e^{5t}$, $y = e^{5t}$ corresponding to choosing $\alpha = 1$ and $\beta = 0$, and another solution $x = -2e^{2t}$, $y = e^{2t}$ corresponding to choosing $\alpha = 0$ and $\beta = 1$. Thus the general solution is a linear combination of much simpler solutions, and this suggests that we might be able to solve such systems by looking for these simpler solutions. So the idea is to search for solutions of the form $x = Ce^{\lambda t}$, $y = De^{\lambda t}$, and then form linear combinations of such solutions in order to find the general solution. There is only one minor problem – we have to convince ourselves that a linear combination of two solutions is itself a solution.

Suppose that $\mathbf{x}_1$ and $\mathbf{x}_2$ are solutions of the matrix equation $\dot{\mathbf{x}} = \mathbf{A}\mathbf{x}$; then $\dot{\mathbf{x}}_1 = \mathbf{A}\mathbf{x}_1$ and $\dot{\mathbf{x}}_2 = \mathbf{A}\mathbf{x}_2$. If α and β are arbitrary constants, then

$$\frac{d}{dt}(\alpha\mathbf{x}_1 + \beta\mathbf{x}_2) = \alpha\dot{\mathbf{x}}_1 + \beta\dot{\mathbf{x}}_2 = \alpha\mathbf{A}\mathbf{x}_1 + \beta\mathbf{A}\mathbf{x}_2 = \mathbf{A}(\alpha\mathbf{x}_1 + \beta\mathbf{x}_2),$$

so $\alpha\mathbf{x}_1 + \beta\mathbf{x}_2$ is indeed a solution. This is a particular case of a more general result known as the *principle of superposition* that you will meet later (in Theorem 2).

You met the principle of superposition in the case of second-order differential equations in Unit 1.

We apply the above technique in the following example.

Example 1

(a) For the following pair of equations, find a solution of the form $x = Ce^{\lambda t}$, $y = De^{\lambda t}$, and hence find the general solution:

$$\begin{cases} \dot{x} = 3x + 2y, \\ \dot{y} = x + 4y. \end{cases} \tag{11}$$

(b) Find the particular solution for which $x(0) = 1$ and $y(0) = 4$.

Solution

(a) We investigate possible solutions of the form

$$x = Ce^{\lambda t}, \quad y = De^{\lambda t},$$

where C and D are constants. Since $\dot{x} = C\lambda e^{\lambda t}$ and $\dot{y} = D\lambda e^{\lambda t}$, substituting the expressions for x and y into equations (11) gives

$$\begin{cases} C\lambda e^{\lambda t} = 3Ce^{\lambda t} + 2De^{\lambda t}, \\ D\lambda e^{\lambda t} = Ce^{\lambda t} + 4De^{\lambda t}. \end{cases}$$

$e^{\lambda t}$ can never be zero.

Cancelling the $e^{\lambda t}$ terms, we obtain the simultaneous linear equations

$$\begin{cases} C\lambda = 3C + 2D, \\ D\lambda = C + 4D, \end{cases} \tag{12}$$

Note that equations (12) can be expressed in matrix form:

$$\begin{pmatrix} 3 & 2 \\ 1 & 4 \end{pmatrix} \begin{pmatrix} C \\ D \end{pmatrix} = \lambda \begin{pmatrix} C \\ D \end{pmatrix}.$$

which can be rearranged to give

$$\begin{cases} (3-\lambda)C + 2D = 0, \\ C + (4-\lambda)D = 0. \end{cases} \tag{13}$$

See the summary of results for non-invertible matrices in Unit 5.

This system of linear equations has non-zero solutions for C and D only if the determinant of the coefficient matrix is 0, that is, if

$$\begin{vmatrix} 3-\lambda & 2 \\ 1 & 4-\lambda \end{vmatrix} = 0.$$

Expanding this determinant gives $(3-\lambda)(4-\lambda) - 2 = 0$, which simplifies to $\lambda^2 - 7\lambda + 10 = 0$, and we deduce that $\lambda = 5$ or $\lambda = 2$. We now substitute these values of λ in turn into equations (13).

- For $\lambda = 5$, equations (13) become

$$-2C + 2D = 0,$$
$$C - D = 0,$$

You will see later that choosing any non-zero value will work.

which reduce to the single equation $C = D$. Choosing $C = D = 1$ provides us with the solution $x = e^{5t}$, $y = e^{5t}$.

- For $\lambda = 2$, equations (13) become

$$C + 2D = 0,$$
$$C + 2D = 0,$$

which reduce to the single equation $C = -2D$. Choosing $C = -2$ and $D = 1$ provides us with another solution, $x = -2e^{2t}$, $y = e^{2t}$.

In vector form, these solutions are

$$\mathbf{x}_1 = \begin{pmatrix} 1 \\ 1 \end{pmatrix} e^{5t} \quad \text{and} \quad \mathbf{x}_2 = \begin{pmatrix} -2 \\ 1 \end{pmatrix} e^{2t}.$$

Linear independence of vectors is defined in Unit 5.

(Notice that these solution vectors are linearly independent.)

Thus the general solution can be written in the form

Here we are using the principle of superposition.

$$\begin{pmatrix} x \\ y \end{pmatrix} = \alpha \begin{pmatrix} 1 \\ 1 \end{pmatrix} e^{5t} + \beta \begin{pmatrix} -2 \\ 1 \end{pmatrix} e^{2t}. \tag{14}$$

The fact that $\mathbf{x}_1$ and $\mathbf{x}_2$ are linearly independent ensures that this expression contains *two* arbitrary constants (in other words, one term cannot be absorbed into the other). Note that this general solution is identical to that expressed in equations (10), found using the earlier method.

We do not prove that this is the case.

(b) We seek the solution for which $x = 1$ and $y = 4$ when $t = 0$. Substituting these values into equation (14) gives the simultaneous linear equations

$$1 = \alpha - 2\beta,$$
$$4 = \alpha + \beta.$$

Solving these equations gives $\alpha = 3$, $\beta = 1$, so the required particular solution is

$$\begin{pmatrix} x \\ y \end{pmatrix} = \begin{pmatrix} 3 \\ 3 \end{pmatrix} e^{5t} + \begin{pmatrix} -2 \\ 1 \end{pmatrix} e^{2t}.$$

You may have noticed that the method in Example 1(a) is similar to that used for calculating eigenvalues and eigenvectors in Unit 5. This similarity is not coincidental. Indeed, if we write the system of differential equations (11) in matrix form $\dot{\mathbf{x}} = \mathbf{A}\mathbf{x}$, that is,

$$\begin{pmatrix} \dot{x} \\ \dot{y} \end{pmatrix} = \begin{pmatrix} 3 & 2 \\ 1 & 4 \end{pmatrix} \begin{pmatrix} x \\ y \end{pmatrix},$$

then the numbers $\lambda = 5$ and $\lambda = 2$ arising in the general solution (14) turn out to be the *eigenvalues* of the coefficient matrix

$$\mathbf{A} = \begin{pmatrix} 3 & 2 \\ 1 & 4 \end{pmatrix},$$

and the vectors $(1 \quad 1)^T$ and $(-2 \quad 1)^T$ appearing in the general solution are corresponding *eigenvectors*.

You may like to check that

$$\mathbf{A}\begin{pmatrix} 1 \\ 1 \end{pmatrix} = 5 \begin{pmatrix} 1 \\ 1 \end{pmatrix}$$

and

$$\mathbf{A}\begin{pmatrix} -2 \\ 1 \end{pmatrix} = 2 \begin{pmatrix} -2 \\ 1 \end{pmatrix}.$$

To see why this happens, consider a general system of homogeneous linear constant-coefficient first-order differential equations $\dot{\mathbf{x}} = \mathbf{A}\mathbf{x}$, of any size. Suppose that there is a solution of the form $\mathbf{x} = \mathbf{v}e^{\lambda t}$, where $\mathbf{v}$ is a constant column vector. Then $\dot{\mathbf{x}} = \mathbf{v}\lambda e^{\lambda t}$, and the system of differential equations becomes $\mathbf{v}\lambda e^{\lambda t} = \mathbf{A}\mathbf{v}e^{\lambda t}$. Dividing the latter equation by $e^{\lambda t}$ (which is never 0) and rearranging, we have

$$\mathbf{A}\mathbf{v} = \lambda \mathbf{v}.$$

Thus $\mathbf{v}$ is an eigenvector of $\mathbf{A}$, and λ is the corresponding eigenvalue.

Conversely, we have the following result.

Theorem 1

If λ is an eigenvalue of the matrix $\mathbf{A}$ corresponding to an eigenvector $\mathbf{v}$, then $\mathbf{x} = \mathbf{v}e^{\lambda t}$ is a solution of the system of differential equations $\dot{\mathbf{x}} = \mathbf{A}\mathbf{x}$.

This theorem holds because if $\mathbf{x} = \mathbf{v}e^{\lambda t}$, then $\dot{\mathbf{x}} = \lambda \mathbf{v}e^{\lambda t} = \mathbf{A}\mathbf{v}e^{\lambda t} = \mathbf{A}\mathbf{x}$.

Example 2

A particle moves in the (x, y)-plane in such a way that its position (x, y) at any time t satisfies the simultaneous differential equations

$$\dot{x} = x + 4y,$$
$$\dot{y} = x - 2y.$$

Find the position (x, y) at time t if $x(0) = 2$ and $y(0) = 3$.

Solution

Note that the differential equations can be written in the form $\dot{\mathbf{x}} = \mathbf{A}\mathbf{x}$, where the matrix of coefficients is

$$\mathbf{A} = \begin{pmatrix} 1 & 4 \\ 1 & -2 \end{pmatrix}.$$

These eigenvectors and eigenvalues were found in Unit 5, Exercise 9(a).

The eigenvectors of $\mathbf{A}$ are $(4 \quad 1)^T$ with corresponding eigenvalue 2, and $(1 \quad -1)^T$ with corresponding eigenvalue -3. The general solution is therefore

$$\begin{pmatrix} x \\ y \end{pmatrix} = \alpha \begin{pmatrix} 4 \\ 1 \end{pmatrix} e^{2t} + \beta \begin{pmatrix} 1 \\ -1 \end{pmatrix} e^{-3t},$$

where α and β are arbitrary constants.

Since $x(0) = 2$ and $y(0) = 3$, we have, on putting $t = 0$,

$$2 = 4\alpha + \beta,$$
$$3 = \alpha - \beta.$$

Solving these equations gives $\alpha = 1$, $\beta = -2$, so the required particular solution is

$$\begin{pmatrix} x \\ y \end{pmatrix} = \begin{pmatrix} 4 \\ 1 \end{pmatrix} e^{2t} + \begin{pmatrix} -2 \\ 2 \end{pmatrix} e^{-3t}.$$

In the above example the particle starts at the point $(2, 3)$ when $t = 0$, and follows a certain path as t increases. The ultimate direction of this path is easy to determine because e^{-3t} is small when t is large, so we have $(x \quad y)^T \simeq (4 \quad 1)^T e^{2t}$, that is, $x \simeq 4e^{2t}$, $y \simeq e^{2t}$, so $x \simeq 4y$ and $y \simeq 0.25x$. Thus the solution approaches the line $y = 0.25x$ as t increases.

Exercise 2

Use the above method to solve the system of differential equations

$$\dot{x} = 5x + 2y,$$
$$\dot{y} = 2x + 5y,$$

given that $x = 4$ and $y = 0$ when $t = 0$.

(The eigenvalues of $\begin{pmatrix} 5 & 2 \\ 2 & 5 \end{pmatrix}$ are 7 and 3, corresponding to eigenvectors $(1 \quad 1)^T$ and $(1 \quad -1)^T$, respectively.)

The above method works equally well for larger systems. Consider the following example of a system of three differential equations.

___

Example 3

Find the general solution of the system of differential equations

$$\dot{x} = 3x + 2y + 2z,$$
$$\dot{y} = 2x + 2y,$$
$$\dot{z} = 2x \quad\quad + 4z.$$

Solution

The matrix of coefficients is

$$\mathbf{A} = \begin{pmatrix} 3 & 2 & 2 \\ 2 & 2 & 0 \\ 2 & 0 & 4 \end{pmatrix}.$$

The eigenvectors of $\mathbf{A}$ are $(2 \quad 1 \quad 2)^T$, $(1 \quad 2 \quad -2)^T$ and $(-2 \quad 2 \quad 1)^T$, corresponding to the eigenvalues $\lambda_1 = 6$, $\lambda_2 = 3$ and $\lambda_3 = 0$, respectively. The general solution is therefore

$$\begin{pmatrix} x \\ y \\ z \end{pmatrix} = \alpha \begin{pmatrix} 2 \\ 1 \\ 2 \end{pmatrix} e^{6t} + \beta \begin{pmatrix} 1 \\ 2 \\ -2 \end{pmatrix} e^{3t} + \gamma \begin{pmatrix} -2 \\ 2 \\ 1 \end{pmatrix},$$

where α, β and γ are arbitrary constants.

These eigenvectors and eigenvalues were found in Unit 5, Example 8.

Note that the last term on the right-hand side corresponds to the term in $e^{\lambda_3 t} = e^{0t} = 1$.

___

Exercise 3

A particle moves in three-dimensional space in such a way that its position (x, y, z) at any time t satisfies the simultaneous differential equations

$$\dot{x} = 5x,$$
$$\dot{y} = \quad x + 2y + \quad z,$$
$$\dot{z} = \quad x + \quad y + 2z.$$

Find the position (x, y, z) at time t if $x(0) = 4$, $y(0) = 6$ and $z(0) = 0$.

(The eigenvectors of $\begin{pmatrix} 5 & 0 & 0 \\ 1 & 2 & 1 \\ 1 & 1 & 2 \end{pmatrix}$ are $(2 \quad 1 \quad 1)^T$, $(0 \quad 1 \quad 1)^T$ and $(0 \quad 1 \quad -1)^T$, corresponding to eigenvalues 5, 3 and 1, respectively.)

___

The above method can be used to solve any system $\dot{\mathbf{x}} = \mathbf{A}\mathbf{x}$ of linear constant-coefficient first-order differential equations for which the matrix $\mathbf{A}$ has distinct real eigenvalues. We summarise the procedure as follows.

> ### Procedure 1   Solving a system of equations when there are distinct real eigenvalues
>
> To solve a system of linear constant-coefficient first-order differential equations $\dot{\mathbf{x}} = \mathbf{A}\mathbf{x}$, where $\mathbf{A}$ is an $n \times n$ matrix with distinct real eigenvalues, carry out the following steps.
>
> 1. Find the eigenvalues $\lambda_1, \lambda_2, \ldots, \lambda_n$ and a corresponding set of eigenvectors $\mathbf{v}_1, \mathbf{v}_2, \ldots, \mathbf{v}_n$.
> 2. Write down the general solution in the form
>
> $$\mathbf{x} = C_1 \mathbf{v}_1 e^{\lambda_1 t} + C_2 \mathbf{v}_2 e^{\lambda_2 t} + \cdots + C_n \mathbf{v}_n e^{\lambda_n t}, \qquad (15)$$
>
> where $C_1, C_2, \ldots, C_n$ are arbitrary constants.

In the next subsection we investigate what happens when the eigenvalues of the matrix $\mathbf{A}$ are not distinct, or when they are complex numbers.

2.2 Two variations

This result is not obvious; we ask you to take it on trust.

The above method relies on the fact that eigenvectors corresponding to distinct eigenvalues are linearly independent, which ensures that the solution given in equation (15) contains n arbitrary constants hence is the required general solution. If the eigenvalues are not distinct, then we may not be able to write down n linearly independent eigenvectors, so when we attempt to construct the solution for $\mathbf{x}$ given in equation (15), we find that it contains too few constants. In the following example we are able to find a sufficient number of eigenvectors in spite of the fact that an eigenvalue is repeated.

Example 4

Find the general solution of the system of differential equations

$$\begin{aligned}
\dot{x} &= 5x &&+ 3z, \\
\dot{y} &= 3x + 2y &&+ 3z, \\
\dot{z} &= -6x &&- 4z.
\end{aligned}$$

Solution

The matrix of coefficients is

$$\mathbf{A} = \begin{pmatrix} 5 & 0 & 3 \\ 3 & 2 & 3 \\ -6 & 0 & -4 \end{pmatrix}.$$

Using the techniques of Unit 5, we can calculate the eigenvalues of $\mathbf{A}$. They are $\lambda = -1$ and $\lambda = 2$ (repeated), corresponding to eigenvectors $(1 \quad 1 \quad -2)^T$ and $(0 \quad 1 \quad 0)^T$, respectively.

You need to understand what goes wrong before we show you how to put it right, so suppose that we try to follow Procedure 1, and let

$$\mathbf{x} = C_1(1 \quad 1 \quad -2)^T e^{-t} + C_2(0 \quad 1 \quad 0)^T e^{2t}.$$

This is certainly a solution, but it is not the general solution because it contains only two arbitrary constants and we require three.

The answer to our difficulty lies in our method of calculating the eigenvectors when the eigenvalue is repeated. The eigenvector equations are

$$\begin{aligned}(5-\lambda)x &&+ && 3z &= 0,\\ 3x + (2-\lambda)y &&+ && 3z &= 0,\\ -6x &&+ (-4-\lambda)z &= 0.\end{aligned}$$

For $\lambda = 2$, the eigenvector equations become

$$3x + 3z = 0, \quad 3x + 3z = 0 \quad \text{and} \quad -6x - 6z = 0.$$

All three equations give $z = -x$, but there is no restriction on y. It follows that any vector of the form $(k \quad l \quad -k)^T$ is an eigenvector corresponding to $\lambda = 2$, where k and l are any real numbers, not both zero. (In particular, the vector $(0 \quad 1 \quad 0)^T$ mentioned above is an eigenvector corresponding to $\lambda = 2$.)

Remember that we need to find three linearly independent eigenvectors, and it might appear that we have found only two, namely $(1 \quad 1 \quad -2)^T$ corresponding to $\lambda = -1$ and $(k \quad l \quad -k)^T$ corresponding to $\lambda = 2$. However, the numbers k and l are arbitrary, so there are infinitely many vectors in the second category; our task is to choose two that are linearly independent. If we write

$$(k \quad l \quad -k)^T = k(1 \quad 0 \quad -1)^T + l(0 \quad 1 \quad 0)^T,$$

then we see at once that $(1 \quad 0 \quad -1)^T$ and $(0 \quad 1 \quad 0)^T$ are suitable candidates (corresponding to $k = 1$, $l = 0$ and $k = 0$, $l = 1$, respectively, but of course other combinations are also possible).

Thus

$$\begin{pmatrix} x \\ y \\ z \end{pmatrix} = C_1 \begin{pmatrix} 1 \\ 1 \\ -2 \end{pmatrix} e^{-t} + \left(C_2 \begin{pmatrix} 1 \\ 0 \\ -1 \end{pmatrix} + C_3 \begin{pmatrix} 0 \\ 1 \\ 0 \end{pmatrix} \right) e^{2t},$$

where C_1, C_2 and C_3 are arbitrary constants, is a solution, by Theorem 1 and the principle of superposition. The fact that the three eigenvectors are linearly independent ensures that there are three arbitrary constants, and hence that this is the general solution.

This approach to finding eigenvectors corresponding to repeated eigenvalues was touched on in Unit 5, Exercise 31.

Exercise 4

A particle moves in three-dimensional space in such a way that its position (x, y, z) at any time t satisfies the simultaneous differential equations

$$\dot{x} = z,$$
$$\dot{y} = y,$$
$$\dot{z} = x.$$

Find the position (x, y, z) at time t if $x(0) = 7$, $y(0) = 5$ and $z(0) = 1$.

(The eigenvalues of $\begin{pmatrix} 0 & 0 & 1 \\ 0 & 1 & 0 \\ 1 & 0 & 0 \end{pmatrix}$ are $\lambda = -1$, corresponding to an eigenvector $(1 \quad 0 \quad -1)^T$, and $\lambda = 1$ (repeated), corresponding to an eigenvector $(k \quad l \quad k)^T$.)

In Example 4 we were able to determine the general solution even though there were only two distinct eigenvalues. This is because we were able to find three linearly independent eigenvectors. We now consider a situation in which there are too few linearly independent eigenvectors.

Suppose that we try to apply the above method to find the general solution of the system of differential equations

$$\dot{x} = x,$$
$$\dot{y} = x + y.$$

The matrix of coefficients is

$$\mathbf{A} = \begin{pmatrix} 1 & 0 \\ 1 & 1 \end{pmatrix},$$

and the eigenvalues are $\lambda = 1$ (repeated). We now substitute this eigenvalue into the eigenvector equations

$$(1 - \lambda)x \qquad\quad = 0,$$
$$x + (1 - \lambda)y = 0.$$

For $\lambda = 1$, the eigenvector equations become $0 = 0$ and $x = 0$. The first equation tells us nothing; the second equation gives $x = 0$, but imposes no restriction on y. It follows that $(0 \quad k)^T$ is an eigenvector corresponding to $\lambda = 1$, for any non-zero value of k. Thus choosing $k = 1$, we have the solution

$$\begin{pmatrix} x \\ y \end{pmatrix} = C \begin{pmatrix} 0 \\ 1 \end{pmatrix} e^t.$$

But this is clearly not the general solution, since it has only one arbitrary constant instead of two; the procedure has failed.

Before extending our matrix procedure to cover the above case, it is illuminating to solve the given system of differential equations directly.

Since $\mathbf{A}$ is a triangular matrix, the eigenvalues are simply the diagonal entries.

The first equation, $\dot{x} = x$, has solution $x = De^t$, where D is an arbitrary constant. Substituting this solution into the second equation gives $\dot{y} = y + De^t$, which can be solved by the integrating factor method of Unit 1 to give $y = Ce^t + Dte^t$. Thus the solution for which we are searching is

$$\begin{pmatrix} x \\ y \end{pmatrix} = C \underbrace{\begin{pmatrix} 0 \\ 1 \end{pmatrix}}_{\text{eigenvector}} e^t + D \underbrace{\begin{pmatrix} 1 \\ t \end{pmatrix}}_{\text{notice the } t \text{ here}} e^t,$$

and this is the general solution since it contains two arbitrary constants.

The above solution provides a clue to a general method. The origins of the first term on the right-hand side are clear – it corresponds to an eigenvector – but let us look more closely at the second term on the right-hand side. We have

> There are *two* arbitrary constants since $(0\ \ 1)^T$ and $(1\ \ t)^T$ are linearly independent.

$$D \begin{pmatrix} 1 \\ t \end{pmatrix} e^t = D \underbrace{\begin{pmatrix} 0 \\ 1 \end{pmatrix}}_{\text{eigenvector}} te^t + D \begin{pmatrix} 1 \\ 0 \end{pmatrix} e^t = D \left(\begin{pmatrix} 0 \\ 1 \end{pmatrix} t + \begin{pmatrix} 1 \\ 0 \end{pmatrix} \right) e^t.$$

This suggests that if we wish to solve the system $\dot{\mathbf{x}} = \mathbf{A}\mathbf{x}$ for which $\mathbf{A}$ has a repeated eigenvalue λ, giving rise to too few eigenvectors, it may be helpful to search for solutions of the form

$$\mathbf{x} = (\mathbf{v}t + \mathbf{b})e^{\lambda t},$$

where $\mathbf{v}$ is an eigenvector corresponding to λ, and $\mathbf{b}$ is to be determined.

Let us suppose that our system has a solution of this form, and examine the consequences. Substituting this proposed solution into $\dot{\mathbf{x}} = \mathbf{A}\mathbf{x}$ gives

$$\lambda(\mathbf{v}t + \mathbf{b})e^{\lambda t} + \mathbf{v}e^{\lambda t} = \mathbf{A}(\mathbf{v}t + \mathbf{b})e^{\lambda t},$$

or, on dividing by $e^{\lambda t}$ and rearranging,

$$\mathbf{A}(\mathbf{v}t + \mathbf{b}) - \lambda(\mathbf{v}t + \mathbf{b}) = \mathbf{v},$$

and a further rearrangement leads to

$$(\mathbf{A}\mathbf{v} - \lambda\mathbf{v})t + (\mathbf{A}\mathbf{b} - \lambda\mathbf{b}) = \mathbf{v}.$$

The first term disappears because $\mathbf{v}$ is an eigenvector of $\mathbf{A}$ corresponding to the eigenvalue λ (so $\mathbf{A}\mathbf{v} = \lambda\mathbf{v}$), and we are left with $(\mathbf{A} - \lambda\mathbf{I})\mathbf{b} = \mathbf{v}$. If this equation can be solved for $\mathbf{b}$, then we will have found a solution of the required form.

For example, in the above case we had $\mathbf{A} = \begin{pmatrix} 1 & 0 \\ 1 & 1 \end{pmatrix}$ and $\lambda = 1$, so

$$\mathbf{A} - \lambda\mathbf{I} = \mathbf{A} - \mathbf{I} = \begin{pmatrix} 0 & 0 \\ 1 & 0 \end{pmatrix} \quad \text{and} \quad \mathbf{v} = \begin{pmatrix} 0 \\ 1 \end{pmatrix}.$$

Thus if $\mathbf{b} = (b_1\ \ b_2)^T$, the equation $(\mathbf{A} - \lambda\mathbf{I})\mathbf{b} = \mathbf{v}$ becomes

$$\begin{pmatrix} 0 & 0 \\ 1 & 0 \end{pmatrix} \begin{pmatrix} b_1 \\ b_2 \end{pmatrix} = \begin{pmatrix} 0 \\ 1 \end{pmatrix}.$$

The value of b_2 is irrelevant, since it is absorbed into the arbitrary constant.

Any solution of this equation for b_1 and b_2 is acceptable. In fact, this equation gives just $b_1 = 1$ (with no condition on b_2), and we can take $\mathbf{b}$ to be $(1 \quad 0)^T$, giving the solution

$$\left(\begin{pmatrix} 0 \\ 1 \end{pmatrix} t + \begin{pmatrix} 1 \\ 0 \end{pmatrix} \right) e^t = \begin{pmatrix} 1 \\ t \end{pmatrix} e^t.$$

Now we have two linearly independent solutions of our system of differential equations, namely $(0 \quad 1)^T e^t$ and $(1 \quad t)^T e^t$, so the general solution is

$$\begin{pmatrix} x \\ y \end{pmatrix} = C \underbrace{\begin{pmatrix} 0 \\ 1 \end{pmatrix} e^t}_{\substack{\text{solution} \\ \mathbf{v}e^{\lambda t}}} + D \underbrace{\begin{pmatrix} 1 \\ t \end{pmatrix} e^t}_{\substack{\text{solution} \\ (\mathbf{v}t + \mathbf{b})e^{\lambda t}}},$$

as we found before.

Procedure 2   Solving a system of equations when there are repeated real eigenvalues

To solve a system of linear constant-coefficient first-order differential equations $\dot{\mathbf{x}} = \mathbf{A}\mathbf{x}$, where $\mathbf{A}$ is an $n \times n$ matrix with some repeated real eigenvalues (where any eigenvalue is repeated at most once), carry out the following steps.

This procedure covers only the case where an eigenvalue is repeated once. It could be extended to cover the case where an eigenvalue is repeated several times, but we choose not to generalise.

1. For the non-repeated eigenvalues $\lambda_1, \lambda_2, \ldots, \lambda_k$ and corresponding eigenvectors $\mathbf{v}_1, \mathbf{v}_2, \ldots, \mathbf{v}_k$, write down the set S of solutions of the form $\mathbf{v}_i e^{\lambda_i t}$.

2. Examine the eigenvector equations corresponding to each repeated eigenvalue, and attempt to construct two linearly independent eigenvectors to add two solutions to S.

    If this fails, then for each repeated eigenvalue λ_i that gives rise to only one eigenvector $\mathbf{v}_i$, construct a solution $(\mathbf{v}_i t + \mathbf{b}_i)e^{\lambda_i t}$ for which $(\mathbf{A} - \lambda_i \mathbf{I})\mathbf{b}_i = \mathbf{v}_i$, and add this and the solution $\mathbf{v}_i e^{\lambda_i t}$ to the set S.

This arbitrary linear combination will contain n arbitrary constants.

3. If S contains n linearly independent solutions, then the general solution of the system of differential equations is an arbitrary linear combination of the solutions in S.

Exercise 5

A particle moves in the plane in such a way that its position (x, y) at any time t satisfies the simultaneous differential equations

$$\dot{x} = 2x + 3y,$$
$$\dot{y} = \phantom{2x + {}} 2y.$$

Find the position (x, y) of the particle at time t if its position is $(4, 3)$ at time $t = 0$.

So far, all our examples and exercises have involved *real* eigenvalues. We now investigate what happens when the characteristic equation has at least one complex root (giving a *complex eigenvalue*). In fact, since the arguments leading to Procedure 1 did not rely on the eigenvalues being real, Procedure 1 applies *whenever* the eigenvalues are distinct – it does not matter whether they are real or complex. However, using Procedure 1 for complex eigenvalues leads to a complex-valued solution involving complex arbitrary constants. For a system of differential equations with real coefficients, we would generally want real-valued solutions. So here we see how to adapt Procedure 1 to obtain a real-valued solution when some of the eigenvalues are complex.

For matrices that are real (ours always are), complex roots occur as complex conjugate pairs $a \pm bi$.

We begin with an example that is simple enough for us to be able to apply a direct method in order to find the general solution. We then solve the system again by applying a matrix method based on Procedure 1, which has the advantage that it can be extended to larger systems of equations.

Example 5

Solve the system of differential equations

$$\begin{cases} \dot{x} = y, \\ \dot{y} = -x. \end{cases} \tag{16}$$

Solution

If we differentiate the first equation, giving $\ddot{x} = \dot{y}$, and substitute for $\dot{y}$ in the second equation, we obtain $\ddot{x} = -x$, so $\ddot{x} + x = 0$. This second-order differential equation has auxiliary equation $\lambda^2 + 1 = 0$, so the general solution is $x = C\cos t + D\sin t$. Therefore $y = \dot{x} = -C\sin t + D\cos t$. Thus the general solution of equations (16) is

See Unit 1.

$$\begin{pmatrix} x \\ y \end{pmatrix} = C\begin{pmatrix} \cos t \\ -\sin t \end{pmatrix} + D\begin{pmatrix} \sin t \\ \cos t \end{pmatrix}.$$

Note that if we want *real* solutions, then C and D must be real.

Now we will obtain the same general solution using a matrix method based on Procedure 1.

The matrix of coefficients is

$$\mathbf{A} = \begin{pmatrix} 0 & 1 \\ -1 & 0 \end{pmatrix}.$$

The characteristic equation is $\lambda^2 + 1 = 0$, giving the complex eigenvalues $\lambda = i$ and $\lambda = -i$. The eigenvector equations are

$$-\lambda x + y = 0 \quad \text{and} \quad -x - \lambda y = 0.$$

- For $\lambda = i$, the eigenvector equations become

$$-ix + y = 0 \quad \text{and} \quad -x - iy = 0,$$

which reduce to the single equation $y = ix$. It follows that $(1 \quad i)^T$ is an eigenvector corresponding to $\lambda = i$.

Note that the first equation is i times the second equation.

to the general solution (where C and D are arbitrary complex constants). To obtain a real-valued solution, this expression can be rewritten in the form

$$\alpha \operatorname{Re}(\mathbf{v}e^{\lambda t}) + \beta \operatorname{Im}(\mathbf{v}e^{\lambda t}),$$

where α and β are arbitrary real constants.

The components of $\operatorname{Re}(\mathbf{v}e^{\lambda t})$ and $\operatorname{Im}(\mathbf{v}e^{\lambda t})$ are sinusoidal functions.

Procedure 3 Solving a system of equations when there are complex eigenvalues

To obtain a real-valued solution of a system of linear constant-coefficient first-order differential equations $\dot{\mathbf{x}} = \mathbf{A}\mathbf{x}$, where $\mathbf{A}$ is an $n \times n$ matrix with distinct eigenvalues, some of which are complex (occurring in complex conjugate pairs λ and $\overline{\lambda}$, with corresponding complex conjugate eigenvectors $\mathbf{v}$ and $\overline{\mathbf{v}}$), carry out the following steps.

If any of the real eigenvalues are repeated, this procedure will need to be adapted as in Procedure 2.

1. Find the eigenvalues $\lambda_1, \lambda_2, \ldots, \lambda_n$ and a corresponding set of eigenvectors $\mathbf{v}_1, \mathbf{v}_2, \ldots, \mathbf{v}_n$.

2. Write down the general solution in the form

$$\mathbf{x} = C_1 \mathbf{v}_1 e^{\lambda_1 t} + C_2 \mathbf{v}_2 e^{\lambda_2 t} + \cdots + C_n \mathbf{v}_n e^{\lambda_n t}, \tag{17}$$

where $C_1, C_2, \ldots, C_n$ are arbitrary complex constants.

3. Replace the terms $\mathbf{v}e^{\lambda t}$ and $\overline{\mathbf{v}}e^{\overline{\lambda} t}$ appearing in the general solution with $\operatorname{Re}(\mathbf{v}e^{\lambda t})$ and $\operatorname{Im}(\mathbf{v}e^{\lambda t})$.

The general solution will then be real-valued for real $C_1, C_2, \ldots, C_n$.

Example 6

Solve the system of differential equations

$$\dot{x} = 3x - y,$$
$$\dot{y} = 2x + y,$$

given that $x = 3$ and $y = 1$ when $t = 0$.

Solution

The matrix of coefficients is $\mathbf{A} = \begin{pmatrix} 3 & -1 \\ 2 & 1 \end{pmatrix}$.

The eigenvalues of $\mathbf{A}$ are $\lambda = 2 + i$ and $\overline{\lambda} = 2 - i$, corresponding to eigenvectors $\mathbf{v} = (1 \quad 1 - i)^T$ and $\overline{\mathbf{v}} = (1 \quad 1 + i)^T$, respectively. So the general solution can be written as

$$\mathbf{x} = C\mathbf{v}e^{\lambda t} + D\overline{\mathbf{v}}e^{\overline{\lambda} t} = C \begin{pmatrix} 1 \\ 1 - i \end{pmatrix} e^{(2+i)t} + D \begin{pmatrix} 1 \\ 1 + i \end{pmatrix} e^{(2-i)t},$$

where C and D are arbitrary complex constants.

To obtain a real-valued solution, we follow Procedure 3 and write

$$\mathbf{v}e^{\lambda t} = \begin{pmatrix} 1 \\ 1-i \end{pmatrix} e^{(2+i)t}$$

$$= e^{2t} \begin{pmatrix} 1 \\ 1-i \end{pmatrix} e^{it}$$

$$= e^{2t} \begin{pmatrix} 1 \\ 1-i \end{pmatrix} (\cos t + i \sin t)$$

$$= e^{2t} \begin{pmatrix} \cos t + i \sin t \\ (1-i)(\cos t + i \sin t) \end{pmatrix}$$

$$= e^{2t} \begin{pmatrix} \cos t + i \sin t \\ (\cos t + \sin t) + i(\sin t - \cos t) \end{pmatrix}$$

$$= \underbrace{e^{2t} \begin{pmatrix} \cos t \\ \cos t + \sin t \end{pmatrix}}_{\text{real part}} + \underbrace{i\, e^{2t} \begin{pmatrix} \sin t \\ \sin t - \cos t \end{pmatrix}}_{\text{imaginary part}}.$$

The real-valued general solution of the given system of equations is therefore

$$\begin{pmatrix} x \\ y \end{pmatrix} = \alpha\, e^{2t} \begin{pmatrix} \cos t \\ \cos t + \sin t \end{pmatrix} + \beta\, e^{2t} \begin{pmatrix} \sin t \\ \sin t - \cos t \end{pmatrix}, \tag{18}$$

where α and β are arbitrary real constants.

In order to find the required particular solution, we substitute $x = 3$, $y = 1$ and $t = 0$ into equation (18), to obtain

$$\begin{pmatrix} 3 \\ 1 \end{pmatrix} = \alpha \begin{pmatrix} 1 \\ 1 \end{pmatrix} + \beta \begin{pmatrix} 0 \\ -1 \end{pmatrix},$$

so $3 = \alpha$ and $1 = \alpha - \beta$, giving $\beta = 2$, and the solution is therefore

$$\begin{pmatrix} x \\ y \end{pmatrix} = \begin{pmatrix} e^{2t}(3\cos t + 2\sin t) \\ e^{2t}(\cos t + 5\sin t) \end{pmatrix}.$$

We will ask you to solve systems of linear constant-coefficient first-order differential equations by hand only for 2×2 and 3×3 coefficient matrices, but you may well encounter larger systems when you use a computer algebra package.

Exercise 6

Using the eigenvalues and eigenvectors given, find the real-valued solution of each of the following systems of differential equations, given that $x = y = 1$ when $t = 0$.

(a) $\begin{cases} \dot{x} = 2x + 3y \\ \dot{y} = 2x + y \end{cases}$

(The matrix $\begin{pmatrix} 2 & 3 \\ 2 & 1 \end{pmatrix}$ has eigenvalues 4 and -1, corresponding to eigenvectors $(3 \quad 2)^T$ and $(1 \quad -1)^T$, respectively.)

(b) $\begin{cases} \dot{x} = -3x - 2y \\ \dot{y} = 4x + y \end{cases}$

(The matrix $\begin{pmatrix} -3 & -2 \\ 4 & 1 \end{pmatrix}$ has eigenvalues $-1 + 2i$ and $-1 - 2i$,

corresponding to eigenvectors $(1 \quad -1 - i)^T$ and $(1 \quad -1 + i)^T$,
respectively.)

Exercise 7

Write down the general solution of each of the following systems of
equations.

(a) $\begin{cases} \dot{x} = x - z \\ \dot{y} = x + 2y + z \\ \dot{z} = 2x + 2y + 3z \end{cases}$

(The matrix $\begin{pmatrix} 1 & 0 & -1 \\ 1 & 2 & 1 \\ 2 & 2 & 3 \end{pmatrix}$ has eigenvalues 1, 2 and 3, corresponding to

eigenvectors $(1 \quad -1 \quad 0)^T$, $(-2 \quad 1 \quad 2)^T$ and $(1 \quad -1 \quad -2)^T$,
respectively.)

(b) $\begin{cases} \dot{x} = 5x - 6y - 6z \\ \dot{y} = -x + 4y + 2z \\ \dot{z} = 3x - 6y - 4z \end{cases}$

(The matrix $\begin{pmatrix} 5 & -6 & -6 \\ -1 & 4 & 2 \\ 3 & -6 & -4 \end{pmatrix}$ has eigenvalues 1 and 2 (repeated), with

corresponding eigenvectors $(3 \quad -1 \quad 3)^T$ and $(2l + 2k \quad l \quad k)^T$,
respectively, where k and l are arbitrary real numbers, not both zero.)

Exercise 8

Find the general real-valued solution of the system of equations

$$\dot{x} = x + z,$$
$$\dot{y} = y,$$
$$\dot{z} = -x + y.$$

Find the solution for which $x = y = 1$ and $z = 2$ when $t = 0$.

(The matrix $\begin{pmatrix} 1 & 0 & 1 \\ 0 & 1 & 0 \\ -1 & 1 & 0 \end{pmatrix}$ has eigenvalues 1, $\lambda = \frac{1}{2} + \frac{\sqrt{3}}{2}i$ and

$\bar{\lambda} = \frac{1}{2} - \frac{\sqrt{3}}{2}i$, corresponding to the eigenvectors $(1 \quad 1 \quad 0)^T$,
$\mathbf{v} = (1 \quad 0 \quad -\frac{1}{2} + \frac{\sqrt{3}}{2}i)^T$ and $\bar{\mathbf{v}} = (1 \quad 0 \quad -\frac{1}{2} - \frac{\sqrt{3}}{2}i)^T$, respectively.)

---

3 First-order inhomogeneous systems

Here we write $\mathbf{h}(t)$ to emphasise that $\mathbf{h}$ is a function of t. Henceforth we will abbreviate this to $\mathbf{h}$.

In the previous section you saw how to solve a system of differential equations of the form $\dot{\mathbf{x}} = \mathbf{A}\mathbf{x}$, where $\mathbf{A}$ is a given constant-coefficient matrix. We now extend our discussion to systems of the form

$$\dot{\mathbf{x}} = \mathbf{A}\mathbf{x} + \mathbf{h}(t),$$

where $\mathbf{h}(t)$ is a given function of t. Our method involves finding a 'particular integral' for the system, and mirrors the approach taken for inhomogeneous second-order differential equations in Unit 1.

3.1 A basic result

In Unit 1 we discussed inhomogeneous differential equations such as

See Unit 1, Example 18.

$$\frac{d^2 y}{dx^2} + 9y = 2e^{3x} + 18x + 18. \tag{19}$$

To solve such an equation, we proceed as follows.

- We first find the *complementary function* of the corresponding homogeneous equation

$$\frac{d^2 y}{dx^2} + 9y = 0,$$

  which is

$$y_c = C_1 \cos 3x + C_2 \sin 3x,$$

  where C_1 and C_2 are arbitrary constants.

- We then find a *particular integral* of the inhomogeneous equation (19):

$$y_p = \tfrac{1}{9}e^{3x} + 2x + 2.$$

The general solution y of the original equation is then obtained by adding these two functions (using the principle of superposition) to give

$$y = y_c + y_p = (C_1 \cos 3x + C_2 \sin 3x) + \left(\tfrac{1}{9}e^{3x} + 2x + 2\right). \tag{20}$$

A similar situation holds for *systems* of linear first-order differential equations. For example, in order to find the general solution of the inhomogeneous system

$$\begin{cases} \dot{x} = 3x + 2y + 4e^{3t}, \\ \dot{y} = x + 4y - e^{3t}, \end{cases} \tag{21}$$

which in matrix form becomes

This is $\dot{\mathbf{x}} = \mathbf{A}\mathbf{x} + \mathbf{h}$, where $\mathbf{h} = (4e^{3t} \quad -e^{3t})^T$.

$$\begin{pmatrix} \dot{x} \\ \dot{y} \end{pmatrix} = \begin{pmatrix} 3 & 2 \\ 1 & 4 \end{pmatrix} \begin{pmatrix} x \\ y \end{pmatrix} + \begin{pmatrix} 4e^{3t} \\ -e^{3t} \end{pmatrix},$$

we first find the general solution of the corresponding homogeneous system

$$\begin{cases} \dot{x} = 3x + 2y, \\ \dot{y} = x + 4y, \end{cases}$$

which is the *complementary function*

$$\begin{pmatrix} x_c \\ y_c \end{pmatrix} = \alpha \begin{pmatrix} 1 \\ 1 \end{pmatrix} e^{5t} + \beta \begin{pmatrix} -2 \\ 1 \end{pmatrix} e^{2t},$$

where α and β are arbitrary constants (see Example 1(a)).

We next find a particular solution, or *particular integral*, of the original system (21), namely

$$\begin{pmatrix} x_p \\ y_p \end{pmatrix} = \begin{pmatrix} 3 \\ -2 \end{pmatrix} e^{3t},$$

as we will show in Subsection 3.2 (Example 9). The general solution of the original system (21) is then obtained by adding these two:

$$\begin{pmatrix} x \\ y \end{pmatrix} = \begin{pmatrix} x_c \\ y_c \end{pmatrix} + \begin{pmatrix} x_p \\ y_p \end{pmatrix} = \alpha \begin{pmatrix} 1 \\ 1 \end{pmatrix} e^{5t} + \beta \begin{pmatrix} -2 \\ 1 \end{pmatrix} e^{2t} + \begin{pmatrix} 3 \\ -2 \end{pmatrix} e^{3t}.$$

To describe the above expression as 'the general solution' is perhaps premature, because it is not immediately obvious that it is even a solution. In order to establish that this is the case, we may use the following general result.

We use the term *particular integral* rather than particular solution. The latter is more appropriately used for the solution of system (21) that satisfies given initial or boundary conditions.

Theorem 2   Principle of superposition

If $\mathbf{x}_1$ is a solution of the system $\dot{\mathbf{x}} = \mathbf{Ax} + \mathbf{h}_1$ and $\mathbf{x}_2$ is a solution of the system $\dot{\mathbf{x}} = \mathbf{Ax} + \mathbf{h}_2$, then $p\mathbf{x}_1 + q\mathbf{x}_2$ is a solution of the system $\dot{\mathbf{x}} = \mathbf{Ax} + p\mathbf{h}_1 + q\mathbf{h}_2$, where p and q are constants.

This result is easy to prove, for we have

$$\frac{d}{dt}(p\mathbf{x}_1 + q\mathbf{x}_2) = p\dot{\mathbf{x}}_1 + q\dot{\mathbf{x}}_2$$
$$= p(\mathbf{Ax}_1 + \mathbf{h}_1) + q(\mathbf{Ax}_2 + \mathbf{h}_2)$$
$$= \mathbf{A}(p\mathbf{x}_1 + q\mathbf{x}_2) + p\mathbf{h}_1 + q\mathbf{h}_2.$$

The particular case that is relevant here corresponds to choosing $\mathbf{h}_1 = \mathbf{0}$ and $\mathbf{h}_2 = \mathbf{h}$, say, and putting $p = q = 1$, $\mathbf{x}_1 = \mathbf{x}_c$, the complementary function, and $\mathbf{x}_2 = \mathbf{x}_p$, a particular integral. Then the above result gives rise to the following theorem.

Theorem 3

If $\mathbf{x}_c$ is the complementary function of the homogeneous system $\dot{\mathbf{x}} = \mathbf{Ax}$, and $\mathbf{x}_p$ is a particular integral of the system $\dot{\mathbf{x}} = \mathbf{Ax} + \mathbf{h}$, then $\mathbf{x}_c + \mathbf{x}_p$ is the general solution of the system $\dot{\mathbf{x}} = \mathbf{Ax} + \mathbf{h}$.

Exercise 9

Write down the general solution of the system

$$\dot{x} = 3x + 2y + t,$$
$$\dot{y} = x + 4y + 7t,$$

given that a particular integral is

$$x_\mathrm{p} = t + \tfrac{4}{5}, \quad y_\mathrm{p} = -2t - \tfrac{7}{10}.$$

(The matrix $\begin{pmatrix} 3 & 2 \\ 1 & 4 \end{pmatrix}$ has eigenvalues 5 and 2, corresponding to eigenvectors $(1 \quad 1)^T$ and $(-2 \quad 1)^T$, respectively.)

At this stage it is natural to ask how we were able to find the above particular integral (although it is easy to verify that it *is* a solution to the given system, by direct substitution). Before we address that question in detail, we should emphasise the importance of the principle of superposition. Consider the following example, paying particular attention to the form of **h**, which is made up of both exponential and linear terms.

Example 7

Find the general solution of the system

$$\dot{x} = 3x + 2y + 4e^{3t} + 2t,$$
$$\dot{y} = x + 4y - e^{3t} + 14t.$$

Here $\mathbf{h} = \begin{pmatrix} 4e^{3t} + 2t \\ -e^{3t} + 14t \end{pmatrix}$.

Solution

Choosing $\mathbf{h}_1 = (4e^{3t} \quad -e^{3t})^T$, we see from the results derived for equations (21) that $\mathbf{x}_1 = (3 \quad -2)^T e^{3t}$ is a solution of $\dot{\mathbf{x}} = \mathbf{Ax} + \mathbf{h}_1$. Also, choosing $\mathbf{h}_2 = (t \quad 7t)^T$ gives $\mathbf{x}_2 = (t + \tfrac{4}{5} \quad -2t - \tfrac{7}{10})^T$ as a solution of $\dot{\mathbf{x}} = \mathbf{Ax} + \mathbf{h}_2$, from Exercise 9. Thus from the principle of superposition, $\mathbf{x}_1 + 2\mathbf{x}_2$ is a particular integral of the given system written as $\dot{\mathbf{x}} = \mathbf{Ax} + \mathbf{h}_1 + 2\mathbf{h}_2$. Hence by Theorem 3, using the complementary function in Exercise 9, the general solution is

$$\begin{pmatrix} x \\ y \end{pmatrix} = \left(\alpha \begin{pmatrix} 1 \\ 1 \end{pmatrix} e^{5t} + \beta \begin{pmatrix} -2 \\ 1 \end{pmatrix} e^{2t} \right) + \left(\begin{pmatrix} 3 \\ -2 \end{pmatrix} e^{3t} + \begin{pmatrix} 2t + \tfrac{8}{5} \\ -4t - \tfrac{7}{5} \end{pmatrix} \right).$$

Example 7 illustrates a general technique, the principle of which is to break down the term **h** into a sum of manageable components.

3.2 Finding particular integrals

We now show you how to find a particular integral $\mathbf{x}_\mathrm{p}$ in some special cases. We consider the system $\dot{\mathbf{x}} = \mathbf{A}\mathbf{x} + \mathbf{h}$ in the situations where $\mathbf{h}$ is a vector whose components are:

- polynomial functions
- exponential functions.

Our treatment will be similar to that of Unit 1, where we found particular integrals for linear second-order differential equations using the method of undetermined coefficients. As in that unit, a number of exceptional cases arise, where our methods need to be slightly modified.

To illustrate the ideas involved, we consider the system

$$\dot{\mathbf{x}} = \mathbf{A}\mathbf{x} + \mathbf{h}, \quad \text{where } \mathbf{A} = \begin{pmatrix} 3 & 2 \\ 1 & 4 \end{pmatrix}. \tag{22}$$

The first stage in solving any inhomogeneous system is to find the complementary function, that is, the solution of the system $\dot{\mathbf{x}} = \mathbf{A}\mathbf{x}$, which you saw in Subsection 3.1 is

$$\begin{pmatrix} x_\mathrm{c} \\ y_\mathrm{c} \end{pmatrix} = \alpha \begin{pmatrix} 1 \\ 1 \end{pmatrix} e^{5t} + \beta \begin{pmatrix} -2 \\ 1 \end{pmatrix} e^{2t}. \tag{23}$$

To this complementary function we add a particular integral that depends on the form of $\mathbf{h}$. We now look at examples of the above two forms for $\mathbf{h}$, and derive a particular integral in each case.

Example 8

Find the general solution of the system

$$\dot{x} = 3x + 2y + t,$$
$$\dot{y} = x + 4y + 7t.$$

Solution

The complementary function is given in equation (23).

We note that $\mathbf{h} = (t \quad 7t)^T$ consists entirely of linear functions, so it seems natural to seek a particular integral of the form

$$\begin{pmatrix} x \\ y \end{pmatrix} = \begin{pmatrix} at + b \\ ct + d \end{pmatrix},$$

where a, b, c and d are constants that we need to determine. We find them by substituting $x = at + b$, $y = ct + d$ into the original system. This gives the simultaneous equations

$$a = 3(at + b) + 2(ct + d) + t,$$
$$c = (at + b) + 4(ct + d) + 7t,$$

which give, on rearranging,

$$\begin{cases} (3a + 2c + 1)t + (3b + 2d - a) = 0, \\ (a + 4c + 7)t + (b + 4d - c) = 0. \end{cases} \tag{24}$$

You may have been tempted to use a simpler trial solution, of the form

$$\begin{pmatrix} x \\ y \end{pmatrix} = \begin{pmatrix} at \\ ct \end{pmatrix}.$$

Unfortunately, this does not work – try it and see! You may recall something similar in Unit 1.

These equations hold for *all* values of t, which means that each of the bracketed terms must be zero.

Equating the coefficients of t to zero in equations (24) gives

$$3a + 2c + 1 = 0,$$
$$a + 4c + 7 = 0,$$

which have the solution

$$a = 1, \quad c = -2.$$

Equating the constant terms to zero in equations (24), and putting $a = 1$, $c = -2$, gives the equations

$$3b + 2d - 1 = 0,$$
$$b + 4d + 2 = 0,$$

which have the solution

$$b = \tfrac{4}{5}, \quad d = -\tfrac{7}{10}.$$

Thus the required particular integral is

$$\begin{pmatrix} x_p \\ y_p \end{pmatrix} = \begin{pmatrix} t + \tfrac{4}{5} \\ -2t - \tfrac{7}{10} \end{pmatrix},$$

and the general solution is

$$\begin{pmatrix} x \\ y \end{pmatrix} = \begin{pmatrix} x_c \\ y_c \end{pmatrix} + \begin{pmatrix} x_p \\ y_p \end{pmatrix}$$

$$= \alpha \begin{pmatrix} 1 \\ 1 \end{pmatrix} e^{5t} + \beta \begin{pmatrix} -2 \\ 1 \end{pmatrix} e^{2t} + \begin{pmatrix} t + \tfrac{4}{5} \\ -2t - \tfrac{7}{10} \end{pmatrix}.$$

Exercise 10

Find the general solution of the system

$$\dot{x} = x + 4y - \ t + 2,$$
$$\dot{y} = x - 2y + 5t.$$

(*Hint*: For the complementary function, see Example 2.)

Example 9

Find the general solution of the system

$$\dot{x} = 3x + 2y + 4e^{3t},$$
$$\dot{y} = \ x + 4y - \ e^{3t}.$$

Solution

The complementary function is given in equation (23).

We note that $\mathbf{h} = (4e^{3t} \quad -e^{3t})^T$ consists entirely of exponentials, so it seems natural to seek a particular integral of the form

$$\begin{pmatrix} x \\ y \end{pmatrix} = \begin{pmatrix} ae^{3t} \\ be^{3t} \end{pmatrix} = \begin{pmatrix} a \\ b \end{pmatrix} e^{3t},$$

where a and b are constants that we need to determine. We find them by substituting $x = ae^{3t}$, $y = be^{3t}$ into the original system. This gives the simultaneous equations

$$3ae^{3t} = 3ae^{3t} + 2be^{3t} + 4e^{3t},$$
$$3be^{3t} = ae^{3t} + 4be^{3t} - e^{3t},$$

or, on dividing by e^{3t},

$$3a = 3a + 2b + 4,$$
$$3b = a + 4b - 1.$$

Rearranging these equations gives

$$2b = -4,$$
$$a + b = 1,$$

which have the solution

$$a = 3, \quad b = -2.$$

Thus the required particular integral is

$$\begin{pmatrix} x_{\mathrm{p}} \\ y_{\mathrm{p}} \end{pmatrix} = \begin{pmatrix} 3e^{3t} \\ -2e^{3t} \end{pmatrix} = \begin{pmatrix} 3 \\ -2 \end{pmatrix} e^{3t},$$

and the general solution is

$$\begin{pmatrix} x \\ y \end{pmatrix} = \begin{pmatrix} x_{\mathrm{c}} \\ y_{\mathrm{c}} \end{pmatrix} + \begin{pmatrix} x_{\mathrm{p}} \\ y_{\mathrm{p}} \end{pmatrix}$$
$$= \alpha \begin{pmatrix} 1 \\ 1 \end{pmatrix} e^{5t} + \beta \begin{pmatrix} -2 \\ 1 \end{pmatrix} e^{2t} + \begin{pmatrix} 3 \\ -2 \end{pmatrix} e^{3t}.$$

This method fails when $\mathbf{h}$ involves e^{5t} or e^{2t}, which occur in the complementary function. We deal with such examples in the 'Exceptional cases' subsection below. You may recall similar failures in Unit 1.

Exercise 11

Find the general solution of the system

$$\dot{x} = x + 4y + 4e^{-t},$$
$$\dot{y} = x - 2y + 5e^{-t}.$$

(*Hint*: For the complementary function, see Exercise 10.)

Exercise 12

Solve the system of differential equations

$$\dot{x} = 2x + 3y + e^{2t},$$
$$\dot{y} = 2x + y + 4e^{2t},$$

subject to the initial conditions $x(0) = \frac{5}{6}$, $y(0) = \frac{2}{3}$.

(The matrix $\begin{pmatrix} 2 & 3 \\ 2 & 1 \end{pmatrix}$ has eigenvectors $(1 \quad -1)^T$ and $(3 \quad 2)^T$, corresponding to eigenvalues -1 and 4, respectively.)

Recall that the technique used in Unit 1, when determining the particular integral of an inhomogeneous differential equation, was to look for a solution of the same form as the right-hand side. Thus if $\mathbf{h}$ contains sinusoidal terms of the form $\cos \omega t$ and/or $\sin \omega t$, the particular integral will be of the form

$$\begin{pmatrix} x_{\mathrm{p}} \\ y_{\mathrm{p}} \end{pmatrix} = \begin{pmatrix} a \\ c \end{pmatrix} \cos \omega t + \begin{pmatrix} b \\ d \end{pmatrix} \sin \omega t.$$

There is a more efficient way of treating this case, by exploiting the relationship between the sinusoidal functions and complex exponentials (given by Euler's formula). One then proceeds as with the case for real exponential terms in $\mathbf{h}$, only now with complex-valued undetermined coefficients.

This will generally lead to *four* equations in the undetermined coefficients a, b, c and d. Therefore subsequent calculations tend to be rather long-winded, and for this reason the case when $\mathbf{h}$ consists of sinusoidal functions will not be pursued further in this module.

Procedure 4   Finding a particular integral

To find a particular integral $\mathbf{x}_{\mathrm{p}} = (x_{\mathrm{p}} \quad y_{\mathrm{p}})^T$ for the system $\dot{\mathbf{x}} = \mathbf{A}\mathbf{x} + \mathbf{h}$, carry out the following steps.

1. When the elements of $\mathbf{h}$ are polynomials of degree less than or equal to k, choose x_{p} and y_{p} to be polynomials of degree k.

   When the elements of $\mathbf{h}$ are multiples of the same exponential function, choose x_{p} and y_{p} to be multiples of this exponential function.

2. To determine the coefficients in x_{p} and y_{p}, substitute into the system of differential equations, and equate coefficients.

Exercise 13

Using the information from Exercise 12, find the general solution of the system of differential equations

$$\dot{x} = 2x + 3y + t,$$
$$\dot{y} = 2x + y + 4e^{-2t}.$$

(*Hint*: Use the principle of superposition.)

Exceptional cases

In Unit 1 we discussed the differential equation

$$\frac{d^2y}{dx^2} - 4y = 2e^{2x}.$$

From Unit 1, Exercise 18(c), the complementary function is $y_c = \alpha e^{-2x} + \beta e^{2x}$, where α and β are arbitrary constants. For the particular integral, it would be natural to try $y = ke^{2x}$, where k is a constant to be determined. However, as you saw in Unit 1, Example 16, this fails since e^{2x} is already included in the complementary function. So we insert an extra factor x, and try a particular integral of the form $y = kxe^{2x}$.

The situation is similar for systems of linear differential equations in cases where the usual trial solution is part of the complementary function, as we show in the following example.

Example 10

Find the general solution of the system

$$\begin{cases} \dot{x} = 3x + 2y + 6e^{2t}, \\ \dot{y} = x + 4y + 3e^{2t}. \end{cases} \tag{25}$$

Solution

From equation (23), the complementary function is

$$\begin{pmatrix} x_c \\ y_c \end{pmatrix} = \alpha \begin{pmatrix} 1 \\ 1 \end{pmatrix} e^{5t} + \beta \begin{pmatrix} -2 \\ 1 \end{pmatrix} e^{2t},$$

where α and β are arbitrary constants.

Since the complementary function includes an e^{2t} term, a particular integral (suggested by $\mathbf{h} = (6e^{2t} \quad 3e^{2t})^T$) of the form

$$\begin{pmatrix} x \\ y \end{pmatrix} = \begin{pmatrix} a_1 e^{2t} \\ a_2 e^{2t} \end{pmatrix} = \begin{pmatrix} a_1 \\ a_2 \end{pmatrix} e^{2t}$$

will not work. That is, if we substitute this into equations (25), we obtain

$$2a_1 e^{2t} = 3a_1 e^{2t} + 2a_2 e^{2t} + 6e^{2t},$$
$$2a_2 e^{2t} = a_1 e^{2t} + 4a_2 e^{2t} + 3e^{2t},$$

or, on dividing by e^{2t} and rearranging,

$$a_1 + 2a_2 = -6,$$
$$a_1 + 2a_2 = -3.$$

These equations clearly have no solution, so the method fails.

However, there is a method that will succeed. First write $\mathbf{v}_1 = (1 \quad 1)^T$, $\mathbf{v}_2 = (-2 \quad 1)^T$, $\lambda_1 = 5$, $\lambda_2 = 2$, so that $\mathbf{v}_1$, $\mathbf{v}_2$ are eigenvectors corresponding respectively to the eigenvalues λ_1, λ_2, and write $\mathbf{h} = \mathbf{k}e^{\lambda_2 t}$, where $\mathbf{k} = (6 \quad 3)^T$.

Recall from Unit 5, Section 1 that any n-dimensional vector $\mathbf{v}$ can be written as a linear combination of n linearly independent n-dimensional vectors.

Now $\mathbf{k}$ can be written as a linear combination of the linearly independent eigenvectors $\mathbf{v}_1$ and $\mathbf{v}_2$:

$$\mathbf{k} = p\mathbf{v}_1 + q\mathbf{v}_2.$$

In this case, $(6 \quad 3)^T = p(1 \quad 1)^T + q(-2 \quad 1)^T$, so $p = 4$ and $q = -1$.

Next we look for a trial solution of the form

$$\mathbf{x} = (a\mathbf{v}_1 + b\mathbf{v}_2 t)e^{\lambda_2 t}.$$

Substituting this and $\mathbf{h} = \mathbf{k}e^{\lambda_2 t} = p\mathbf{v}_1 e^{\lambda_2 t} + q\mathbf{v}_2 e^{\lambda_2 t}$ into $\dot{\mathbf{x}} = \mathbf{A}\mathbf{x} + \mathbf{h}$ gives

$$b\mathbf{v}_2 e^{\lambda_2 t} + \lambda_2 (a\mathbf{v}_1 + b\mathbf{v}_2 t)e^{\lambda_2 t} = \mathbf{A}(a\mathbf{v}_1 + b\mathbf{v}_2 t)e^{\lambda_2 t} + p\mathbf{v}_1 e^{\lambda_2 t} + q\mathbf{v}_2 e^{\lambda_2 t}.$$

Dividing by $e^{\lambda_2 t}$ and using the fact that $\mathbf{A}\mathbf{v}_1 = \lambda_1 \mathbf{v}_1$ and $\mathbf{A}\mathbf{v}_2 = \lambda_2 \mathbf{v}_2$, we obtain

$$a(\lambda_2 - \lambda_1)\mathbf{v}_1 + b\mathbf{v}_2 = p\mathbf{v}_1 + q\mathbf{v}_2.$$

Equating coefficients is appropriate as $\mathbf{v}_1$ and $\mathbf{v}_2$ are linearly independent. Also, a is well defined since $\lambda_1 \neq \lambda_2$.

Equating the coefficients of $\mathbf{v}_1$ and $\mathbf{v}_2$ gives

$$a = p/(\lambda_2 - \lambda_1) \quad \text{and} \quad b = q.$$

We know $\lambda_1 = 5$, $\lambda_2 = 2$, $p = 4$ and $q = -1$, so $a = -\frac{4}{3}$ and $b = -1$, and a particular integral is

$$\mathbf{x}_\mathrm{p} = \left(-\frac{4}{3} \begin{pmatrix} 1 \\ 1 \end{pmatrix} - 1 \begin{pmatrix} -2 \\ 1 \end{pmatrix} t \right) e^{2t} = \begin{pmatrix} 2t - \frac{4}{3} \\ -t - \frac{4}{3} \end{pmatrix} e^{2t}.$$

So the general solution of equations (25) is

$$\mathbf{x} = \alpha \begin{pmatrix} 1 \\ 1 \end{pmatrix} e^{5t} + \beta \begin{pmatrix} -2 \\ 1 \end{pmatrix} e^{2t} + \begin{pmatrix} 2t - \frac{4}{3} \\ -t - \frac{4}{3} \end{pmatrix} e^{2t}.$$

The method used in Example 10 works in general, provided that the eigenvalues are distinct.

Procedure 5 Finding a particular integral – special case

To find a particular integral $\mathbf{x}_\mathrm{p} = (x_\mathrm{p} \quad y_\mathrm{p})^T$ for the system $\dot{\mathbf{x}} = \mathbf{A}\mathbf{x} + \mathbf{h}$, where $\mathbf{A}$ has distinct real eigenvalues λ_1 and λ_2, with corresponding eigenvectors $\mathbf{v}_1$ and $\mathbf{v}_2$, respectively, and $\mathbf{h} = \mathbf{k}e^{\lambda_2 t}$, first determine p and q such that

$$\mathbf{k} = p\mathbf{v}_1 + q\mathbf{v}_2.$$

Then a particular integral has the form

$$\mathbf{x}_\mathrm{p} = (a\mathbf{v}_1 + b\mathbf{v}_2 t)e^{\lambda_2 t}, \tag{26}$$

where $a = p/(\lambda_2 - \lambda_1)$ and $b = q$.

A similar procedure can be followed if $\mathbf{h}$ contains polynomial components, but we do not go into the details here.

Exercise 14

Using the information from Exercise 12, find the general solution of the
system of differential equations

$$\dot{x} = 2x + 3y + e^{4t},$$
$$\dot{y} = 2x + y + 2e^{4t}.$$

4   Second-order systems

In this section we show how the methods introduced earlier in this unit can
be adapted to finding the solutions of certain systems of homogeneous
second-order differential equations. We then consider a particular case in
which the solutions are all sinusoidal. Such cases arise often in connection
with oscillating mechanical systems or electrical circuits.

4.1   Homogeneous second-order systems

We now turn our attention to systems of linear constant-coefficient
second-order differential equations of the form $\ddot{\mathbf{x}} = \mathbf{A}\mathbf{x}$. You have seen
that the general solution of a first-order system $\dot{\mathbf{x}} = \mathbf{A}\mathbf{x}$ of n equations can
be written as a linear combination of n linearly independent solutions
involving n arbitrary constants. In a similar way, it can be shown that the
general solution of a second-order system $\ddot{\mathbf{x}} = \mathbf{A}\mathbf{x}$ of n equations can be
written as a linear combination of $2n$ linearly independent solutions
involving $2n$ arbitrary constants. The following example will show you
what is involved in the solution of such systems; the treatment is similar to
that of Example 1.

We do not prove this.

Example 11

Find the general solution of the system of differential equations

$$\begin{cases} \ddot{x} = x + 4y, \\ \ddot{y} = x - 2y. \end{cases} \tag{27}$$

Solution

In order to find the general solution of this pair of equations, it is sufficient
to find four linearly independent solutions and write down an arbitrary
linear combination of them.

We begin by attempting to find solutions of the form

$$x = Ce^{\mu t}, \quad y = De^{\mu t},$$

where C and D are constants.

*The reason for using μ rather
than λ will become apparent as
we proceed.*

Since $\ddot{x} = C\mu^2 e^{\mu t}$ and $\ddot{y} = D\mu^2 e^{\mu t}$, we have, on substituting the expressions for x and y into equations (27),

$$C\mu^2 e^{\mu t} = Ce^{\mu t} + 4De^{\mu t},$$
$$D\mu^2 e^{\mu t} = Ce^{\mu t} - 2De^{\mu t}.$$

Dividing through by $e^{\mu t}$, we obtain

$$\begin{pmatrix} 1 & 4 \\ 1 & -2 \end{pmatrix} \begin{pmatrix} C \\ D \end{pmatrix} = \mu^2 \begin{pmatrix} C \\ D \end{pmatrix},$$

so μ^2 is an eigenvalue of $\mathbf{A} = \begin{pmatrix} 1 & 4 \\ 1 & -2 \end{pmatrix}$. However, from Example 2 we know that the eigenvalues of $\mathbf{A}$ are 2 and -3, so $\mu = \pm\sqrt{2}$ or $\mu = \pm\sqrt{3}i$.

The eigenvalue 2 corresponds to an eigenvector $(4 \quad 1)^T$, and it is easy to verify that the values $\mu = \pm\sqrt{2}$ provide us with two linearly independent solutions of equations (27), namely

The verification can be done by direct substitution.

$$\mathbf{x}_1 = \begin{pmatrix} 4 \\ 1 \end{pmatrix} e^{\sqrt{2}t} \quad \text{and} \quad \mathbf{x}_2 = \begin{pmatrix} 4 \\ 1 \end{pmatrix} e^{-\sqrt{2}t}.$$

The eigenvalue -3 corresponds to an eigenvector $(1 \quad -1)^T$, and choosing $\mu = \sqrt{3}i$ gives a further solution

$$\begin{pmatrix} 1 \\ -1 \end{pmatrix} e^{\sqrt{3}it} = \begin{pmatrix} 1 \\ -1 \end{pmatrix} (\cos\sqrt{3}t + i\sin\sqrt{3}t);$$

Here we use Euler's formula to write down the exponential in terms of sinusoids.

we can verify that the real and imaginary parts of the expression on the right-hand side are both solutions of equations (27). (Choosing $\mu = -\sqrt{3}i$ leads to the same two linearly independent solutions.)

Thus we have found two more linearly independent solutions of equations (27), namely

$$\mathbf{x}_3 = \begin{pmatrix} 1 \\ -1 \end{pmatrix} \cos\sqrt{3}t \quad \text{and} \quad \mathbf{x}_4 = \begin{pmatrix} 1 \\ -1 \end{pmatrix} \sin\sqrt{3}t.$$

We do not prove this.

Using a version of the principle of superposition applicable to second-order systems, we can now take linear combinations of $\mathbf{x}_1$, $\mathbf{x}_2$, $\mathbf{x}_3$ and $\mathbf{x}_4$ to find further solutions. The expression

$$\mathbf{x} = C_1\mathbf{x}_1 + C_2\mathbf{x}_2 + C_3\mathbf{x}_3 + C_4\mathbf{x}_4,$$

Note that there are four arbitrary constants, as expected.

where C_1, C_2, C_3, C_4 are arbitrary constants, is the general solution of equations (27).

Comparing the above solution with that of Example 2, we notice many similarities. The main difference is that λ is replaced by μ^2, giving rise to four values for μ, instead of two for λ. Consequently, we obtain a general solution with four arbitrary constants.

This discussion mirrors the corresponding discussion in Section 2.

In general, consider a system of differential equations of the form $\ddot{\mathbf{x}} = \mathbf{A}\mathbf{x}$. If we try an exponential solution of the form $\mathbf{x} = \mathbf{v}e^{\mu t}$, where $\mathbf{v}$ is a constant column vector, then $\ddot{\mathbf{x}} = \mathbf{v}\mu^2 e^{\mu t}$, and the system of differential equations becomes $\mathbf{v}\mu^2 e^{\mu t} = \mathbf{A}\mathbf{v}e^{\mu t}$.

Dividing this equation by $e^{\mu t}$ and rearranging, we have

$$\mathbf{A}\mathbf{v} = \mu^2 \mathbf{v}.$$

Thus $\mathbf{v}$ is an eigenvector of $\mathbf{A}$, and μ^2 is the corresponding eigenvalue.

> **Theorem 4**
>
> If μ^2 is an eigenvalue of the matrix $\mathbf{A}$ corresponding to an eigenvector $\mathbf{v}$, then $\mathbf{x} = \mathbf{v}e^{\mu t}$ is a solution of the system of differential equations $\ddot{\mathbf{x}} = \mathbf{A}\mathbf{x}$.

If $\mathbf{x} = \mathbf{v}e^{\mu t}$, then $\dot{\mathbf{x}} = \mu \mathbf{v}e^{\mu t}$ and $\ddot{\mathbf{x}} = \mu^2 \mathbf{v}e^{\mu t} = \mathbf{A}\mathbf{v}e^{\mu t} = \mathbf{A}\mathbf{x}$.

Example 12

Find the general solution of the system of differential equations

$$\ddot{x} = 3x + 2y,$$
$$\ddot{y} = x + 4y.$$

Solution

The matrix of coefficients is

$$\mathbf{A} = \begin{pmatrix} 3 & 2 \\ 1 & 4 \end{pmatrix}.$$

From Example 1, the eigenvectors of $\mathbf{A}$ are $(1 \quad 1)^T$ and $(-2 \quad 1)^T$, corresponding to the eigenvalues $\lambda = 5$ and $\lambda = 2$, respectively.

Using the notation of Example 11, it follows that μ has the values $\sqrt{5}$, $-\sqrt{5}$, $\sqrt{2}$ and $-\sqrt{2}$, and that the general solution is

$$\begin{pmatrix} x \\ y \end{pmatrix} = C_1 \begin{pmatrix} 1 \\ 1 \end{pmatrix} e^{\sqrt{5}t} + C_2 \begin{pmatrix} 1 \\ 1 \end{pmatrix} e^{-\sqrt{5}t} + C_3 \begin{pmatrix} -2 \\ 1 \end{pmatrix} e^{\sqrt{2}t} + C_4 \begin{pmatrix} -2 \\ 1 \end{pmatrix} e^{-\sqrt{2}t}.$$

Exercise 15

Find the general solution of the system of differential equations

$$\ddot{x} = 5x + 2y,$$
$$\ddot{y} = 2x + 5y.$$

(The matrix $\begin{pmatrix} 5 & 2 \\ 2 & 5 \end{pmatrix}$ has eigenvectors $(1 \quad 1)^T$ and $(1 \quad -1)^T$, corresponding to eigenvalues 7 and 3, respectively.)

The above ideas can be formalised in the following procedure.

Complex eigenvalues and repeated real eigenvalues are not discussed here, but they can be dealt with in a fashion similar to that for the first-order case.

> ## Procedure 6 Solving a second-order homogeneous linear system
>
> To solve a system $\ddot{\mathbf{x}} = \mathbf{A}\mathbf{x}$, where $\mathbf{A}$ is an $n \times n$ matrix with n distinct real eigenvalues, carry out the following steps.
>
> 1. Find the eigenvalues $\lambda_1, \lambda_2, \ldots, \lambda_n$ of $\mathbf{A}$, and a corresponding set of eigenvectors $\mathbf{v}_1, \mathbf{v}_2, \ldots, \mathbf{v}_n$.
>
> 2. Each *positive* eigenvalue, μ^2 say, corresponding to an eigenvector $\mathbf{v}$, gives rise to two linearly independent solutions
>
> $$\mathbf{v}e^{\mu t} \quad \text{and} \quad \mathbf{v}e^{-\mu t}.$$
>
> Each *negative* eigenvalue, $-\omega^2$ say, corresponding to an eigenvector $\mathbf{v}$, gives rise to two linearly independent solutions
>
> $$\mathbf{v}\cos \omega t \quad \text{and} \quad \mathbf{v}\sin \omega t.$$
>
> A *zero* eigenvalue corresponding to an eigenvector $\mathbf{v}$ gives rise to two linearly independent solutions
>
> $$\mathbf{v} \quad \text{and} \quad \mathbf{v}t.$$
>
> 3. The general solution is then an arbitrary linear combination of the $2n$ linearly independent solutions found in step 2, involving $2n$ arbitrary constants.

We do not show this here, but you can verify it in any particular case (see Example 13 below). It is analogous to the case of a single second-order differential equation with both roots of the auxiliary equation equal to zero.

We illustrate this procedure in the following example.

Example 13

Find the general solution of the system of differential equations

$$\ddot{x} = 3x + 2y + 2z,$$
$$\ddot{y} = 2x + 2y,$$
$$\ddot{z} = 2x \qquad + 4z.$$

Solution

The matrix of coefficients is $\mathbf{A} = \begin{pmatrix} 3 & 2 & 2 \\ 2 & 2 & 0 \\ 2 & 0 & 4 \end{pmatrix}$.

The eigenvectors of $\mathbf{A}$ are $(2 \quad 1 \quad 2)^T$, corresponding to the eigenvalue $\lambda = 6$, $(1 \quad 2 \quad -2)^T$, corresponding to the eigenvalue $\lambda = 3$, and $(-2 \quad 2 \quad 1)^T$, corresponding to the eigenvalue $\lambda = 0$. It follows from Procedure 6 that the general solution of the above system is

$$\begin{pmatrix} x \\ y \\ z \end{pmatrix} = \begin{pmatrix} 2 \\ 1 \\ 2 \end{pmatrix} (C_1 e^{\sqrt{6}t} + C_2 e^{-\sqrt{6}t}) + \begin{pmatrix} 1 \\ 2 \\ -2 \end{pmatrix} (C_3 e^{\sqrt{3}t} + C_4 e^{-\sqrt{3}t})$$

$$+ \begin{pmatrix} -2 \\ 2 \\ 1 \end{pmatrix} (C_5 + C_6 t).$$

You may like to verify that $(-2 \quad 2 \quad 1)^T$ and $(-2 \quad 2 \quad 1)^T t$ are both solutions of the system.

Exercise 16

Find the general solution of the system of equations

$$\ddot{x} = x + 4y,$$
$$\ddot{y} = x + \ y.$$

Exercise 17

Find the general solution of the system of differential equations

$$\ddot{x} = 2x + \ y - \ z,$$
$$\ddot{y} = \qquad -3y + 2z,$$
$$\ddot{z} = \qquad\qquad 4z.$$

(The matrix $\begin{pmatrix} 2 & 1 & -1 \\ 0 & -3 & 2 \\ 0 & 0 & 4 \end{pmatrix}$ has eigenvalues 2, -3 and 4, corresponding to eigenvectors $(1 \quad 0 \quad 0)^T$, $(1 \quad -5 \quad 0)^T$ and $(-5 \quad 4 \quad 14)^T$, respectively.)

4.2 Simple harmonic motion

Simple harmonic motion is an often observed phenomenon. It arises, for example, if a quantity satisfies a second-order differential equation of the form

$$\ddot{x} = -\omega^2 x,$$

where ω is a constant. In this case solutions are of the form

$$x = \alpha \cos \omega t + \beta \sin \omega t,$$

where α and β are arbitrary constants.

In Subsection 1.3 we developed a model for the horizontal motion of a ball-bearing within a bowl of specified shape. The resulting equations were

$$\begin{cases} \ddot{x} = -5x + 4y, \\ \ddot{y} = \ \ 4x - 5y, \end{cases} \tag{28}$$

where $x(t)$ and $y(t)$ are the coordinates of the ball-bearing at time t. These second-order differential equations may be expressed in matrix form as

$$\begin{pmatrix} \ddot{x} \\ \ddot{y} \end{pmatrix} = \begin{pmatrix} -5 & 4 \\ 4 & -5 \end{pmatrix} \begin{pmatrix} x \\ y \end{pmatrix}.$$

The matrix $\begin{pmatrix} -5 & 4 \\ 4 & -5 \end{pmatrix}$ has eigenvectors $\begin{pmatrix} 1 \\ 1 \end{pmatrix}$ and $\begin{pmatrix} 1 \\ -1 \end{pmatrix}$, corresponding to eigenvalues -1 and -9, respectively.

It follows from Procedure 6 that the general solution is

$$\begin{pmatrix} x \\ y \end{pmatrix} = \begin{pmatrix} 1 \\ 1 \end{pmatrix} (C_1 \cos t + C_2 \sin t) + \begin{pmatrix} 1 \\ -1 \end{pmatrix} (C_3 \cos 3t + C_4 \sin 3t),$$

where C_1, C_2, C_3 and C_4 are arbitrary constants.

The initial conditions are chosen so that the ball-bearing is kept sufficiently close to the lowest point of the bowl (i.e. the origin). Recall that this was the assumption underlying the linear approximation leading to equations (28).

Let us now consider the paths that a ball-bearing takes for given initial conditions. The following list gives just four of the many possibilities.

(a) $x(0) = 0.1$, $y(0) = 0.1$, $\dot{x}(0) = 0$, $\dot{y}(0) = 0$.
(b) $x(0) = 0.1$, $y(0) = -0.1$, $\dot{x}(0) = 0$, $\dot{y}(0) = 0$.
(c) $x(0) = 0.1$, $y(0) = 0$, $\dot{x}(0) = 0$, $\dot{y}(0) = 0$.
(d) $x(0) = 0.1$, $y(0) = 0.2$, $\dot{x}(0) = -0.1$, $\dot{y}(0) = 0.1$.

In case (a) we find $C_1 = 0.1$ and $C_2 = C_3 = C_4 = 0$, so the solution is

$$(x \quad y)^T = (0.1 \quad 0.1)^T \cos t,$$

and the ball-bearing performs simple harmonic motion in the direction of the vector $(1 \quad 1)^T$, that is, along the line $y = x$, with angular frequency 1 (as shown in Figure 6(a)).

In case (b) we find $C_3 = 0.1$ and $C_1 = C_2 = C_4 = 0$, so the solution is

$$(x \quad y)^T = (0.1 \quad -0.1)^T \cos 3t,$$

and the ball-bearing performs simple harmonic motion in the direction of the vector $(1 \quad -1)^T$, that is, along the line $y = -x$, with angular frequency 3 (as shown in Figure 6(b)).

Note that cases (a) and (b) consist of motion with a *single* angular frequency – these are the *normal modes* of the system, which will be the subject of Unit 11.

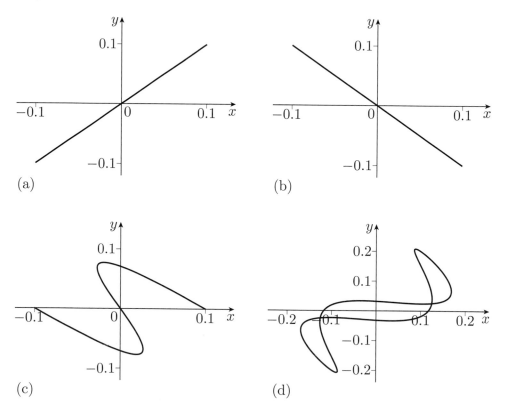

Figure 6 Paths of the ball-bearing for initial conditions (a), (b), (c) and (d)

In case (c) we find $C_1 = C_3 = 0.05$ and $C_2 = C_4 = 0$, so the solution is

$$(x \quad y)^T = 0.05 \, (1 \quad 1)^T \cos t + 0.05 \, (1 \quad -1)^T \cos 3t,$$

which is a combination of the previous motions (as shown in Figure 6(c)).

In case (d) we find $C_1 = 0.15$, $C_3 = -0.05$, $C_2 = 0$ and $C_4 = -\frac{1}{30}$, so the solution is

$$(x \quad y)^T = (1 \quad 1)^T (0.15 \cos t) + (1 \quad -1)^T (-0.05 \cos 3t - \tfrac{1}{30} \sin 3t)$$

(as shown in Figure 6(d)).

Cases (c) and (d) consist of superpositions of the two normal modes.

Note that the coefficients in equations (28) have been contrived so that the resulting angular frequencies ω are rational numbers, and this implies periodic motion for the ball-bearing. In general, this need not be so – irrational ω could give non-periodic motion. More accurately, the motion is in general *non-periodic* if the *ratio* of the two angular frequencies (normal mode frequencies) is *irrational*; otherwise, the motion is always periodic.

Exercise 18

An object moves in a plane so that its coordinates at time t satisfy the equations

$$\ddot{x} = -\tfrac{25}{7}x + \tfrac{6}{7}y,$$
$$\ddot{y} = \tfrac{9}{7}x - \tfrac{10}{7}y.$$

Find two directions in which the object can describe simple harmonic motion along a straight line. Give the angular frequencies of such motions.

Learning outcomes

After studying this unit, you should be able to:

- understand and use the terminology associated with systems of linear constant-coefficient differential equations

- obtain the general solution of a homogeneous system of two or three first-order differential equations, by applying knowledge of the eigenvalues and eigenvectors of the coefficient matrix

- obtain a particular solution of an inhomogeneous system of two first-order differential equations in certain simple cases, by using a trial solution

- understand the role of the principle of superposition in determining a particular integral of an inhomogeneous linear system of differential equations

- obtain the general solution of an inhomogeneous system of two or three first-order differential equations, by combining its complementary function and a particular integral

- apply given initial conditions to obtain the solution of an initial-value problem that features a system of two first-order differential equations

- obtain the general solution of a homogeneous system of two or three second-order equations, by applying knowledge of the eigenvalues and eigenvectors of the coefficient matrix

- appreciate how systems of linear constant-coefficient differential equations arise in mathematical models of the real world.

Solutions to exercises

Solution to Exercise 1

(a) $\begin{pmatrix} \dot{x} \\ \dot{y} \end{pmatrix} = \begin{pmatrix} 2 & 1 \\ 1 & 0 \end{pmatrix} \begin{pmatrix} x \\ y \end{pmatrix} + \begin{pmatrix} 1 \\ -2 \end{pmatrix}$; inhomogeneous.

(b) $\begin{pmatrix} \dot{x} \\ \dot{y} \end{pmatrix} = \begin{pmatrix} 0 & 1 \\ 0 & 0 \end{pmatrix} \begin{pmatrix} x \\ y \end{pmatrix} + \begin{pmatrix} 0 \\ t \end{pmatrix}$; inhomogeneous.

(c) $\begin{pmatrix} \dot{x} \\ \dot{y} \\ \dot{z} \end{pmatrix} = \begin{pmatrix} 5 & 0 & 0 \\ 1 & 2 & 1 \\ 1 & 1 & 2 \end{pmatrix} \begin{pmatrix} x \\ y \\ z \end{pmatrix}$; homogeneous.

Solution to Exercise 2

The matrix of coefficients is $\mathbf{A} = \begin{pmatrix} 5 & 2 \\ 2 & 5 \end{pmatrix}$.

We are given that the eigenvectors of $\mathbf{A}$ are $(1 \quad 1)^T$ with corresponding eigenvalue $\lambda = 7$, and $(1 \quad -1)^T$ with corresponding eigenvalue $\lambda = 3$. The general solution is therefore

$$\begin{pmatrix} x \\ y \end{pmatrix} = \alpha \begin{pmatrix} 1 \\ 1 \end{pmatrix} e^{7t} + \beta \begin{pmatrix} 1 \\ -1 \end{pmatrix} e^{3t}.$$

Since $x = 4$ and $y = 0$ when $t = 0$, we have

$4 = \alpha + \beta,$
$0 = \alpha - \beta.$

Thus $\alpha = 2$ and $\beta = 2$, so

$$\begin{pmatrix} x \\ y \end{pmatrix} = 2 \begin{pmatrix} 1 \\ 1 \end{pmatrix} e^{7t} + 2 \begin{pmatrix} 1 \\ -1 \end{pmatrix} e^{3t} = \begin{pmatrix} 2 \\ 2 \end{pmatrix} e^{7t} + \begin{pmatrix} 2 \\ -2 \end{pmatrix} e^{3t}.$$

Solution to Exercise 3

The matrix of coefficients is $\mathbf{A} = \begin{pmatrix} 5 & 0 & 0 \\ 1 & 2 & 1 \\ 1 & 1 & 2 \end{pmatrix}$.

We are given that the eigenvectors of $\mathbf{A}$ are $(2 \quad 1 \quad 1)^T$, $(0 \quad 1 \quad 1)^T$ and $(0 \quad 1 \quad -1)^T$, corresponding to the eigenvalues 5, 3 and 1, respectively.

The general solution is therefore

$$\begin{pmatrix} x \\ y \\ z \end{pmatrix} = \alpha \begin{pmatrix} 2 \\ 1 \\ 1 \end{pmatrix} e^{5t} + \beta \begin{pmatrix} 0 \\ 1 \\ 1 \end{pmatrix} e^{3t} + \gamma \begin{pmatrix} 0 \\ 1 \\ -1 \end{pmatrix} e^{t}.$$

Since $x = 4$, $y = 6$ and $z = 0$ when $t = 0$, we have

$4 = 2\alpha,$
$6 = \alpha + \beta + \gamma,$
$0 = \alpha + \beta - \gamma.$

Thus $\alpha = 2$, $\beta = 1$ and $\gamma = 3$, so

$$\begin{pmatrix} x \\ y \\ z \end{pmatrix} = 2 \begin{pmatrix} 2 \\ 1 \\ 1 \end{pmatrix} e^{5t} + \begin{pmatrix} 0 \\ 1 \\ 1 \end{pmatrix} e^{3t} + 3 \begin{pmatrix} 0 \\ 1 \\ -1 \end{pmatrix} e^{t}$$

$$= \begin{pmatrix} 4 \\ 2 \\ 2 \end{pmatrix} e^{5t} + \begin{pmatrix} 0 \\ 1 \\ 1 \end{pmatrix} e^{3t} + \begin{pmatrix} 0 \\ 3 \\ -3 \end{pmatrix} e^{t}.$$

Solution to Exercise 4

The matrix of coefficients is $\mathbf{A} = \begin{pmatrix} 0 & 0 & 1 \\ 0 & 1 & 0 \\ 1 & 0 & 0 \end{pmatrix}$.

We are given that the eigenvectors are $(1 \quad 0 \quad -1)^T$ and $(k \quad l \quad k)^T$, corresponding to the eigenvalues -1 and 1 (repeated), respectively. But

$$(k \quad l \quad k)^T = k(1 \quad 0 \quad 1)^T + l(0 \quad 1 \quad 0)^T,$$

so the general solution is

$$\begin{pmatrix} x \\ y \\ z \end{pmatrix} = \alpha \begin{pmatrix} 1 \\ 0 \\ -1 \end{pmatrix} e^{-t} + \beta \begin{pmatrix} 1 \\ 0 \\ 1 \end{pmatrix} e^{t} + \gamma \begin{pmatrix} 0 \\ 1 \\ 0 \end{pmatrix} e^{t}.$$

Since $x = 7$, $y = 5$ and $z = 1$ when $t = 0$, we have

$$7 = \alpha + \beta, \quad 5 = \gamma \quad \text{and} \quad 1 = -\alpha + \beta.$$

Thus $\alpha = 3$, $\beta = 4$ and $\gamma = 5$, so

$$\begin{pmatrix} x \\ y \\ z \end{pmatrix} = 3 \begin{pmatrix} 1 \\ 0 \\ -1 \end{pmatrix} e^{-t} + 4 \begin{pmatrix} 1 \\ 0 \\ 1 \end{pmatrix} e^{t} + 5 \begin{pmatrix} 0 \\ 1 \\ 0 \end{pmatrix} e^{t}$$

$$= \begin{pmatrix} 3 \\ 0 \\ -3 \end{pmatrix} e^{-t} + \begin{pmatrix} 4 \\ 5 \\ 4 \end{pmatrix} e^{t}.$$

Solution to Exercise 5

The matrix of coefficients is $\mathbf{A} = \begin{pmatrix} 2 & 3 \\ 0 & 2 \end{pmatrix}$, and the eigenvalues are $\lambda = 2$ (repeated).

The eigenvector equations are

$$(2 - \lambda)x + 3y = 0 \quad \text{and} \quad (2 - \lambda)y = 0,$$

which reduce, when $\lambda = 2$, to

$$3y = 0 \quad \text{and} \quad 0 = 0,$$

so $y = 0$. It follows that an eigenvector corresponding to $\lambda = 2$ is $(1 \quad 0)^T$, and that one solution is $(1 \quad 0)^T e^{2t}$.

To find the general solution, we solve the equation $(\mathbf{A} - \lambda\mathbf{I})\mathbf{b} = \mathbf{v}$, where

$$\mathbf{A} - \lambda\mathbf{I} = \mathbf{A} - 2\mathbf{I} = \begin{pmatrix} 0 & 3 \\ 0 & 0 \end{pmatrix}, \quad \mathbf{v} = \begin{pmatrix} 1 \\ 0 \end{pmatrix} \quad \text{and} \quad \mathbf{b} = \begin{pmatrix} b_1 \\ b_2 \end{pmatrix}.$$

This gives

$$\begin{pmatrix} 0 & 3 \\ 0 & 0 \end{pmatrix} \begin{pmatrix} b_1 \\ b_2 \end{pmatrix} = \begin{pmatrix} 1 \\ 0 \end{pmatrix},$$

which reduces to $3b_2 = 1$ with no condition on b_1, so $b_2 = \frac{1}{3}$ and we can take $b_1 = 0$, giving a solution

$$\left(\begin{pmatrix} 1 \\ 0 \end{pmatrix} t + \begin{pmatrix} 0 \\ \frac{1}{3} \end{pmatrix} \right) e^{2t} = \begin{pmatrix} t \\ \frac{1}{3} \end{pmatrix} e^{2t}.$$

Thus the general solution is

$$\begin{pmatrix} x \\ y \end{pmatrix} = \alpha \begin{pmatrix} 1 \\ 0 \end{pmatrix} e^{2t} + \beta \begin{pmatrix} t \\ \frac{1}{3} \end{pmatrix} e^{2t}.$$

Since $x = 4$ and $y = 3$ when $t = 0$, we have

$$4 = \alpha \quad \text{and} \quad 3 = \tfrac{1}{3}\beta,$$

giving $\alpha = 4$ and $\beta = 9$. Thus the required solution is

$$\begin{pmatrix} x \\ y \end{pmatrix} = 4 \begin{pmatrix} 1 \\ 0 \end{pmatrix} e^{2t} + 9 \begin{pmatrix} t \\ \frac{1}{3} \end{pmatrix} e^{2t} = \begin{pmatrix} 9t + 4 \\ 3 \end{pmatrix} e^{2t}.$$

Solution to Exercise 6

(a) The matrix of coefficients is $\mathbf{A} = \begin{pmatrix} 2 & 3 \\ 2 & 1 \end{pmatrix}$.

Using the given eigenvalues and eigenvectors, we obtain the general solution

$$\begin{pmatrix} x \\ y \end{pmatrix} = \alpha \begin{pmatrix} 3 \\ 2 \end{pmatrix} e^{4t} + \beta \begin{pmatrix} 1 \\ -1 \end{pmatrix} e^{-t}.$$

Since $x = y = 1$ when $t = 0$, we have

$$1 = 3\alpha + \beta \quad \text{and} \quad 1 = 2\alpha - \beta,$$

giving $\alpha = \frac{2}{5}$ and $\beta = -\frac{1}{5}$. The required solution is therefore

$$\begin{pmatrix} x \\ y \end{pmatrix} = \tfrac{2}{5} \begin{pmatrix} 3 \\ 2 \end{pmatrix} e^{4t} - \tfrac{1}{5} \begin{pmatrix} 1 \\ -1 \end{pmatrix} e^{-t}$$

$$= \begin{pmatrix} \frac{6}{5} \\ \frac{4}{5} \end{pmatrix} e^{4t} + \begin{pmatrix} -\frac{1}{5} \\ \frac{1}{5} \end{pmatrix} e^{-t}.$$

(b) The matrix of coefficients is $\mathbf{A} = \begin{pmatrix} -3 & -2 \\ 4 & 1 \end{pmatrix}$.

Using the given eigenvalues and eigenvectors, we obtain the general solution

$$\begin{pmatrix} x \\ y \end{pmatrix} = C \begin{pmatrix} 1 \\ -1-i \end{pmatrix} e^{(-1+2i)t} + D \begin{pmatrix} 1 \\ -1+i \end{pmatrix} e^{(-1-2i)t}.$$

Now

$$\begin{pmatrix} 1 \\ -1-i \end{pmatrix} e^{(-1+2i)t} = \begin{pmatrix} \cos 2t + i \sin 2t \\ (-1-i)(\cos 2t + i \sin 2t) \end{pmatrix} e^{-t}$$

$$= \begin{pmatrix} \cos 2t + i \sin 2t \\ (\sin 2t - \cos 2t) - i(\sin 2t + \cos 2t) \end{pmatrix} e^{-t}.$$

So we have

$$\mathrm{Re}\left(\begin{pmatrix} 1 \\ -1-i \end{pmatrix} e^{(-1+2i)t}\right) = \begin{pmatrix} \cos 2t \\ \sin 2t - \cos 2t \end{pmatrix} e^{-t},$$

$$\mathrm{Im}\left(\begin{pmatrix} 1 \\ -1-i \end{pmatrix} e^{(-1+2i)t}\right) = \begin{pmatrix} \sin 2t \\ -\sin 2t - \cos 2t \end{pmatrix} e^{-t},$$

and the general real-valued solution can be written as

$$\begin{pmatrix} x \\ y \end{pmatrix} = C \begin{pmatrix} \cos 2t \\ \sin 2t - \cos 2t \end{pmatrix} e^{-t} + D \begin{pmatrix} \sin 2t \\ -\sin 2t - \cos 2t \end{pmatrix} e^{-t}.$$

Since $x = y = 1$ when $t = 0$, we have

$$1 = C \quad \text{and} \quad 1 = -C - D,$$

so $C = 1$, $D = -2$, and the required particular solution is

$$\begin{pmatrix} x \\ y \end{pmatrix} = \begin{pmatrix} \cos 2t - 2\sin 2t \\ 3\sin 2t + \cos 2t \end{pmatrix} e^{-t}.$$

Solution to Exercise 7

(a) $\begin{pmatrix} x \\ y \\ z \end{pmatrix} = \alpha \begin{pmatrix} 1 \\ -1 \\ 0 \end{pmatrix} e^t + \beta \begin{pmatrix} -2 \\ 1 \\ 2 \end{pmatrix} e^{2t} + \gamma \begin{pmatrix} 1 \\ -1 \\ -2 \end{pmatrix} e^{3t}.$

(b) $\begin{pmatrix} x \\ y \\ z \end{pmatrix} = \alpha \begin{pmatrix} 3 \\ -1 \\ 3 \end{pmatrix} e^t + \beta \begin{pmatrix} 2 \\ 1 \\ 0 \end{pmatrix} e^{2t} + \gamma \begin{pmatrix} 2 \\ 0 \\ 1 \end{pmatrix} e^{2t}.$

Solution to Exercise 8

Using the given eigenvalues and eigenvectors in Procedure 3, we have

$$
\mathbf{v}e^{\lambda t} = \begin{pmatrix} 1 \\ 0 \\ -\tfrac{1}{2} + \tfrac{\sqrt{3}}{2}i \end{pmatrix} e^{(\tfrac{1}{2} + \tfrac{\sqrt{3}}{2}i)t}
$$

$$
= e^{t/2} \begin{pmatrix} 1 \\ 0 \\ -\tfrac{1}{2} + \tfrac{\sqrt{3}}{2}i \end{pmatrix} \left(\cos\left(\tfrac{\sqrt{3}}{2}t\right) + i\sin\left(\tfrac{\sqrt{3}}{2}t\right) \right)
$$

$$
= e^{t/2} \begin{pmatrix} \cos\left(\tfrac{\sqrt{3}}{2}t\right) + i\sin\left(\tfrac{\sqrt{3}}{2}t\right) \\ 0 \\ \left(-\tfrac{1}{2} + \tfrac{\sqrt{3}}{2}i\right)\left(\cos\left(\tfrac{\sqrt{3}}{2}t\right) + i\sin\left(\tfrac{\sqrt{3}}{2}t\right)\right) \end{pmatrix}
$$

$$
= \underbrace{e^{t/2} \begin{pmatrix} \cos\left(\tfrac{\sqrt{3}}{2}t\right) \\ 0 \\ -\tfrac{1}{2}\cos\left(\tfrac{\sqrt{3}}{2}t\right) - \tfrac{\sqrt{3}}{2}\sin\left(\tfrac{\sqrt{3}}{2}t\right) \end{pmatrix}}_{\text{real part}}
$$

$$
+ \underbrace{i\,e^{t/2} \begin{pmatrix} \sin\left(\tfrac{\sqrt{3}}{2}t\right) \\ 0 \\ \tfrac{\sqrt{3}}{2}\cos\left(\tfrac{\sqrt{3}}{2}t\right) - \tfrac{1}{2}\sin\left(\tfrac{\sqrt{3}}{2}t\right) \end{pmatrix}}_{\text{imaginary part}}.
$$

Thus the general real-valued solution is

$$
\begin{pmatrix} x \\ y \\ z \end{pmatrix} = C_1 \begin{pmatrix} 1 \\ 1 \\ 0 \end{pmatrix} e^t + C_2 \begin{pmatrix} \cos\left(\tfrac{\sqrt{3}}{2}t\right) \\ 0 \\ -\tfrac{1}{2}\cos\left(\tfrac{\sqrt{3}}{2}t\right) - \tfrac{\sqrt{3}}{2}\sin\left(\tfrac{\sqrt{3}}{2}t\right) \end{pmatrix} e^{t/2}
$$

$$
+ C_3 \begin{pmatrix} \sin\left(\tfrac{\sqrt{3}}{2}t\right) \\ 0 \\ \tfrac{\sqrt{3}}{2}\cos\left(\tfrac{\sqrt{3}}{2}t\right) - \tfrac{1}{2}\sin\left(\tfrac{\sqrt{3}}{2}t\right) \end{pmatrix} e^{t/2},
$$

where C_1, C_2 and C_3 are real constants.

Putting $x = y = 1$ and $z = 2$ when $t = 0$, we have

$$
\begin{pmatrix} 1 \\ 1 \\ 2 \end{pmatrix} = C_1 \begin{pmatrix} 1 \\ 1 \\ 0 \end{pmatrix} + C_2 \begin{pmatrix} 1 \\ 0 \\ -\tfrac{1}{2} \end{pmatrix} + C_3 \begin{pmatrix} 0 \\ 0 \\ \tfrac{\sqrt{3}}{2} \end{pmatrix},
$$

so $C_1 + C_2 = 1$, $C_1 = 1$ and $-\tfrac{1}{2}C_2 + \tfrac{\sqrt{3}}{2}C_3 = 2$, which give $C_2 = 0$ and $C_3 = \tfrac{4}{\sqrt{3}}$.

Thus the required solution is

$$\begin{pmatrix} x \\ y \\ z \end{pmatrix} = \begin{pmatrix} 1 \\ 1 \\ 0 \end{pmatrix} e^t + \tfrac{4}{\sqrt{3}} \begin{pmatrix} \sin\left(\frac{\sqrt{3}}{2}t\right) \\ 0 \\ \frac{\sqrt{3}}{2}\cos\left(\frac{\sqrt{3}}{2}t\right) - \tfrac{1}{2}\sin\left(\frac{\sqrt{3}}{2}t\right) \end{pmatrix} e^{t/2}.$$

Solution to Exercise 9

$$\begin{pmatrix} x \\ y \end{pmatrix} = \alpha \begin{pmatrix} 1 \\ 1 \end{pmatrix} e^{5t} + \beta \begin{pmatrix} -2 \\ 1 \end{pmatrix} e^{2t} + \begin{pmatrix} t + \frac{4}{5} \\ -2t - \frac{7}{10} \end{pmatrix}.$$

Solution to Exercise 10

From Example 2, the complementary function is

$$\begin{pmatrix} x_{\mathrm{c}} \\ y_{\mathrm{c}} \end{pmatrix} = \alpha \begin{pmatrix} 4 \\ 1 \end{pmatrix} e^{2t} + \beta \begin{pmatrix} 1 \\ -1 \end{pmatrix} e^{-3t}.$$

For a particular integral, we try

$$\begin{pmatrix} x \\ y \end{pmatrix} = \begin{pmatrix} at + b \\ ct + d \end{pmatrix},$$

where a, b, c, d are constants to be determined.

Substituting $x = at + b$, $y = ct + d$ into the differential equations gives

$$a = (at + b) + 4(ct + d) - t + 2,$$
$$c = (at + b) - 2(ct + d) + 5t,$$

which become

$$(a + 4c - 1)t + (b + 4d + 2 - a) = 0,$$
$$(a - 2c + 5)t + (b - 2d - c) = 0.$$

Equating the coefficients of t to zero gives

$$a + 4c - 1 = 0,$$
$$a - 2c + 5 = 0,$$

which have the solution $a = -3$, $c = 1$.

Equating the constant terms to zero, and putting $a = -3$, $c = 1$, gives

$$b + 4d + 5 = 0,$$
$$b - 2d - 1 = 0,$$

which have the solution $b = -1$, $d = -1$.

Thus the required particular integral is

$$\begin{pmatrix} x_{\mathrm{p}} \\ y_{\mathrm{p}} \end{pmatrix} = \begin{pmatrix} -3t - 1 \\ t - 1 \end{pmatrix},$$

and the general solution is

$$\begin{pmatrix} x \\ y \end{pmatrix} = \begin{pmatrix} x_{\mathrm{c}} \\ y_{\mathrm{c}} \end{pmatrix} + \begin{pmatrix} x_{\mathrm{p}} \\ y_{\mathrm{p}} \end{pmatrix} = \alpha \begin{pmatrix} 4 \\ 1 \end{pmatrix} e^{2t} + \beta \begin{pmatrix} 1 \\ -1 \end{pmatrix} e^{-3t} + \begin{pmatrix} -3t - 1 \\ t - 1 \end{pmatrix}.$$

Solution to Exercise 11

From Exercise 10, the complementary function is

$$\begin{pmatrix} x_c \\ y_c \end{pmatrix} = \alpha \begin{pmatrix} 4 \\ 1 \end{pmatrix} e^{2t} + \beta \begin{pmatrix} 1 \\ -1 \end{pmatrix} e^{-3t}.$$

For a particular integral, we try

$$\begin{pmatrix} x \\ y \end{pmatrix} = \begin{pmatrix} a \\ b \end{pmatrix} e^{-t},$$

where a and b are constants to be determined.

Substituting $x = ae^{-t}$, $y = be^{-t}$ into the differential equations gives

$$-ae^{-t} = ae^{-t} + 4be^{-t} + 4e^{-t},$$
$$-be^{-t} = ae^{-t} - 2be^{-t} + 5e^{-t},$$

which, on dividing by e^{-t} and rearranging, become

$$2a + 4b = -4,$$
$$a - b = -5.$$

These equations have the solution $a = -4$, $b = 1$.

Thus the required particular integral is

$$\begin{pmatrix} x_p \\ y_p \end{pmatrix} = \begin{pmatrix} -4 \\ 1 \end{pmatrix} e^{-t},$$

and the general solution is

$$\begin{pmatrix} x \\ y \end{pmatrix} = \begin{pmatrix} x_c \\ y_c \end{pmatrix} + \begin{pmatrix} x_p \\ y_p \end{pmatrix}$$
$$= \alpha \begin{pmatrix} 4 \\ 1 \end{pmatrix} e^{2t} + \beta \begin{pmatrix} 1 \\ -1 \end{pmatrix} e^{-3t} + \begin{pmatrix} -4 \\ 1 \end{pmatrix} e^{-t}.$$

Solution to Exercise 12

The complementary function is

$$\begin{pmatrix} x_c \\ y_c \end{pmatrix} = \alpha \begin{pmatrix} 1 \\ -1 \end{pmatrix} e^{-t} + \beta \begin{pmatrix} 3 \\ 2 \end{pmatrix} e^{4t}.$$

We try a particular integral of the form

$$\begin{pmatrix} x \\ y \end{pmatrix} = \begin{pmatrix} a \\ b \end{pmatrix} e^{2t}.$$

Then

$$2ae^{2t} = 2ae^{2t} + 3be^{2t} + e^{2t},$$
$$2be^{2t} = 2ae^{2t} + be^{2t} + 4e^{2t},$$

which give $3b + 1 = 0$ and $b - 2a = 4$, so $b = -\frac{1}{3}$ and $a = -\frac{13}{6}$. The general solution is therefore

$$\begin{pmatrix} x \\ y \end{pmatrix} = \alpha \begin{pmatrix} 1 \\ -1 \end{pmatrix} e^{-t} + \beta \begin{pmatrix} 3 \\ 2 \end{pmatrix} e^{4t} - \frac{1}{6} \begin{pmatrix} 13 \\ 2 \end{pmatrix} e^{2t}.$$

Putting $t = 0$, we obtain

$$\tfrac{5}{6} = \alpha + 3\beta - \tfrac{13}{6}, \quad \tfrac{2}{3} = -\alpha + 2\beta - \tfrac{1}{3},$$

so $\alpha + 3\beta = 3$ and $-\alpha + 2\beta = 1$, which give $\alpha = \tfrac{3}{5}$ and $\beta = \tfrac{4}{5}$.

The required solution is therefore

$$\begin{pmatrix} x \\ y \end{pmatrix} = \tfrac{3}{5} \begin{pmatrix} 1 \\ -1 \end{pmatrix} e^{-t} + \tfrac{4}{5} \begin{pmatrix} 3 \\ 2 \end{pmatrix} e^{4t} - \tfrac{1}{6} \begin{pmatrix} 13 \\ 2 \end{pmatrix} e^{2t}.$$

Solution to Exercise 13

These equations are of the form

$$\dot{\mathbf{x}} = \mathbf{A}\mathbf{x} + \mathbf{h}_1 + 4\mathbf{h}_2,$$

where

$$\mathbf{x} = \begin{pmatrix} x \\ y \end{pmatrix}, \quad \mathbf{A} = \begin{pmatrix} 2 & 3 \\ 2 & 1 \end{pmatrix}, \quad \mathbf{h}_1 = \begin{pmatrix} t \\ 0 \end{pmatrix} \quad \text{and} \quad \mathbf{h}_2 = \begin{pmatrix} 0 \\ e^{-2t} \end{pmatrix}.$$

Choosing a particular integral

$$\mathbf{x}_1 = (at + b \quad ct + d)^T$$

with $\mathbf{h}_1 = (t \quad 0)^T$, and substituting into $\dot{\mathbf{x}} = \mathbf{A}\mathbf{x} + \mathbf{h}_1$, we obtain

$$a = 2(at + b) + 3(ct + d) + t,$$
$$c = 2(at + b) + (ct + d),$$

so

$$\begin{array}{rrrl} 2a & + 3c & & = -1, \\ 2a & + c & & = 0, \\ -a + 2b & & + 3d = & 0, \\ & 2b - & c + & d = 0, \end{array}$$

which have the solution $a = \tfrac{1}{4}$, $b = -\tfrac{7}{16}$, $c = -\tfrac{1}{2}$, $d = \tfrac{3}{8}$. Hence a particular integral of the system $\dot{\mathbf{x}} = \mathbf{A}\mathbf{x} + \mathbf{h}_1$ is given by

$$\mathbf{x}_1 = \tfrac{1}{16} \begin{pmatrix} 4t - 7 \\ -8t + 6 \end{pmatrix}.$$

For $\mathbf{h}_2 = (0 \quad e^{-2t})^T$, we try a particular integral

$$\mathbf{x}_2 = (a \quad b)^T e^{-2t},$$

which is substituted into $\dot{\mathbf{x}} = \mathbf{A}\mathbf{x} + \mathbf{h}_2$, followed by dividing through by e^{-2t}, to obtain

$$-2a = 2a + 3b,$$
$$-2b = 2a + b + 1,$$

which simplify to

$$4a + 3b = 0,$$
$$2a + 3b = -1,$$

giving the solution $a = \tfrac{1}{2}$ and $b = -\tfrac{2}{3}$.

Hence a particular integral of the system $\dot{\mathbf{x}} = \mathbf{A}\mathbf{x} + \mathbf{h}_2$ is given by

$$\mathbf{x}_2 = \tfrac{1}{6} \begin{pmatrix} 3 \\ -4 \end{pmatrix} e^{-2t}.$$

Using the complementary function from Exercise 12 and the principle of superposition, the required general solution is

$$\begin{pmatrix} x \\ y \end{pmatrix} = \alpha \begin{pmatrix} 1 \\ -1 \end{pmatrix} e^{-t} + \beta \begin{pmatrix} 3 \\ 2 \end{pmatrix} e^{4t} + \mathbf{x}_1 + 4\mathbf{x}_2$$

$$= \alpha \begin{pmatrix} 1 \\ -1 \end{pmatrix} e^{-t} + \beta \begin{pmatrix} 3 \\ 2 \end{pmatrix} e^{4t} + \tfrac{1}{16} \begin{pmatrix} 4t - 7 \\ -8t + 6 \end{pmatrix} + \tfrac{2}{3} \begin{pmatrix} 3 \\ -4 \end{pmatrix} e^{-2t}.$$

Solution to Exercise 14

These equations are of the form $\dot{\mathbf{x}} = \mathbf{A}\mathbf{x} + \mathbf{k}e^{4t}$, where

$$\mathbf{x} = \begin{pmatrix} x \\ y \end{pmatrix}, \quad \mathbf{A} = \begin{pmatrix} 2 & 3 \\ 2 & 1 \end{pmatrix} \quad \text{and} \quad \mathbf{k} = \begin{pmatrix} 1 \\ 2 \end{pmatrix}.$$

From Exercise 12, $\lambda_1 = -1$ and $\lambda_2 = 4$ are the eigenvalues corresponding to eigenvectors $\mathbf{v}_1 = (1 \quad -1)^T$ and $\mathbf{v}_2 = (3 \quad 2)^T$, respectively.

We need to use Procedure 5 because $e^{4t} = e^{\lambda_2 t}$. We have $\mathbf{k} = p\mathbf{v}_1 + q\mathbf{v}_2$ for some numbers p and q, that is, $(1 \quad 2)^T = p(1 \quad -1)^T + q(3 \quad 2)^T$, which gives $p = -\tfrac{4}{5}$ and $q = \tfrac{3}{5}$. A particular integral is of the form $\mathbf{x}_p = (a\mathbf{v}_1 + b\mathbf{v}_2 t)e^{4t}$, where $a = p/(\lambda_2 - \lambda_1)$ and $b = q$. Substituting our values for p and q into these expressions gives $a = -\tfrac{4}{5}/5 = -\tfrac{4}{25}$ and $b = \tfrac{3}{5}$, hence a particular integral is

$$\mathbf{x}_p = \left(-\tfrac{4}{25} \begin{pmatrix} 1 \\ -1 \end{pmatrix} + \tfrac{3}{5} \begin{pmatrix} 3 \\ 2 \end{pmatrix} t \right) e^{4t}.$$

The required general solution is therefore

$$\mathbf{x} = \alpha \begin{pmatrix} 1 \\ -1 \end{pmatrix} e^{-t} + \beta \begin{pmatrix} 3 \\ 2 \end{pmatrix} e^{4t} + \tfrac{1}{25} \begin{pmatrix} 45t - 4 \\ 30t + 4 \end{pmatrix} e^{4t}.$$

Solution to Exercise 15

The matrix of coefficients is $\mathbf{A} = \begin{pmatrix} 5 & 2 \\ 2 & 5 \end{pmatrix}$, and we are given that the eigenvectors are $(1 \quad 1)^T$ corresponding to the eigenvalue $\lambda = 7$, and $(1 \quad -1)^T$ corresponding to the eigenvalue $\lambda = 3$.

It follows that the general solution is

$$\begin{pmatrix} x \\ y \end{pmatrix} = C_1 \begin{pmatrix} 1 \\ 1 \end{pmatrix} e^{\sqrt{7}t} + C_2 \begin{pmatrix} 1 \\ 1 \end{pmatrix} e^{-\sqrt{7}t} + C_3 \begin{pmatrix} 1 \\ -1 \end{pmatrix} e^{\sqrt{3}t} + C_4 \begin{pmatrix} 1 \\ -1 \end{pmatrix} e^{-\sqrt{3}t}.$$

Solution to Exercise 16

The matrix of coefficients is $\mathbf{A} = \begin{pmatrix} 1 & 4 \\ 1 & 1 \end{pmatrix}$.

The characteristic equation is $\lambda^2 - 2\lambda - 3 = 0$, so the eigenvalues are $\lambda = 3$ and $\lambda = -1$. Solving the eigenvector equations, we obtain eigenvectors $(2 \quad 1)^T$ and $(-2 \quad 1)^T$, respectively. Using Procedure 6, we then have

$$\begin{pmatrix} x \\ y \end{pmatrix} = \begin{pmatrix} 2 \\ 1 \end{pmatrix} \left(C_1 e^{\sqrt{3}t} + C_2 e^{-\sqrt{3}t} \right) + \begin{pmatrix} -2 \\ 1 \end{pmatrix} (C_3 \cos t + C_4 \sin t).$$

Solution to Exercise 17

Using the given eigenvalues and eigenvectors, we obtain the general solution

$$\begin{pmatrix} x \\ y \\ z \end{pmatrix} = C_1 \begin{pmatrix} 1 \\ 0 \\ 0 \end{pmatrix} e^{\sqrt{2}t} + C_2 \begin{pmatrix} 1 \\ 0 \\ 0 \end{pmatrix} e^{-\sqrt{2}t}$$

$$+ C_3 \begin{pmatrix} 1 \\ -5 \\ 0 \end{pmatrix} \cos(\sqrt{3}t) + C_4 \begin{pmatrix} 1 \\ -5 \\ 0 \end{pmatrix} \sin(\sqrt{3}t)$$

$$+ C_5 \begin{pmatrix} -5 \\ 4 \\ 14 \end{pmatrix} e^{2t} + C_6 \begin{pmatrix} -5 \\ 4 \\ 14 \end{pmatrix} e^{-2t}.$$

Solution to Exercise 18

The matrix of coefficients is $\mathbf{A} = \begin{pmatrix} -\frac{25}{7} & \frac{6}{7} \\ \frac{9}{7} & -\frac{10}{7} \end{pmatrix}$.

The characteristic equation of $\mathbf{A}$ is $\lambda^2 + 5\lambda + 4 = 0$, so the eigenvalues are $\lambda = -4$ and $\lambda = -1$.

The eigenvector equations are

$$(-\tfrac{25}{7} - \lambda)x + \tfrac{6}{7}y = 0,$$
$$\tfrac{9}{7}x + (-\tfrac{10}{7} - \lambda)y = 0.$$

- For $\lambda = -4$, the eigenvector equations become

$$\tfrac{3}{7}x + \tfrac{6}{7}y = 0,$$
$$\tfrac{9}{7}x + \tfrac{18}{7}y = 0,$$

 which reduce to the equation $-2y = x$, so a corresponding eigenvector is $(-2 \quad 1)^T$.

- For $\lambda = -1$, the eigenvector equations become

$$-\tfrac{18}{7}x + \tfrac{6}{7}y = 0,$$
$$\tfrac{9}{7}x - \tfrac{3}{7}y = 0,$$

 which reduce to the equation $y = 3x$, so a corresponding eigenvector is $(1 \quad 3)^T$.

The general solution is therefore

$$\begin{pmatrix} x \\ y \end{pmatrix} = \begin{pmatrix} -2 \\ 1 \end{pmatrix} (C_1 \cos 2t + C_2 \sin 2t) + \begin{pmatrix} 1 \\ 3 \end{pmatrix} (C_3 \cos t + C_4 \sin t).$$

The object describes simple harmonic motion along the eigenvectors, so there are two possibilities for simple harmonic motion along a straight line:

- motion in the direction of the vector $(-2 \quad 1)^T$ (i.e. the line $x + 2y = 0$) with angular frequency 2 (corresponding to $C_3 = C_4 = 0$)

- motion in the direction of the vector $(1 \quad 3)^T$ (i.e. the line $y = 3x$) with angular frequency 1 (corresponding to $C_1 = C_2 = 0$).

Acknowledgements

Grateful acknowledgement is made to the following source:

Figure 1: © British Motor Industry Heritage Trust.

Every effort has been made to contact copyright holders. If any have been inadvertently overlooked, the publishers will be pleased to make the necessary arrangements at the first opportunity.

Unit 7

Functions of several variables

Introduction

So far in this module, most of the mathematical models have concerned physical quantities that vary with respect to a single variable, which has usually been time. In this unit we look at models that depend on more than one variable.

As a simple example, let us consider the illumination from a street lamp, as shown in Figure 1. (That is, we are considering the illumination falling on, say, a flat paving slab at the point P, due to a street lamp placed at the point Q.) There are a number of variable quantities here. To simplify things a little, let us assume that the power rating of the light bulb is fixed at 1000 watts. Nevertheless, the height h of the bulb above the street, the distance x of P from the base of the lamp, the distance r from P to Q, and the angle θ (as shown) are all features that could be taken into consideration.

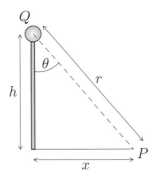

Figure 1 Street lamp placed at point Q, illuminating a paving slab at point P

It is possible to express h and x in terms of r and θ, or to express r and θ in terms of h and x. The quantities h and x are easy to measure, but the physics of the situation gives the illumination at P more readily in terms of the two variables r and θ, via the equation

$$I = \frac{1000 \cos \theta}{r^2}, \tag{1}$$

where I is the 'brightness' of the illumination per square metre falling on the slab at P.

The technical term for 'brightness' in this sense is *luminance*. The form of its dependence on r is due to the fact that the surface area of a sphere of radius r is proportional to r^2. The reason for its dependence on θ is that the light is falling obliquely on the slab.

In order to express I in terms of h and x rather than r and θ, we use the formulas $\cos \theta = h/\sqrt{h^2 + x^2}$ and $r^2 = h^2 + x^2$, giving

$$I(h, x) = \frac{1000h}{(h^2 + x^2)^{3/2}}. \tag{2}$$

In equation (1) the two independent variables are r and θ, while in equation (2) the independent variables are h and x. Thus the initial choice of variables in a problem can affect the form of the function that we need to consider, and may well affect the difficulty of our calculations. In this case, it is quite reasonable to represent I as a function of the two variables h and x, so let us suppose that we have made that choice.

Often, we wish to gain some physical insight into a problem, but, as with equation (2), the practical implications of a particular formula are not obvious. However, we can gain some understanding of this situation if we keep the height h fixed, at say $h = 3$, and vary the distance x. The function $I = I(h, x)$ now becomes a function of the single variable x, so we can sketch its graph, as shown in Figure 2. We can now see that the point of brightest illumination is when P is immediately below the lamp (as intuition might lead us to expect).

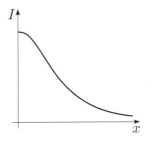

Figure 2 Plot of $I(3, x)$ against x

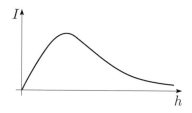

Figure 3   Plot of $I(h, 10)$ against h

A *surface* here is a set of points in space where coordinates satisfy a particular equation.

Suppose now that we keep the point P fixed, at say $x = 10$, but vary the height of the lamp. Once again, I becomes a function of a single variable, in this case h, and again we can sketch a graph, as shown in Figure 3. This time the result is perhaps a little more unexpected, for our graph tells us that there is an optimum height for the lamp at which the illumination on the horizontal slab at P is greatest. (This is because as h increases, there is a trade-off between the increasing distance of the lamp from P, which tends to decrease the illumination, and the decreasing obliqueness of the angle, which tends to increase the illumination.)

You may well wonder if it is possible to sketch a graph that represents the variation of I when both variables h and x are allowed to change. Indeed it is, but we need more than two dimensions, and the resulting surface can be hard to interpret. (We will look at such surfaces in Section 1.)

In order to deal sensibly with functions of two or more variables, we need mathematical tools similar to those that we have at our disposal for functions of a single variable. We should like to be able to differentiate these functions, to locate the points at which they take their greatest (or least) values, and to approximate them by polynomials. This may enable us to understand the behaviour of such functions and so give us an insight into the physical situations from which they arise. In fact, we need to develop a form of calculus that applies to such functions, and that is the purpose of this unit.

Section 1 concentrates on functions of two variables. We show how such functions may be used to define a surface, then extend the notion of derivative in order to investigate the slope of such a surface. Section 2 provides a brief discussion of Taylor polynomials for functions of one variable, then extends the discussion to Taylor polynomials for functions of several variables. Section 3 discusses the main topic of the unit: the classification of stationary points (where the first derivatives are zero) for functions of two or more variables.

1   Functions of two variables

Our main objective in this section is to extend some of the ideas of the calculus of functions of one variable – most importantly, the concepts of *derivative*, *stationary point*, *local maximum* and *local minimum*. However, before we discuss the *calculus* of functions of two variables, we need to discuss the *concept* of a function of two variables. We introduce the concept by considering a physical situation.

1.1 Introducing functions of two variables

Imagine an experiment in which a thin flat metal disc of radius 2 metres is heated (see Figure 4(a)). At a particular moment, we record the temperatures at various points on the upper surface of the disc.

(a)

We could specify the points on the surface of the disc by means of a Cartesian coordinate system, using the centre of the disc as the origin, as shown in Figure 4(b). The temperature may well vary over the surface of the disc, so that the temperature at O is higher than at P, for example. Nevertheless, at any given moment, each point (x, y) of the disc has a well-defined temperature (Θ, say, in degrees Celsius). We could denote this temperature by $\Theta(x, y)$ to remind ourselves that the value of Θ depends on our particular choice of x and y. We say that Θ is a function of the two variables x and y, and that the *dependent variable* Θ is a function of the two *independent variables* x and y.

There is a natural restriction on the independent variables x and y arising from the physical situation: $\Theta(x, y)$ is defined only for points (x, y) lying on the disc. That is, the domain of the function Θ is the set of points (x, y) in the plane such that $x^2 + y^2 \leq 4$.

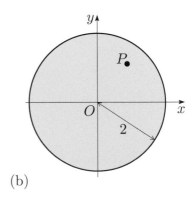

(b)

Figure 4 (a) Bunsen burner heating the centre of a metal disc of radius 2 metres. (b) Surface of the disc depicted in the (x, y)-plane.

Suppose that a mathematical model of this situation predicts that

$$\Theta(x, y) = 10(10e^{-(x^2+y^2)} + 1) \quad (\text{for } x^2 + y^2 \leq 4).$$

Then it is a simple matter to calculate the predicted temperature at any point on the disc. For example, at the point $(1, 1.5)$, the predicted temperature (in degrees Celsius) is

$$\Theta(1, 1.5) = 10(10e^{-(1^2+1.5^2)} + 1) = 10(10e^{-3.25} + 1) \simeq 13.9.$$

Exercise 1

Given $f(x, y) = 3x^2 - 2y^3$, evaluate the following.

(a) $f(2, 3)$ (b) $f(3, 2)$ (c) $f(a, b)$ (d) $f(b, a)$

(e) $f(2a, b)$ (f) $f(a - b, 0)$ (g) $f(x, 2)$ (h) $f(y, x)$

Exercise 2

Figure 5 shows a double pendulum consisting of two light model rods OA and AB, each of length a, with a smooth joint at A. The rods move in a vertical plane, with O attached to a fixed point by means of a frictionless hinge. A particle of mass m is attached to B, and the angles θ and ϕ are as shown.

In this system the *potential energy* is given by mg multiplied by the vertical displacement from O (where g is the magnitude of the acceleration due to gravity). (You will learn more about potential energy in Unit 9.) Express the potential energy U of the system in terms of the independent variables θ and ϕ. What is the least possible value of U?

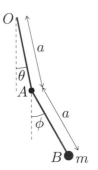

Figure 5 Double pendulum, fixed to point O, consisting of two light rods articulated at A and supporting a particle of mass m at B

1.2 Geometric interpretation

A function of two variables expresses a dependent variable in terms of two independent variables, so there are three varying quantities altogether. Thus a graph of such a function will require three dimensions.

Each variable is in the set of real numbers $\mathbb{R}$, hence the domain of a function of two variables is denoted by $\mathbb{R}^2$.

> **Functions of two variables and surfaces**
>
> A **function of two variables** is a function f whose domain is $\mathbb{R}^2$ (or a subset of $\mathbb{R}^2$) and whose codomain is $\mathbb{R}$. Thus for each point (x, y) in the domain of f, there is a unique value z defined by
>
> $$z = f(x, y).$$
>
> The set of all points with coordinates $(x, y, z) = (x, y, f(x, y))$, plotted in a three-dimensional Cartesian coordinate system, is the **surface** with equation $z = f(x, y)$.

The definition of a function of two variables generalises in a straightforward way: a **function of n variables** is a function whose domain is $\mathbb{R}^n$ (or a subset of $\mathbb{R}^n$) and whose codomain is $\mathbb{R}$.

The simplest of all surfaces $z = f(x, y)$ for a function of two variables arises from choosing f to be the zero function. We then have the equation $z = 0$, and the surface is the plane that contains the x- and y-axes, known as the (x, y)-plane.

More generally, the surface corresponding to any *linear* function of two variables $z = f(x, y) = Ax + By + C$ (where A, B and C are constants) is a **plane**.

For example, the equation $z = f(x, y) = -\frac{2}{3}x - 2y + 2$ represents a plane passing through the three points $(3, 0, 0)$, $(0, 1, 0)$ and $(0, 0, 2)$, and extending indefinitely. Part of this plane is illustrated in Figure 6.

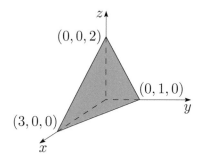

Figure 6   Part of the plane $z = -\frac{2}{3}x - 2y + 2$

A plane can be described geometrically by specifying a point through which it passes, say (a, b, c), and a unit vector that is normal (or, in other words, perpendicular) to the plane, denoted by $\widehat{\mathbf{n}}$, which is unique up to a sign.

Let $\mathbf{a} = a\mathbf{i} + b\mathbf{j} + c\mathbf{k}$, and consider $\mathbf{r} = x\mathbf{i} + y\mathbf{j} + z\mathbf{k}$, the position vector of a general point on the plane. The vector $\mathbf{r} - \mathbf{a}$ is in the plane and therefore perpendicular to $\widehat{\mathbf{n}}$, hence the equation for the plane can be expressed in vector form as

$$(\mathbf{r} - \mathbf{a}) \cdot \widehat{\mathbf{n}} = 0. \tag{3}$$

This construction is illustrated in Figure 7. Note that $|\mathbf{a} \cdot \widehat{\mathbf{n}}|$ is the perpendicular distance – i.e. the shortest distance – to the plane from the origin.

Recall from Unit 4 that the solution of simultaneous linear equations can be interpreted in terms of the intersection of planes.

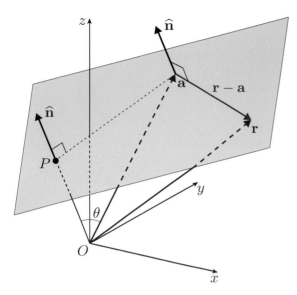

Figure 7   Plane passing through the point represented by vector **a**, with unit vector $\widehat{\mathbf{n}}$ normal to the plane. P is the point on the plane closest to the origin, at distance $|\mathbf{a}|\cos\theta = \mathbf{a}\cdot\widehat{\mathbf{n}}$.

Example 1

Consider the plane $z = -\tfrac{2}{3}x - 2y + 2$ discussed above, and the general situation illustrated in Figure 7.

(a) Write down a vector **n** that is normal to the plane, and hence calculate $\widehat{\mathbf{n}}$.

(b) By expressing the equation of the plane in terms of $\widehat{\mathbf{n}}$ and the position vector **r** of a general point on the plane, show that the shortest distance from the plane to the origin is $6/7$.

Solution

(a) Note that the equation of the plane $z = -\tfrac{2}{3}x - 2y + 2$ can be written as

$$\tfrac{2}{3}x + 2y + z = 2,$$

or as $\mathbf{n}\cdot\mathbf{r} = 2$, where **r** is the position vector and

$$\mathbf{n} = \tfrac{2}{3}\mathbf{i} + 2\mathbf{j} + \mathbf{k},$$

which is normal to the plane, as can be deduced by comparison with equation (3). A unit normal $\widehat{\mathbf{n}}$ is given by $\widehat{\mathbf{n}} = \mathbf{n}/|\mathbf{n}|$, where

$$|\mathbf{n}|^2 = \tfrac{4}{9} + 4 + 1 = 49/9$$

so $|\mathbf{n}| = 7/3$. Thus

$$\widehat{\mathbf{n}} = \tfrac{2}{7}\mathbf{i} + \tfrac{6}{7}\mathbf{j} + \tfrac{3}{7}\mathbf{k}.$$

(b) Multiplying both sides of $\mathbf{n} \cdot \mathbf{r} = 2$ by $1/|\mathbf{n}|$ gives $\hat{\mathbf{n}} \cdot \mathbf{r} = 6/7$, and comparison with equation (3) shows that $\hat{\mathbf{n}} \cdot \mathbf{a}$, the shortest distance from the plane to the origin, is $6/7$, where $\mathbf{a}$ is the vector position of any point in the plane.

The surfaces corresponding to the functions $p(x,y) = x^2 + y^2$ (see Figure 8(a)) and $h(x,y) = y^2 - x^2$ (see Figure 8(b)) are not planes, but you will see later that their behaviour near the origin is of particular interest. The function $p(x,y)$ is a **paraboloid** (which can be obtained by plotting the parabola $z = x^2$ in the (x,z)-plane then rotating it about the z-axis). The function $h(x,y)$ is a **hyperboloid** (which cannot be obtained by rotating a curve about the z-axis or any other axis).

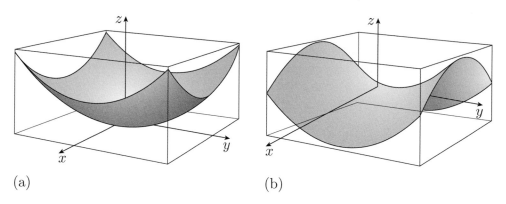

(a)   (b)

Figure 8   Surfaces of (a) the paraboloid $z = p(x,y) = x^2 + y^2$, and (b) the hyperboloid $z = h(x,y) = y^2 - x^2$

Section functions

In general, the surface representing a function may be complicated and difficult to visualise. It is often helpful to consider the function obtained by fixing all the independent variables except one at specific values. In the case of the function $p(x,y) = x^2 + y^2$, for example, we might choose to fix the value of y at 2, in which case we are left with the function of a *single variable*

$$p(x,2) = x^2 + 4.$$

This function is known as a **section function** of $p(x,y) = x^2 + y^2$, with y fixed at 2.

In the case of the surfaces shown in Figure 8, it is worth looking at their behaviour near the origin. The section functions $p(x,0)$ and $p(0,y)$, and $h(x,0)$ and $h(0,y)$, are quite illuminating. They show, very clearly, properties of the surfaces that you may have already observed.

The section functions $p(x,0)$ and $p(0,y)$ are shown in Figures 9 and 10, respectively.

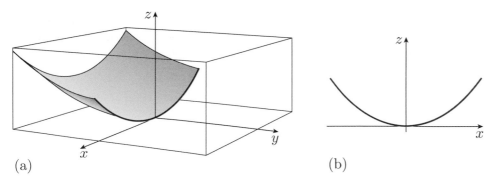

(a)   (b)

Figure 9   (a) The surface $z = p(x, y) = x^2 + y^2$ cut along the plane $y = 0$. (b) The section function $z = p(x, 0)$.

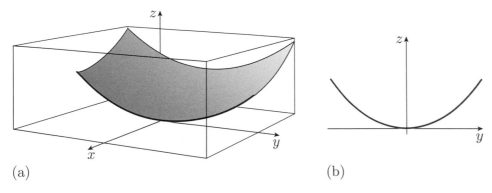

(a)   (b)

Figure 10   (a) The surface $z = p(x, y) = x^2 + y^2$ cut along the plane $x = 0$. (b) The section function $z = p(0, y)$.

The surface $z = p(x, y) = x^2 + y^2$ has a local minimum at the origin; correspondingly, each of the section functions $p(x, 0)$ and $p(0, y)$ has a local minimum there.

The section functions $h(x, 0)$ and $h(0, y)$ are shown in Figures 11 and 12, respectively.

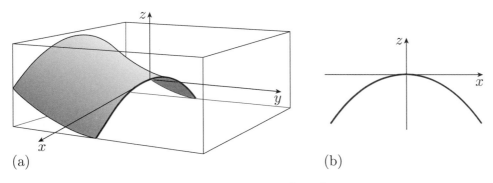

(a)   (b)

Figure 11   (a) The surface $z = h(x, y) = y^2 - x^2$ cut along the plane $y = 0$. (b) The section function $z = h(x, 0)$.

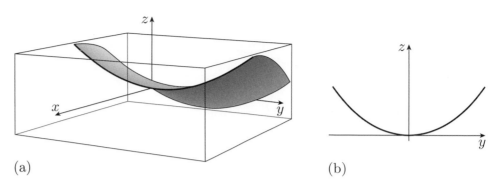

(a)   (b)

Figure 12   (a) The surface $z = h(x, y) = y^2 - x^2$, cut along the plane $x = 0$. (b) The section function $z = h(0, y)$.

The surface $z = h(x, y) = y^2 - x^2$ has neither a local maximum nor a local minimum at the origin, corresponding to the fact that the section function $h(x, 0)$ has a local maximum at the origin, while the section function $h(0, y)$ has a local minimum there.

Of course, we have not yet defined what we mean by a (local) maximum or minimum of a function of two variables (that comes in Section 3), but it is already clear that a surface can behave in a more complicated fashion than the graph of a function of one variable.

It is worth spending a little time at this point to recall how to use calculus to justify that the section functions $h(x, 0)$ and $h(0, y)$ have a local maximum and a local minimum, respectively, at the origin.

A standard method in this context is the *second derivative test*, which applies to 'sufficiently smooth' functions of one variable. (In this context, 'sufficiently smooth' means that the first and second derivatives exist.) If $f(x)$ is a function whose first and second derivatives exist, and at some point $x = a$ we have $f'(a) = 0$, then a is a **stationary point** of $f(x)$. Often (but not always) it will be a local maximum or a local minimum.

The **second derivative test** is based on the evaluation of $f''(x)$ at a. There are three possibilities:

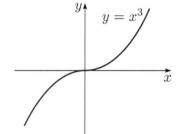

Figure 13   The curve $y = f(x) = x^3$, with a point of inflection at the origin

- If $f''(a)$ is *negative*, then f has a *local maximum* at a.

- If $f''(a)$ is *positive*, then f has a *local minimum* at a.

- If $f''(a) = 0$, then the test is inconclusive. There may still be a local maximum or a local minimum at a, but another possibility is that there is a *point of inflection*, such as occurs at $x = 0$ for the function $f(x) = x^3$ (see Figure 13).

Example 2

For $h(x, y) = y^2 - x^2$, use the second derivative test to verify that the section function $h(x, 0)$ has a local maximum at $x = 0$ and that the section function $h(0, y)$ has a local minimum at $y = 0$.

Solution

We have $h(x,0) = -x^2$, and

$$\frac{d}{dx}(-x^2) = -2x,$$

which is zero when $x = 0$. Thus $h(x,0)$ has a stationary point at $x = 0$. Now

$$\frac{d^2}{dx^2}(-x^2) = -2,$$

which is negative for all values of x, so this stationary point is a local maximum.

We have $h(0,y) = y^2$, and

$$\frac{d}{dy}(y^2) = 2y,$$

which is zero when $y = 0$. Thus $h(0,y)$ has a stationary point at $y = 0$. Now

$$\frac{d^2}{dy^2}(y^2) = 2,$$

which is positive for all values of y, so this stationary point is a local minimum.

Exercise 3

Show that the section function of $F(x,y) = 100e^{-(x^2+y^2)}$ with y fixed at 0 has a local maximum at $x = 0$.

The concept of a section function can be extended easily to functions of more than two variables. For example, the section function of

$$w(x,y,t) = \frac{x}{y + 2t}$$

with x fixed at 3 and t fixed at 1 is

$$w(3,y,1) = \frac{3}{y + 2},$$

The domain of w should be restricted so that $y + 2t$ can never be zero.

which is a function of y only. (Section functions are always functions of *one* variable, so we have to fix the values of all the variables except one to obtain a section function.) One obvious advantage of considering section functions (rather than the original function of two or more variables) is that we can apply the familiar calculus techniques for functions of one variable.

Contour maps

Another way to visualise a function of two variables on a plane is to use contour maps. Consider a continuous function $f(x, y)$. A curve in the (x, y)-plane defined by the equation $f(x, y) = c$, for some constant c, is called a **contour curve** of $f(x, y)$. By plotting contour curves of $f(x, y)$ for different values of c chosen from a discrete set of constants, $c_1, c_2, \ldots$ say, we obtain a family of contour curves in the (x, y)-plane. Such a plot is called a **contour map**. It is reminiscent of the contours found on Ordnance Survey maps, which are curves joining points on land that are at a constant elevation above sea level.

As an example, consider contour maps for the paraboloid $p(x, y) = x^2 + y^2$ (Figure 14(a)) and the hyperboloid $h(x, y) = y^2 - x^2$ (Figure 14(b)), seen earlier.

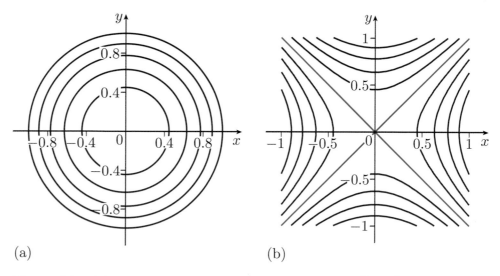

(a)   (b)

Figure 14 (a) Contours of the paraboloid $p(x, y) = x^2 + y^2$, given by red circles with radii increasing with increasing values of $c = p(x, y)$, where $c > 0$. If $c = 0$, the contour is just a single point. Clearly, there are no contours with $c < 0$. (b) Contours of the hyperboloid $h(x, y) = y^2 - x^2$, given by $h(x, y) = c$; contours with $c > 0$ are depicted in red, those with $c < 0$ in blue, and those with $c = 0$ in green.

Exercise 4

Sketch a contour map for the function $f(x, y) = x^2 + y$, considering contours with positive, negative and zero values.

1.3   First-order partial derivatives

As a first step towards our goal of extending the ideas of calculus to functions of two (or more) variables, we begin by recalling the role played by the tangent to a graph in the calculus of functions of one variable. If we imagine a tangent line sliding along a graph, then each time the line is horizontal, we have a stationary point. We apply the same idea to functions of two variables, only this time we slide a *tangent plane* over the surface. Let us be a little more precise about this.

In many cases, the tangent line to a curve C at a point P on C is the straight line that *touches* C at P, but does not *cross* the curve at that point. Sometimes, however, even if C is a smooth curve as it goes through P, it is not possible to find a line with the 'non-crossing' property. Suppose, for example, that C is the graph of $y = x^3$ (see Figure 15) and P is the origin. Then every straight line through the origin 'crosses' C, as you may verify by placing a ruler at various angles through the origin on Figure 15. Nevertheless, the line that is the x-axis seems to be a good candidate for the 'tangent line' to C at $(0,0)$; intuitively, it seems to pass through the curve at a 'zero angle'. Let us try to make this idea more mathematically robust.

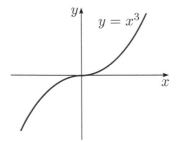

Figure 15   The curve $y = f(x) = x^3$

Consider again a general curve C and a point P on C at which we wish to find a tangent line (see Figure 16). If Q is a point on the curve close to P, then the **chord** through P and Q is the straight line through these points. If C is smooth enough to have a derivative at P, then as Q approaches P, the chord through P and Q approaches a well-defined line through P, which is defined to be the **tangent line** to C at P.

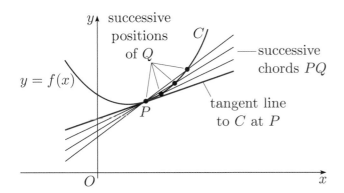

Figure 16   Chords PQ of a general curve C; as point Q approaches point P, the chord PQ tends to the tangent to C at P

The tangent line at P is the line that has the same *slope* as C at that point. To return to the case of the curve $y = f(x) = x^3$ (see Figure 15), since $f'(0) = 0$, the slope of C at $(0,0)$ is 0, so the tangent line to C at $(0,0)$ is the x-axis, that is, the line $y = 0$.

More generally, if the curve C is defined by the function $y = f(x)$, then at the point $P = (a, f(a)) = (a, b)$, the slope of C is $f'(a)$ and the equation of the tangent line is $y - b = f'(a)(x - a)$, this being the equation of a line through (a, b) with slope $f'(a)$.

In a similar way, a smooth surface without breaks or folds has a *tangent plane*. In the cases of the paraboloid and hyperboloid in Figure 8, the surface is horizontal at the point $(0,0,0)$, so for each of these surfaces, the tangent plane at $(0,0,0)$ is the (x,y)-plane, that is, $z = 0$. In the case of the paraboloid, the (x,y)-plane touches the surface at that point, but does not cut through it. The hyperboloid, however, lies partly above and partly below the (x,y)-plane, so (as with the tangent line at $(0,0)$ to $y = x^3$) the (x,y)-plane cuts the hyperboloid – despite having the same 'slope in any direction' as the hyperboloid at $(0,0,0)$.

The tangent plane can be defined by a 'limiting' construction similar to that for the tangent line. We need three points to define a plane, so if P is a point on a smooth surface S, we must take two further points Q and R on the surface, and we must ensure that P, Q and R never lie on a straight line (when projected onto the (x,y)-plane). Then as Q and R separately approach P (from distinct directions), the plane through P, Q and R will approach a well-defined plane, the **tangent plane** at P (see Figure 17).

Just as the slope of a curve C at a point P on C is equal to the slope of the tangent line at P, so the 'slope' of the surface S at the point P on S is equal to the 'slope' of the tangent plane at P. But what *is* this slope?

Imagine that the surface is a hillside and that you are walking across it (see Figure 18). Let us suppose that you want to measure the 'slope' of the hill at some particular point. You immediately encounter a problem: in which direction should you measure the slope? If you choose a direction pointing 'straight up the hill' you will get one value, and if you choose to move 'round the hill' you will get another. We will choose two specific directions in which to measure the slope: the x-direction and the y-direction. On a smooth hill, this will be sufficient to determine the slope in every direction (as you will see in Subsection 1.4). So we start by examining the rate at which a function of two variables changes when we keep one of the variables fixed.

There are some technicalities concerning the choice of Q and R, but they are not important in this context.

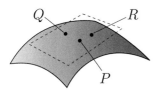

Figure 17   Plane passing through points P, Q and R on a curved surface; as Q and R approach P from different directions, the plane becomes tangent to the surface at P

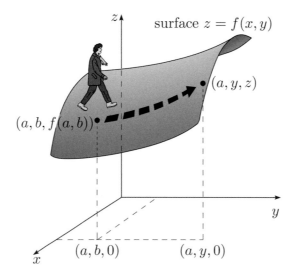

Figure 18   Path travelled on a surface defined by the equation $z = f(x,y)$

Suppose that you are walking over the surface defined by the equation $z = f(x, y)$ and that you are at the point $(a, b, f(a, b)) = (a, b, c)$. If $c > 0$, then directly below you is the point $(a, b, 0)$ lying in the (x, y)-plane (see Figure 18). Now you begin to move across the surface, taking care to ensure that the value of x stays fixed at a. As you move, the value of y changes, and your height z above the (x, y)-plane varies. We are going to investigate the rate of change of the height z with y, which you would recognise as the slope (at some particular point) of the path along which you are walking. We refer to this slope as the *slope of the surface in the y-direction* (at the point in question).

As a specific example, consider the function

$$f(x, y) = x^2 - y^3 + 2xy^2.$$

Suppose that we are trying to find the slope of this surface in the y-direction at the point $(2, 1, 7)$ on the surface. First, we construct the section function of $f(x, y)$ with x fixed at 2:

$$f(2, y) = 4 - y^3 + 4y^2.$$

Then we differentiate this function with respect to y, to obtain

$$\frac{df}{dy}(2, y) = -3y^2 + 8y.$$

Finally, we put $y = 1$ into this expression and obtain the value 5 for the slope of the surface in the y-direction at $(2, 1, 7)$.

This process would be the same for any fixed value of x thus can be generalised: fix x at some constant value, then differentiate $f(x, y)$ with respect to y, using all the standard rules of differentiation and *treating x as a constant*. The result is the expression $-3y^2 + 4xy$. This is the *partial derivative* of the function $f(x, y) = x^2 - y^3 + 2xy^2$ with respect to y, denoted by $\partial f / \partial y$. So we have

The use of the 'partial dee' symbol ∂ (rather than d) for partial derivatives distinguishes them from ordinary derivatives. It is important that there is a clear distinction between these symbols in written work.

$$\frac{\partial f}{\partial y}(x, y) = -3y^2 + 4xy.$$

If we put $x = 2$ and $y = 1$ in this expression, then we obtain

$$\frac{\partial f}{\partial y}(2, 1) = 5,$$

which is the same value as we found above.

The same method can be used to find the slope in the x-direction, but this time we keep y fixed and differentiate with respect to x. We obtain

$$\frac{\partial f}{\partial x}(x, y) = 2x + 2y^2.$$

Putting $x = 2$ and $y = 1$ into this expression, we obtain the value 6 for the slope of the surface in the x-direction at $(2, 1, 7)$.

The ordinary derivative of $f(t)$ with respect to t is formally defined as
$$\frac{df}{dt} = \lim_{h \to 0} \frac{f(t+h) - f(t)}{h}.$$

More formally, the partial derivatives of a function $f(x,y)$ with respect to x and y are given by

$$\frac{\partial f}{\partial x} = \lim_{\delta x \to 0} \frac{f(x + \delta x, y) - f(x,y)}{\delta x} \tag{4}$$

and

$$\frac{\partial f}{\partial y} = \lim_{\delta y \to 0} \frac{f(x, y + \delta y) - f(x,y)}{\delta y}, \tag{5}$$

where δx and δy denote (small) *increments* (i.e. changes) in the values of x and y, respectively.

Note the important difference between the symbols:

the 'delta' symbol δ represents an increment;

the 'partial dee' symbol ∂ represents partial differentiation.

We will need the more formal definitions later, but for now the following definitions will suffice.

The expression $\partial f / \partial x$ is read as 'partial dee f by dee x'.

First-order partial derivatives

Given a function f of two variables x and y, the **partial derivative** $\partial f / \partial x$ is obtained by differentiating $f(x,y)$ with respect to x while treating y as a constant. Similarly, the partial derivative $\partial f / \partial y$ is obtained by differentiating $f(x,y)$ with respect to y while treating x as a constant.

We will define second-order and higher-order partial derivatives in Section 2.

The partial derivatives $\partial f / \partial x$ and $\partial f / \partial y$ represent the slopes of the surface $z = f(x,y)$ at the point $(x, y, f(x,y))$ in the x- and y-directions, respectively. These partial derivatives are the **first-order partial derivatives** or the **first partial derivatives** of the function f.

We will also use the alternative notation f_x for $\partial f / \partial x$ and f_y for $\partial f / \partial y$.

Example 3

Calculate $\partial f / \partial x$ and $\partial f / \partial y$ for

$$f(x,y) = \sqrt{xy} + xy^2 \quad (x > 0, \ y > 0).$$

Find the slopes of the corresponding surface $z = \sqrt{xy} + xy^2$ in the x- and y-directions at the point $(4, 1, 6)$ on the surface.

Solution

First, we treat y as a constant and differentiate with respect to x (remembering that $\sqrt{xy} = \sqrt{x}\sqrt{y}$), to obtain

$$\frac{\partial f}{\partial x} = \frac{\sqrt{y}}{2\sqrt{x}} + y^2.$$

So the slope in the x-direction at $(4, 1, 6)$ is

$$\frac{\sqrt{1}}{2\sqrt{4}} + 1 = \tfrac{5}{4}.$$

Now we treat x as a constant and differentiate f with respect to y, to obtain

$$\frac{\partial f}{\partial y} = \frac{\sqrt{x}}{2\sqrt{y}} + 2xy.$$

So the slope in the y-direction at $(4, 1, 6)$ is

$$\frac{\sqrt{4}}{2\sqrt{1}} + (2 \times 4 \times 1) = 9.$$

In general, $\partial f/\partial x$ and $\partial f/\partial y$ are functions of the two variables x and y, so in Example 3 we could write

$$\frac{\partial f}{\partial x}(x, y) = \frac{\sqrt{y}}{2\sqrt{x}} + y^2, \quad \frac{\partial f}{\partial y}(x, y) = \frac{\sqrt{x}}{2\sqrt{y}} + 2xy,$$

or alternatively,

$$f_x(x, y) = \frac{\sqrt{y}}{2\sqrt{x}} + y^2, \quad f_y(x, y) = \frac{\sqrt{x}}{2\sqrt{y}} + 2xy,$$

if we wish to emphasise the fact that the partial derivatives are themselves functions. Thus we could write

$$f_x(4, 1) = \tfrac{5}{4}, \quad f_y(4, 1) = 9,$$

for the slopes in the x- and y-directions, respectively, at the point in question.

Exercise 5

Given

$$f(x, y) = x^3 \cos y + y^2 \sin x,$$

calculate $\partial f/\partial x$ and $\partial f/\partial y$.

Exercise 6

Given

$$f(x, y) = (x^2 + y^3) \sin(xy),$$

calculate $\partial f/\partial x$ and $\partial f/\partial y$.

Of course, the two independent variables need not be denoted by x and y; any variable names will do, as the next example shows.

Example 4

Given $f(\alpha, t) = \alpha \sin(\alpha t)$, calculate $f_\alpha\left(\tfrac{\pi}{2}, 1\right)$ and $f_t\left(\tfrac{\pi}{2}, 1\right)$.

Solution

Differentiating partially with respect to α gives $f_\alpha = \sin(\alpha t) + \alpha t \cos(\alpha t)$, so

$$f_\alpha \left(\tfrac{\pi}{2}, 1 \right) = \sin \tfrac{\pi}{2} + \tfrac{\pi}{2} \cos \tfrac{\pi}{2} = 1.$$

Differentiating partially with respect to t gives $f_t = \alpha^2 \cos(\alpha t)$, so

$$f_t \left(\tfrac{\pi}{2}, 1 \right) = \left(\tfrac{\pi}{2} \right)^2 \cos \tfrac{\pi}{2} = 0.$$

Exercise 7

Given $u(\theta, \phi) = \sin \theta + \phi \tan \theta$, calculate u_θ and u_ϕ. Hence evaluate $u_\theta \left(\tfrac{\pi}{4}, \tfrac{\pi}{2} \right)$ and $u_\phi \left(\tfrac{\pi}{4}, \tfrac{\pi}{2} \right)$.

Often, a mathematical model will generate a relationship between variables. For example, we have the formula $V = \tfrac{1}{3} \pi r^2 h$ for the volume V of a cone in terms of the radius r of its circular base and its height h. We could introduce a function $f(r, h) = \tfrac{1}{3} \pi r^2 h$ and write the partial derivatives as $\partial f / \partial r$ and $\partial f / \partial h$. But it is often more convenient to let V denote both the variable and the function that defines it, enabling us to write $\partial V / \partial r$ in place of $\partial f / \partial r$, and $\partial V / \partial h$ in place of $\partial f / \partial h$, thus keeping the number of symbols to a minimum.

The notion of partial derivative can be extended to functions of more than two variables. For example, for a function $f(x, y, t)$ of three variables, to calculate $\partial f / \partial x$, we keep y and t fixed, and differentiate with respect to x (and similarly for the other partial derivatives).

Exercise 8

(a) Find all the first partial derivatives of the function
$$f(x, y, t) = x^2 y^3 t^4 + 2xy + 4t^2 x^2 + y.$$

(b) Given $z = (1 + x)^2 + (1 + y)^3$, calculate $\partial z / \partial x$ and $\partial z / \partial y$. Sketch the section functions $z(x, 0)$ and $z(0, y)$. What is the relevance of the value of $(\partial z / \partial x)(0, 0)$ to the graph of $z(x, 0)$, and what is the relevance of the value of $(\partial z / \partial y)(0, 0)$ to the graph of $z(0, y)$?

1.4   Slope in an arbitrary direction

Suppose that the walker in Figure 18 is not walking in either the x-direction or the y-direction, but in some other direction. Can we use the partial derivatives $(\partial f / \partial x)(a, b)$ and $(\partial f / \partial y)(a, b)$ to find the slope at the point (a, b, c) in this other direction?

To answer this question, we start by looking at the formal definitions of partial derivatives in equations (4) and (5), and use them to investigate what happens when we move a small distance in a particular direction.

For a function $z = f(x, y)$, these equations are

$$\frac{\partial f}{\partial x} = \lim_{\delta x \to 0} \frac{f(x + \delta x, y) - f(x, y)}{\delta x},$$

$$\frac{\partial f}{\partial y} = \lim_{\delta y \to 0} \frac{f(x, y + \delta y) - f(x, y)}{\delta y}.$$

Small increments

If we write $\delta z_1 = f(x + \delta x, y) - f(x, y)$ and $\delta z_2 = f(x, y + \delta y) - f(x, y)$, then δz_1 is the change, or *increment*, in the value of z corresponding to a (small) increment δx in the value of x. Similarly, δz_2 is the increment in the value of z corresponding to a (small) increment δy in the value of y. So we have

$$\frac{\partial f}{\partial x} = \lim_{\delta x \to 0} \frac{\delta z_1}{\delta x}, \quad \frac{\partial f}{\partial y} = \lim_{\delta y \to 0} \frac{\delta z_2}{\delta y}. \tag{6}$$

The expressions of the form $\frac{\delta *}{\delta t}$ here are quotients, *not* derivatives. Do not confuse the symbol δ with ∂ or d.

We know from Subsection 1.3 that $\partial f / \partial x$ and $\partial f / \partial y$ are the slopes of $z = f(x, y)$ in the x- and y-directions, respectively. To find the slope of $z = f(x, y)$ in an arbitrary direction, we need to find the increment δz in the value of f when we move a short distance in that direction. Such a movement can be achieved by small increments δx and δy, and equations (6) relate these approximately to the corresponding increments δz_1 and δz_2, as shown below.

Figure 19 shows a small part of the surface $z = f(x, y)$ and the point (a, b) in the (x, y)-plane. We are interested in the effect on z when x and y are increased by the small amounts δx and δy, respectively. The increment δz is produced by moving first from (a, b) to $(a + \delta x, b)$, and then from $(a + \delta x, b)$ to $(a + \delta x, b + \delta y)$. We specify δz_1 to be the increment in z on moving from (a, b) to $(a + \delta x, b)$, and δz_2 to be the increment in z on moving from $(a + \delta x, b)$ to $(a + \delta x, b + \delta y)$.

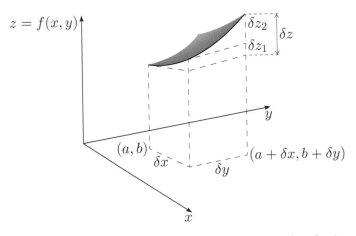

Figure 19   Small part of the surface $z = f(x, y)$ above the point $(x, y) = (a, b)$

The approximation used here holds because for small δx, we can take the slope $\partial f/\partial x$ in the x-direction to be almost constant on the interval between $x = a$ and $x = a + \delta x$. Similarly, for small δy, the slope $\partial f/\partial y$ in the y-direction can be taken to be almost constant on the interval between $y = b$ and $y = b + \delta y$.

We consider δz_1 first. This is $f(a + \delta x, b) - f(a, b)$, the difference between the function values at (a, b) and $(a + \delta x, b)$. Since x has moved from a to $a + \delta x$ while y has remained constant, the increment in z is approximately equal to the increment in x multiplied by the partial derivative with respect to x, that is,

$$\delta z_1 \simeq \frac{\partial f}{\partial x}(a, b)\, \delta x. \tag{7}$$

This follows from the first of equations (6).

The increment δz_2 is obtained by holding x constant at the value $a + \delta x$ while incrementing y from b to $b + \delta y$. It is thus approximately equal to the increment in y multiplied by the partial derivative with respect to y, that is,

$$\delta z_2 \simeq \frac{\partial f}{\partial y}(a + \delta x, b)\, \delta y. \tag{8}$$

At this point in the argument, it is necessary to assume that f is a sufficiently smooth function so that the methods of calculus that we require can be applied. We assume, in particular, that the partial derivatives are continuous. So for small δx we have

$$\frac{\partial f}{\partial y}(a + \delta x, b) \simeq \frac{\partial f}{\partial y}(a, b). \tag{9}$$

Putting equations (7), (8) and (9) together, we now have our expression linking small increments in z with small increments in x and y:

$$\delta z = \delta z_1 + \delta z_2 \simeq \frac{\partial f}{\partial x}(a, b)\, \delta x + \frac{\partial f}{\partial y}(a, b)\, \delta y, \tag{10}$$

which may be easier to remember when written in the form

$$\delta z \simeq \frac{\partial z}{\partial x}\, \delta x + \frac{\partial z}{\partial y}\, \delta y. \tag{11}$$

The approximation (11) has an important application to error analysis, as the next example shows.

Example 5

The volume V of a cone of height h with base radius r is given by

$$V = \tfrac{1}{3}\pi r^2 h.$$

(a) Determine the approximate change in the volume if the radius increases from 2 to $2 + \delta r$ and the height increases from 5 to $5 + \delta h$.

(b) If the radius and height measurements are each subject to an error of magnitude up to 0.01, how accurate is the estimate

$$V \simeq \tfrac{1}{3} \times \pi \times 2^2 \times 5 = \tfrac{20}{3}\pi \ (= 20.94, \text{ to 4 s.f.})$$

of the volume?

Solution

(a) Calculating the partial derivatives of $V = V(r, h)$ with respect to r and h, we have

$$\frac{\partial V}{\partial r} = \tfrac{2}{3}\pi r h, \quad \frac{\partial V}{\partial h} = \tfrac{1}{3}\pi r^2.$$

Setting $r = 2$ and $h = 5$, we calculate

$$\frac{\partial V}{\partial r}(2,5) = \tfrac{2}{3}\pi \times 2 \times 5 = \tfrac{20}{3}\pi, \quad \frac{\partial V}{\partial h}(2,5) = \tfrac{1}{3}\pi \times 2^2 = \tfrac{4}{3}\pi,$$

thus, from approximation (11), the approximate change in volume is

$$\delta V \simeq \tfrac{20}{3}\pi\,\delta r + \tfrac{4}{3}\pi\,\delta h.$$

(b) If the maximum possible magnitudes of δr and δh are 0.01, then the maximum possible magnitude of δV is approximately

$$\left(\tfrac{20}{3} + \tfrac{4}{3}\right)\pi \times 0.01 = 8\pi \times 0.01 \simeq 0.25.$$

Thus the volume estimate of 20.94 may compare with an actual value as high as 21.19 or as low as 20.69. The estimate is accurate to only two significant figures (and should be given as $V = 21$, correct to two significant figures).

Exercise 9

Given $z = (1 + x)^2 + (1 + y)^3$, find the approximate increment δz in z when x is incremented from 0 to δx, and y is incremented from 2 to $2 + \delta y$.

(*Hint*: You may wish to use your solution to Exercise 8(b).)

Rate of change along a curve

Now we focus on the rate of change of $z = f(x, y)$ if (x, y) is constrained to move along a curve in the (x, y)-plane. Let us suppose that x and y are themselves functions of a parameter t, so that as t varies, the point $(x(t), y(t))$ moves along a curve in the (x, y)-plane, passing through (a, b) when $t = t_0$ and through $(a + \delta x, b + \delta y)$ when $t = t_0 + \delta t$. From equation (11) we have

You may recall from previous studies that a curve described in terms of a parameter in this way is called a *parametrised curve*.

$$\frac{\delta z}{\delta t} \simeq \frac{\partial z}{\partial x}\frac{\delta x}{\delta t} + \frac{\partial z}{\partial y}\frac{\delta y}{\delta t}. \tag{12}$$

Having introduced the parameter t, we can think of x, y and z as functions of the single variable t. Thinking of them in this way, we have

$$\delta x = x(t_0 + \delta t) - x(t_0),$$
$$\delta y = y(t_0 + \delta t) - y(t_0),$$
$$\delta z = z(t_0 + \delta t) - z(t_0).$$

Thus

$$\frac{\delta x}{\delta t} = \frac{x(t_0 + \delta t) - x(t_0)}{\delta t},$$

$$\frac{\delta y}{\delta t} = \frac{y(t_0 + \delta t) - y(t_0)}{\delta t},$$

$$\frac{\delta z}{\delta t} = \frac{z(t_0 + \delta t) - z(t_0)}{\delta t}.$$

On the curve, z, x and y are functions of t only, so it is consistent to write, for example, dz/dt rather than $\partial z/\partial t$.

So from the definition of an ordinary derivative, as $\delta t \to 0$, these become the derivatives (not fractions) dx/dt, dy/dt and dz/dt, respectively. Hence as $\delta t \to 0$, approximation (12) becomes

$$\frac{dz}{dt}(t_0) = \frac{\partial z}{\partial x}(a, b)\frac{dx}{dt}(t_0) + \frac{\partial z}{\partial y}(a, b)\frac{dy}{dt}(t_0).$$

This may remind you of the chain rule for the derivative of z with respect to t if z is a function of the single variable x, and x is a function of t; that is, if $z = z(x(t))$, then

$$\frac{dz}{dt} = \frac{dz}{dx}\frac{dx}{dt}.$$

Indeed, the formula for the rate of change along a parametrised curve is the two-dimensional analogue of the chain rule of ordinary differentiation.

> ### Chain rule
>
> Let $z = f(x, y)$ be a function whose first partial derivatives exist and are continuous. Then the rate of change of z with respect to t along a curve parametrised by $(x(t), y(t))$ is given by
>
> $$\frac{dz}{dt} = \frac{\partial z}{\partial x}\frac{dx}{dt} + \frac{\partial z}{\partial y}\frac{dy}{dt}. \qquad (13)$$

Example 6

Given $z = \sin x - 3\cos y$, find the rate of change of z along the curve $(x(t), y(t))$, where $x(t) = t^2$ and $y(t) = 2t$.

Solution

We have

$$\frac{\partial z}{\partial x} = \cos x, \quad \frac{\partial z}{\partial y} = 3\sin y, \quad \frac{dx}{dt} = 2t, \quad \frac{dy}{dt} = 2.$$

Thus

$$\frac{dz}{dt} = \frac{\partial z}{\partial x}\frac{dx}{dt} + \frac{\partial z}{\partial y}\frac{dy}{dt} = 2t\cos x + 6\sin y$$

$$= 2t\cos(t^2) + 6\sin(2t).$$

(Note that the final answer is expressed in terms of t.)

Exercise 10

Given $z = y \sin x$, find the rate of change of z along the curve $(x(t), y(t))$, where $x = e^t$ and $y = t^2$. Evaluate this rate of change at $t = 0$.

The above form of the chain rule is easy to remember, but if there is a reason to emphasise that the partial derivatives are evaluated at a particular point, then it may be convenient to write it as

$$\frac{dz}{dt}(t_0) = \frac{\partial f}{\partial x}(a, b) \times \frac{dx}{dt}(t_0) + \frac{\partial f}{\partial y}(a, b) \times \frac{dy}{dt}(t_0), \tag{14}$$

where $x(t_0) = a$ and $y(t_0) = b$.

The chain rule is of fundamental importance, and we will refer back to it both in this unit and in the remainder of the module. For the moment, we use it to continue our discussion of the slope of a surface.

Writing $z(t)$ is a slight abuse of notation since it suggests that z is a function of just one variable, t (which is true only along the parametrised curve), whereas in general z depends on x and y through $z = f(x, y)$. Rather, $z(t)$ is shorthand for $z(x(t), y(t))$.

Slope in an arbitrary direction

We want to find the slope of the surface $z = f(x, y)$ at a point $(a, b, c) = (a, b, f(a, b))$ on the surface in an arbitrary given direction. This given direction is specified by a straight line through (a, b) in the (x, y)-plane. Suppose that on this line x and y are functions of the parameter t, so that $x = x(t)$ and $y = y(t)$. Let us also take $x(0) = a$ and $y(0) = b$. Then our straight line can be parametrised as

$$x(t) = a + t \cos \alpha, \quad y(t) = b + t \sin \alpha,$$

where α is the anticlockwise angle that the line makes with the positive x-axis, and t measures the distance along this line, as illustrated in Figure 20. As (x, y) moves along this line, the point $(x, y, f(x, y))$ moves along a curve in the surface $z = f(x, y)$ (see Figure 21).

The parametric form of a straight line is discussed in Subsection 2.1 of Unit 2.

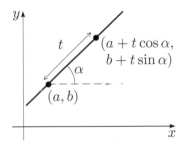

Figure 20   Parametrisation of a straight line passing through the point (a, b) with angle α relative to the x-axis

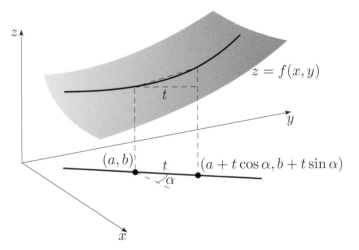

Figure 21   The line in the (x, y)-plane, as plotted in Figure 20, is projected onto the surface $z = f(x, y)$

The advantage of defining the line in terms of the parameter t is that the derivative of z with respect to t is the quantity that we are looking for – the slope of the surface $z = f(x, y)$ at the point (a, b, c), in the direction that makes an angle α with the direction of the x-axis (see Figure 21).

Moreover, we can now use the chain rule given in equation (13). Since $dx/dt = \cos \alpha$ and $dy/dt = \sin \alpha$, we obtain

$$\frac{dz}{dt} = \frac{\partial z}{\partial x} \cos \alpha + \frac{\partial z}{\partial y} \sin \alpha. \tag{15}$$

That is, we have shown that the slope of the surface $z = f(x, y)$ at the point $(a, b, f(a, b))$ in the direction making an anticlockwise angle α with the positive x-axis is

$$\frac{\partial f}{\partial x}(a, b) \cos \alpha + \frac{\partial f}{\partial y}(a, b) \sin \alpha$$

or

$$f_x(a, b) \cos \alpha + f_y(a, b) \sin \alpha.$$

This defines the slope of a surface *in a particular direction*. But what is *the* slope of the surface at $(a, b, f(a, b))$? The answer is that it can be thought of as a vector, with a component $f_x(a, b)$ in the x-direction and a component $f_y(a, b)$ in the y-direction, that is, as the vector $f_x(a, b)\mathbf{i} + f_y(a, b)\mathbf{j}$. The advantage of this formulation is that the slope in the direction of an arbitrary unit vector $\widehat{\mathbf{d}} = (\cos \alpha)\mathbf{i} + (\sin \alpha)\mathbf{j}$ in the (x, y)-plane is the dot product of the vectors $f_x(a, b)\mathbf{i} + f_y(a, b)\mathbf{j}$ and $\widehat{\mathbf{d}}$. This idea is important enough to deserve some terminology of its own.

$|\widehat{\mathbf{d}}|^2 = \cos^2 \alpha + \sin^2 \alpha = 1.$

Gradient

The vector

$$\mathbf{grad}\, f(a, b) = f_x(a, b)\mathbf{i} + f_y(a, b)\mathbf{j} \tag{16}$$

is called the **gradient** of the function $f(x, y)$ at the point (a, b), and is alternatively denoted by $\nabla f(a, b)$.

Thus $\nabla f(x, y)$ is a (vector) function of two variables, called the **gradient function**.

The symbol ∇ is called 'del', or sometimes 'nabla' (after a type of Phoenician harp said to be shaped like an inverted Delta). Note that ∇f is a vector function, so in written work, the symbol must be underlined (note how ∇ has been typeset in bold).

The result concerning the slope of a surface can now be written as follows.

Slope of a surface

Let $z = f(x, y)$ be a surface described by a function whose first partial derivatives exist and are continuous. Then the slope of the surface at the point $(a, b, f(a, b))$ in the direction of the unit vector $\widehat{\mathbf{d}} = (\cos \alpha)\mathbf{i} + (\sin \alpha)\mathbf{j}$ in the (x, y)-plane is the dot product

$$(\nabla f(a, b)) \cdot \widehat{\mathbf{d}} = f_x(a, b) \cos \alpha + f_y(a, b) \sin \alpha. \tag{17}$$

Exercise 11

Consider the surface defined by $z = f(x, y) = 2x^2 y + 3xy^3$.

(a) Find the gradient function $\nabla f(x, y) = f_x \mathbf{i} + f_y \mathbf{j}$.

(b) Find the slope of the surface at the point $(2, 1, 14)$ in the direction of the unit vector $\widehat{\mathbf{d}} = \frac{3}{5}\mathbf{i} + \frac{4}{5}\mathbf{j}$.

Exercise 12

By varying the angle α (measured anticlockwise from the positive x-axis), we can examine the slope of the surface at the fixed point (a, b, c) in any direction we wish.

This exercise is quite difficult.

Calculate the greatest slope of the surface $z = f(x, y) = \frac{1}{2}x^2 + \sqrt{3}y^2$ at the point $(2, 1, 2 + \sqrt{3})$ on the surface. Show that this greatest slope is in the direction of $\nabla f(2, 1)$.

In general, as the result from Exercise 12 illustrates, the direction of the gradient function $\nabla f(x, y)$ at a point (a, b) corresponds to the direction of greatest slope of the surface $z = f(x, y)$ at the point $(a, b, f(a, b))$. To see this, we observe that

$$\nabla f \cdot \widehat{\mathbf{d}} = |\nabla f|\,|\widehat{\mathbf{d}}| \cos \theta = |\nabla f| \cos \theta, \tag{18}$$

where θ is the angle between ∇f and $\widehat{\mathbf{d}}$. Then $\theta = 0$ gives the maximum value.

We can also see from equation (18) that $\nabla f(x, y)$ at (a, b) points in a direction normal to the contour curve passing through (a, b). To see this, recall that $f(x, y)$ is constant along the contour curve, therefore the slope of the surface $z = f(x, y)$ in directions tangential to a contour curve must be zero (since z does not vary along contour curves). Thus if $\widehat{\mathbf{d}}$ is tangential to a contour curve, then $\nabla f \cdot \widehat{\mathbf{d}} = 0$, implying that ∇f is perpendicular to $\widehat{\mathbf{d}}$. This is illustrated in Figure 22.

Figure 22 The vector ∇f points in directions normal to contours of the function $f(x, y)$

Exercise 13

Consider the surface defined by $z = f(x, y) = (x + 2y)^3 - (2x - y)^2$.

(a) Find the gradient function $\nabla f(x, y) = f_x \mathbf{i} + f_y \mathbf{j}$.

(b) Find the slope of the surface at the point $(1, 0, -3)$ in the direction of the vector $\mathbf{i} + \mathbf{j}$.

(c) Find the greatest slope of the surface at the point $(1, 0, -3)$, and the direction of this maximum slope expressed as a unit vector.

(d) Find the direction of a unit vector that is tangential to the contour curve at the point $(1, 0, -3)$.

2 Taylor polynomials

The aim of this unit is to extend the techniques of calculus to functions of two (or more) variables, in order to be able to tackle a wider range of problems in applied mathematics. However, before continuing, it is necessary to review Taylor polynomials and Taylor approximations as they apply to functions of one variable. These are revised in Subsection 2.1. Subsection 2.2 introduces higher-order partial derivatives of functions of two variables (which are conceptually very like their counterparts for functions of one variable). In Subsection 2.3 we generalise Taylor polynomials and Taylor approximations to functions of two variables.

2.1 Functions of one variable

Many useful functions (e.g. trigonometric and exponential functions) cannot generally be evaluated exactly, so the best that we can do is approximate them. Polynomial functions are often used as approximations because they are easy to evaluate and manipulate. In many cases, a good approximation to a function f can be obtained near some point a in the domain of f by finding the polynomial of a chosen degree that agrees with f at a, and also agrees with the first few derivatives of f evaluated at a.

p_1 has been given the subscript 1 because it is a *first*-order polynomial.

For example, the function $f(x) = \sin x$ can be approximated reasonably well near $x = 0$ by the first-order polynomial $p_1(x) = x$ (see Figure 23(a)). So $\sin x \simeq x$ is a good approximation for small x (say $|x| \leq 0.1$). This is because the functions $y = x$ and $y = \sin x$ at $x = 0$ agree in value (they are both 0), in their first derivatives (they are both 1), and in their second derivatives (they are both 0).

Similarly, the function $g(x) = \cos x$ can be approximated quite well near $x = 0$ by the quadratic (second-order) polynomial $p_2(x) = 1 - \frac{1}{2}x^2$ (see Figure 23(b)). This is because $p_2(x)$ and $\cos x$ agree at $x = 0$ in their values, and also in the values of their first, second and third derivatives.

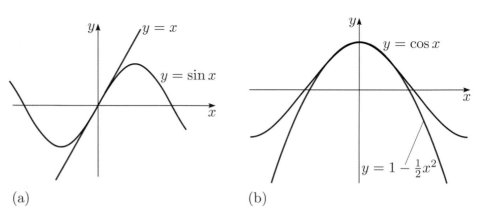

(a)   (b)

Figure 23   (a) First-order polynomial approximation $y = p_1(x) = x$ to $y = f(x) = \sin x$. (b) Second-order polynomial approximation $y = p_2(x) = 1 - \frac{1}{2}x^2$ to $y = g(x) = \cos x$.

Exercise 14

Verify the above statements concerning $p_1(x)$ and $p_2(x)$. That is, check that at $x = 0$, $p_1(x)$ and $f(x) = \sin x$ agree in value and in their first and second derivatives, and that $p_2(x)$ and $g(x) = \cos x$ agree in value and in their first, second and third derivatives.

We call $p_1(x) = x$ the *tangent approximation* to the function $f(x) = \sin x$ near $x = 0$, or the *Taylor polynomial of degree 1* for $f(x) = \sin x$ about $x = 0$. Similarly, $p_2(x) = 1 - \frac{1}{2}x^2$ is the *quadratic approximation* to the function $g(x) = \cos x$ near $x = 0$, or the *Taylor polynomial of degree 2* for $g(x) = \cos x$ about $x = 0$.

In fact, $p_1(x)$ is also the quadratic approximation to $\sin x$, and $p_2(x)$ is also the cubic approximation to $\cos x$.

Taylor polynomials

For a function $f(x)$ that has n continuous derivatives near $x = a$, the **Taylor polynomial of degree n about $x = a$**, or the **nth-order Taylor polynomial about $x = a$**, is

$$p_n(x) = f(a) + f'(a)(x - a) + \frac{1}{2!}f''(a)(x - a)^2 + \frac{1}{3!}f'''(a)(x - a)^3$$

$$+ \cdots + \frac{1}{n!}f^{(n)}(a)(x - a)^n. \tag{19}$$

We use the phrases 'Taylor polynomial of degree n' and 'nth-order Taylor polynomial' synonymously.

Note that at $x = a$, $p_n(x)$ agrees with $f(x)$ in value, and they also agree in the values of their first n derivatives.

If $a = 0$, equation (19) becomes the simpler expression

$$p_n(x) = f(0) + f'(0)x + \frac{1}{2!}f''(0)x^2 + \frac{1}{3!}f'''(0)x^3$$

$$+ \cdots + \frac{1}{n!}f^{(n)}(0)x^n. \tag{20}$$

This is known as a *Maclaurin series*.

Example 7

For the function $f(x) = e^{2x}$, calculate $f(0)$, $f'(0)$, $f''(0)$ and $f'''(0)$. Write down the third-order Taylor polynomial $p_3(x)$ for $f(x)$ about $x = 0$.

Solution

Since $f(x) = e^{2x}$, it follows that

$$f'(x) = 2e^{2x}, \quad f''(x) = 4e^{2x}, \quad f'''(x) = 8e^{2x}.$$

Hence

$$f(0) = 1, \quad f'(0) = 2, \quad f''(0) = 4, \quad f'''(0) = 8.$$

The third-order Taylor polynomial for e^{2x} about $x = 0$ is therefore

$$p_3(x) = 1 + 2x + \frac{4}{2!}x^2 + \frac{8}{3!}x^3 = 1 + 2x + 2x^2 + \tfrac{4}{3}x^3.$$

For the functions that you will meet in the remainder of this module, successive higher-order Taylor polynomials will give successively better approximations, at least for values of x that are reasonably close to a.

Exercise 15

For $f(x) = e^{2x}$ (as in Example 7), write down the Taylor polynomials $p_0(x)$, $p_1(x)$ and $p_2(x)$ about $x = 0$. Evaluate $p_0(0.1)$, $p_1(0.1)$ and $p_2(0.1)$, and compare these values with the value of $f(0.1)$ obtained on a calculator.

One important application of Taylor polynomials is in examining the local behaviour of a function. Suppose that the function $f(t)$ has a stationary point at $t = a$ (so $f'(a) = 0$). It can be shown that close to $t = a$, the behaviour of $f(t)$ will be the same as the behaviour of the second-order Taylor polynomial for $f(t)$ about $t = a$. (This is a consequence of Taylor's theorem.) So we can use the second-order Taylor polynomial about $t = a$ to determine the nature of this stationary point. Close to $t = a$, we have

> The change in independent variable from x to t has no particular significance.

$$f(t) \simeq p_2(t) = f(a) + \frac{1}{2!}f''(a)(t-a)^2.$$

The behaviour of the function $f(t)$ near $t = a$ is determined by the sign of $f''(a)$, assuming that $f''(a) \neq 0$ (see Figure 24). In fact,

$$f(t) - f(a) \simeq \frac{1}{2!}f''(a)(t-a)^2;$$

thus if $f''(a) \neq 0$, the right-hand side of this equation does not change sign near $t = a$. So either $f(t) \geq f(a)$ near $t = a$ (if $f''(a) > 0$), or $f(t) \leq f(a)$ near $t = a$ (if $f''(a) < 0$).

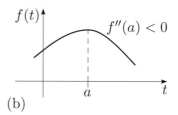

(a)   (b)

Figure 24   Shape of function $f(t)$ near its stationary point at $t = a$: (a) a minimum if $f''(a) > 0$; (b) a maximum if $f''(a) < 0$

So if $f''(a) > 0$, then $f(t)$ has a local minimum at $t = a$, and if $f''(a) < 0$, then $f(t)$ has a local maximum at $t = a$. However, if $f''(a) = 0$, then the polynomial $p_2(t)$ can tell us nothing about the nature of the stationary point of $f(t)$ at $t = a$. This is the result known as the *second derivative test* that you saw in Section 1. To illustrate the usefulness of Taylor polynomials, let us examine the case when $f''(a) = 0$ a little further. (In this case, the second derivative test is of no help.)

Example 8

Suppose that you are told that $f'(a) = f''(a) = 0$, but $f'''(a) \neq 0$, for a function $f(t)$. If $f(t)$ is approximated by its third-order Taylor polynomial $p_3(t)$, what does $p_3(t)$ tell you about the stationary point of $f(t)$ at $t = a$?

When a Taylor polynomial is used to approximate a function, we refer to the polynomial as a *Taylor approximation* to the function.

Solution

We have

$$f(t) \simeq p_3(t) = f(a) + \frac{1}{3!} f'''(a)(t - a)^3,$$

so

$$f(t) - f(a) \simeq \frac{1}{3!} f'''(a)(t - a)^3.$$

This will change sign as t passes through a (whatever the sign of $f'''(a)$). It follows that the stationary point is neither a local maximum nor a local minimum; such a point is a point of inflection.

You should take particular notice of the reasoning in Example 8, because we will apply a similar process in discussing functions of two variables. It is the sign of $f(t) - f(a)$ near $t = a$ that determines the nature of the stationary point at $t = a$.

If we are concerned with the local behaviour of $f(t)$ near $t = a$, then we are interested in the behaviour of $f(t) - f(a)$ when $t - a$ is small (and certainly less than 1). If $t - a$ is small, then $(t - a)^2$ is even smaller, while higher powers of $t - a$ are smaller still. When, for example, we use the second-order Taylor polynomial as an approximation to $f(t)$, we are effectively ignoring terms involving $(t - a)^3$, $(t - a)^4$, ... This is another idea that extends to functions of two variables.

2.2 Higher-order partial derivatives

In the next subsection we will extend the concept of Taylor polynomials to functions of two variables, but first we must develop the concept of partial derivatives a little further.

You saw in Section 1 that we can differentiate a function of two variables $f(x, y)$ partially with respect to x and partially with respect to y, to obtain the partial derivatives $\partial f / \partial x$ and $\partial f / \partial y$. For example, if $f(x, y) = \sin(xy)$, then $\partial f / \partial x = y \cos(xy)$ and $\partial f / \partial y = x \cos(xy)$. The partial derivatives are themselves functions of two variables, so it is possible to calculate *their* partial derivatives. In the case of the function $f(x, y) = \sin(xy)$, we may differentiate $\partial f / \partial x$ partially with respect to x and obtain

$$\frac{\partial}{\partial x}\left(\frac{\partial f}{\partial x}\right) = \frac{\partial}{\partial x}(y \cos(xy)) = -y^2 \sin(xy). \tag{21}$$

Each of $\partial f/\partial x$ and $\partial f/\partial y$ can be partially differentiated with respect to either variable, so for this particular function we have, in addition to equation (21),

$$\frac{\partial}{\partial y}\left(\frac{\partial f}{\partial x}\right) = \frac{\partial}{\partial y}\left(y\cos(xy)\right) = \cos(xy) - xy\sin(xy),$$

$$\frac{\partial}{\partial x}\left(\frac{\partial f}{\partial y}\right) = \frac{\partial}{\partial x}\left(x\cos(xy)\right) = \cos(xy) - xy\sin(xy),$$

$$\frac{\partial}{\partial y}\left(\frac{\partial f}{\partial y}\right) = \frac{\partial}{\partial y}\left(x\cos(xy)\right) = -x^2\sin(xy).$$

Second-order partial derivatives

The **second-order partial derivatives** (or **second partial derivatives**) of a function $f(x, y)$ are

$$\frac{\partial^2 f}{\partial x^2} = \frac{\partial}{\partial x}\left(\frac{\partial f}{\partial x}\right), \quad \frac{\partial^2 f}{\partial y^2} = \frac{\partial}{\partial y}\left(\frac{\partial f}{\partial y}\right),$$

$$\frac{\partial^2 f}{\partial x\,\partial y} = \frac{\partial}{\partial x}\left(\frac{\partial f}{\partial y}\right), \quad \frac{\partial^2 f}{\partial y\,\partial x} = \frac{\partial}{\partial y}\left(\frac{\partial f}{\partial x}\right).$$

They are often abbreviated as f_{xx}, f_{yy}, f_{xy} and f_{yx}, respectively.

Both notations are in common use, and we will use them interchangeably. f_{xy} represents the partial derivative with respect to x of the partial derivative of f with respect to y, that is, differentiate first with respect to y, then differentiate the result with respect to x.

We can extend the ideas here to obtain higher-order partial derivatives of any order. For example, we can obtain third-order partial derivatives by partially differentiating the second-order partial derivatives.

Example 9

Determine the second-order partial derivatives of the function

$$f(x, y) = e^x \cos y + x^2 - y + 1.$$

Solution

We have

$$\frac{\partial f}{\partial x} = e^x \cos y + 2x, \quad \frac{\partial f}{\partial y} = -e^x \sin y - 1,$$

so

$$\frac{\partial^2 f}{\partial x^2} = e^x \cos y + 2, \quad \frac{\partial^2 f}{\partial x\,\partial y} = -e^x \sin y,$$

$$\frac{\partial^2 f}{\partial y\,\partial x} = -e^x \sin y, \quad \frac{\partial^2 f}{\partial y^2} = -e^x \cos y.$$

Exercise 16

Given $f(x, y) = x \sin(xy)$, calculate f_{xx}, f_{yy}, f_{xy} and f_{yx}.

In both Example 9 and Exercise 16 (as well as in the work on $f(x, y) = \sin(xy)$ at the beginning of this subsection), you can see that

$$\frac{\partial^2 f}{\partial x \, \partial y} = \frac{\partial^2 f}{\partial y \, \partial x},$$
(22)

that is, $f_{xy} = f_{yx}$. This is no accident; this result is always true, provided that the function $f(x, y)$ is sufficiently smooth for the second-order partial derivatives to exist and to be continuous.

> **Theorem 1   Mixed derivative theorem**
>
> For any function $f(x, y)$ that is sufficiently smooth for the second-order partial derivatives to exist and to be continuous,
>
> $$\frac{\partial^2 f}{\partial x \, \partial y} = \frac{\partial^2 f}{\partial y \, \partial x}.$$

This can be written as $f_{xy} = f_{yx}$.

We assume throughout the remainder of this unit that the functions that we consider are smooth enough for the mixed derivative theorem to apply.

Exercise 17

Given $f(x, y) = e^{2x+3y}$, calculate $f_x(0,0)$, $f_y(0,0)$, $f_{xx}(0,0)$, $f_{yy}(0,0)$, $f_{xy}(0,0)$ and $f_{yx}(0,0)$.

Exercise 18

Determine the second partial derivatives of $f(x, y) = (x^2 + 2y^2 - 3xy)^3$. Evaluate these partial derivatives at $(1, -1)$.

The ideas in this subsection can be extended to functions of more than two variables, though we do not do so here.

2.3   Functions of two variables

In the case of a function f of one variable, say x, you saw in Subsection 2.1 that the nth-order Taylor polynomial agrees with f in value and in the values of the first n derivatives at the chosen point $x = a$. This property of agreement in function value and values of the derivatives is crucial in the definition of Taylor polynomials, and is the property that we generalise to more than one variable.

Consider, for example, the function
$$f(x, y) = e^{x+2y}.$$

If we wish to find a first-order polynomial $p(x, y)$ that approximates $f(x, y)$ near $(0, 0)$, then it seems that we must ensure that p agrees with f in value and in the values of the first partial derivatives at $(0, 0)$. That is, we need to find a first-order polynomial

A first-order (linear) polynomial in one variable has the form $f(x) = c + mx$, where c and m are constants. A first-order polynomial in two variables has linear terms in both variables, so is of the form $f(x, y) = c + mx + ny$, where c, m and n are constants.

$$p(x, y) = \alpha + \beta x + \gamma y, \tag{23}$$

where α, β and γ are constants, with the properties that
$$p(0, 0) = f(0, 0), \quad p_x(0, 0) = f_x(0, 0), \quad p_y(0, 0) = f_y(0, 0).$$

In our example, $f_x(x, y) = e^{x+2y}$ and $f_y(x, y) = 2e^{x+2y}$, so
$$f(0, 0) = 1, \quad f_x(0, 0) = 1, \quad f_y(0, 0) = 2.$$

Thus, in defining p, we need to choose the coefficients α, β and γ so that
$$p(0, 0) = 1, \quad p_x(0, 0) = 1, \quad p_y(0, 0) = 2.$$

From equation (23), $p(0, 0) = \alpha$, so we need $\alpha = 1$. Also, differentiating equation (23), we obtain
$$p_x(x, y) = \beta, \quad p_y(x, y) = \gamma.$$

In particular,
$$p_x(0, 0) = \beta, \quad p_y(0, 0) = \gamma.$$

So we need $\beta = 1$ and $\gamma = 2$. The required Taylor polynomial is therefore
$$p(x, y) = 1 + x + 2y.$$

More generally, whatever the function $f(x, y)$ may be (provided that we can find its first partial derivatives), we can make $p(x, y) = \alpha + \beta x + \gamma y$ agree with $f(x, y)$ at $(0, 0)$ by setting $\alpha = f(0, 0)$. Also, we can make the first partial derivatives agree at $(0, 0)$ by setting $\beta = f_x(0, 0)$ and $\gamma = f_y(0, 0)$.

First-order Taylor approximation

For a function $f(x, y)$ that is sufficiently smooth near $(x, y) = (0, 0)$, the **first-order Taylor approximation** (or **tangent approximation**) **to** $f(x, y)$ **near** $(0, 0)$ is
$$p_1(x, y) = f(0, 0) + f_x(0, 0)x + f_y(0, 0)y.$$

Exercise 19

Given $f(x, y) = e^{3x-y}$, find the tangent approximation to $f(x, y)$ near $(0, 0)$.

In order to proceed further, we need the notion of higher-order polynomials in two variables.

> ## Nth-order polynomial in two variables
>
> An **Nth-order polynomial** (or **polynomial of degree N**) in two variables, x and y, is a sum of terms $a_{m,n}x^m y^n$ with $m + n \leq N$, where m, n are non-negative integers and $a_{m,n}$ are constants.

As in the case of functions of one variable, we obtain a more accurate approximation than the tangent approximation if we use a second-order polynomial that agrees with the function not only in the above respects, but also in the values of the second partial derivatives at $(0,0)$.

A general second-order polynomial in x and y takes the form

$$q(x,y) = \alpha + \beta x + \gamma y + Ax^2 + Bxy + Cy^2. \tag{24}$$

In order to fit the value of $q(x,y)$ and its first and second partial derivatives at $(0,0)$ to those of a function $f(x,y)$, it is necessary to determine the partial derivatives of q. You are asked to do this in the next exercise.

For the moment, we continue to consider approximations near $(0,0)$, though we will generalise shortly.

In terms of the constants $a_{m,n}$ defined above, we have $a_{0,0} = \alpha$, $a_{1,0} = \beta$, $a_{0,1} = \gamma$, $a_{2,0} = A$, $a_{1,1} = B$ and $a_{0,2} = C$.

Exercise 20

Consider $q(x,y)$ described in equation (24).

(a) Find the functions q_x, q_y, q_{xx}, q_{xy} and q_{yy}.

(b) Evaluate $q(x,y)$ and its first and second partial derivatives at $(0,0)$.

From the results of Exercise 20, it follows that in order to approximate $f(x,y)$ near $(0,0)$ by $q(x,y)$ in equation (24), we must set

$$\alpha = f(0,0), \quad \beta = f_x(0,0), \quad \gamma = f_y(0,0),$$
$$A = \tfrac{1}{2}f_{xx}(0,0), \quad B = f_{xy}(0,0), \quad C = \tfrac{1}{2}f_{yy}(0,0).$$

> ## Second-order Taylor approximation
>
> For a function $f(x,y)$ that is sufficiently smooth near $(x,y) = (0,0)$, the **second-order Taylor approximation** (or **quadratic approximation**) **to $f(x,y)$ near $(0,0)$** is
>
> $$p_2(x,y) = f(0,0) + f_x(0,0)x + f_y(0,0)y$$
> $$+ \tfrac{1}{2}\left(f_{xx}(0,0)x^2 + 2f_{xy}(0,0)xy + f_{yy}(0,0)y^2\right). \tag{25}$$

If we take only the *linear* terms in equation (25), then we obtain the first-order Taylor polynomial. This is the equation of the *tangent plane* at $(0,0)$. The reason why it is called the tangent plane should become clear from the following exercise.

Exercise 21

Verify that

$$z = g(x, y) = f(0,0) + f_x(0,0)x + f_y(0,0)y$$

is the equation of a plane through $(0, 0, f(0,0))$.

Show that the plane has the same gradient as the surface $z = f(x, y)$ at $(0, 0, f(0,0))$; that is, show that $\nabla g(0,0) = \nabla f(0,0)$.

It is also possible to obtain similar approximations for $f(x, y)$ near an arbitrary point (a, b). In this case, x is replaced by $x - a$, y is replaced by $y - b$, and the function f and its partial derivatives are evaluated at (a, b).

Taylor polynomials about arbitrary points

For a function $f(x, y)$ that is sufficiently smooth near $(x, y) = (a, b)$, the **first-order Taylor polynomial for $f(x, y)$ about (a, b)** (or **tangent approximation to $f(x, y)$ near (a, b)**) is

$$p_1(x, y) = f(a, b) + f_x(a, b)(x - a) + f_y(a, b)(y - b).$$

The **tangent plane** to the surface $z = f(x, y)$ at $(a, b, f(a, b))$ is given by $z = p_1(x, y)$.

For a function $f(x, y)$ that is sufficiently smooth near $(x, y) = (a, b)$, the **second-order Taylor polynomial for $f(x, y)$ about (a, b)** (or **quadratic approximation to $f(x, y)$ near (a, b)**) is

$$\begin{aligned}
p_2(x, y) = {} & f(a, b) + f_x(a, b)(x - a) + f_y(a, b)(y - b) \\
& + \tfrac{1}{2}\big(f_{xx}(a, b)(x - a)^2 + 2f_{xy}(a, b)(x - a)(y - b) \\
& + f_{yy}(a, b)(y - b)^2\big).
\end{aligned} \tag{26}$$

Example 10

Determine the Taylor polynomials of degrees 1 and 2 about $(2, 1)$ for the function $f(x, y) = x^3 + xy - 2y^2$.

Solution

Differentiating the function partially with respect to x and partially with respect to y gives

$$f_x = 3x^2 + y, \quad f_y = x - 4y.$$

Differentiating partially again gives

$$f_{xx} = 6x, \quad f_{xy} = 1, \quad f_{yy} = -4.$$

It follows that

$$f(2,1) = 8, \quad f_x(2,1) = 13, \quad f_y(2,1) = -2,$$
$$f_{xx}(2,1) = 12, \quad f_{xy}(2,1) = 1, \quad f_{yy}(2,1) = -4,$$

therefore

$$p_1(x,y) = 8 + 13(x-2) - 2(y-1),$$
$$p_2(x,y) = 8 + 13(x-2) - 2(y-1)$$
$$+ 6(x-2)^2 + (x-2)(y-1) - 2(y-1)^2.$$

Exercise 22

Use the results of Exercise 17 to write down the second-order Taylor polynomial for $f(x,y) = e^{2x+3y}$ about $(0,0)$.

Exercise 23

In Exercise 2 we discussed the potential energy U of the mechanical system shown in Figure 5, and you saw that $U(\theta,\phi) = -mga(\cos\theta + \cos\phi)$. Find the second-order Taylor polynomial for $U(\theta,\phi)$ about $(0,0)$.

Exercise 24

Determine the second-order Taylor polynomial about $(0,0)$ for the function $f(x,y) = e^{xy} + (x+y)^2$.

Exercise 25

(a) Determine the Taylor polynomials of degrees 1 and 2 about $(0,0)$ for the function $f(x,y) = (2+x+2y)^3$. Compare your answers to the expression obtained by expanding $(2+x+2y)^3$.

(b) Determine the Taylor polynomials of degrees 1 and 2 about $(1,-1)$ for the function $f(x,y) = (2+x+2y)^3$.

(c) Putting $X = x-1$ and $Y = y+1$ (so that $X = 0$ when $x = 1$, and $Y = 0$ when $y = -1$), we have

$$f(x,y) = (2+x+2y)^3 = \left(2 + (X+1) + 2(Y-1)\right)^3$$
$$= (1 + X + 2Y)^3.$$

Write down the Taylor polynomials of degrees 1 and 2 about $(0,0)$ for the function $F(X,Y) = (1 + X + 2Y)^3$.

We could extend the arguments of this subsection to define Taylor polynomials of order higher than two, or even for functions of more than two variables, but we do not do so here.

3 Classification of stationary points

The main purpose of this section is to extend to functions of two variables the second derivative test that was discussed in Section 1. If $f(x, y)$ is sufficiently smooth so that the first and second partial derivatives are defined, and $f_x(a, b) = f_y(a, b) = 0$ at some point (a, b), then there is a distinct possibility that $f(x, y)$ has a local maximum or a local minimum at (a, b).

In the case of a function of one variable, the sign of the second derivative at a stationary point is enough to distinguish whether that point is a local maximum or a local minimum (provided that the second derivative is not zero at that point). The situation is more complicated for functions of two variables (for a start, there are three second partial derivatives to consider), but similarly, a knowledge of the values of these derivatives at a stationary point will often tell us whether it is a local maximum, a local minimum, or neither.

3.1 Extrema

In searching for the local maxima and local minima of a function of one variable, the first step is to locate the stationary points, that is, the points where the derivative is zero. The same is true in the case of functions of two or more variables.

The definition of a stationary point can be extended to functions of three or more variables.

> **Stationary points**
>
> A **stationary point** of a function $f(x, y)$ is a point (a, b) in the domain of $f(x, y)$ at which $f_x(a, b) = f_y(a, b) = 0$.
>
> The corresponding point $(a, b, f(a, b))$ on the surface S defined by $z = f(x, y)$ is a **stationary point** on S.

Example 11

Locate the stationary points of the function $f(x, y) = 5 + (x - 1)^3 + y^2$.

Solution

Partially differentiating gives $f_x = 3(x - 1)^2$, which is zero when $x = 1$, and $f_y = 2y$, which is zero when $y = 0$. So $(1, 0)$ is the only stationary point (corresponding to the point $(1, 0, 5)$ on the surface).

Generally, to find the stationary points, we need to solve a pair of simultaneous equations, as the following example shows.

Example 12

Locate the stationary points of the function

$$f(x, y) = x^2 + y^2 + (x - 1)(y + 2).$$

Solution

Partially differentiating gives $f_x = 2x + y + 2$ and $f_y = 2y + x - 1$. To find the stationary points, we need to solve the pair of simultaneous equations

$$2x + y = -2,$$
$$x + 2y = 1.$$

We find that $x = -\frac{5}{3}$ and $y = \frac{4}{3}$. It follows that $\left(-\frac{5}{3}, \frac{4}{3}\right)$ is the only stationary point.

Exercise 26

Locate the stationary points of the function

$$f(x, y) = 3x^2 - 4xy + 2y^2 + 4x - 8y.$$

A word of warning! The simultaneous equations that must be solved in order to find stationary points are in general non-linear. For example, if

$$f(x, y) = e^{x+2y} + x^4 y + xy^3,$$

then $f_x = e^{x+2y} + 4x^3 y + y^3$ and $f_y = 2e^{x+2y} + x^4 + 3xy^2$, so we need to solve the pair of simultaneous equations

$$e^{x+2y} + 4x^3 y + y^3 = 0,$$
$$2e^{x+2y} + x^4 + 3xy^2 = 0.$$

We will not ask you to tackle problems as difficult as this by hand, but the next exercise involves a pair of non-linear equations that can be solved by factorisation.

Exercise 27

Locate the stationary points of the function $f(x, y) = xy(x + y - 3)$.

If a function f of n variables is smooth enough to have first partial derivatives everywhere on $\mathbb{R}^n$, then any local maxima or local minima that exist will occur at stationary points. For a function of one variable, we could apply the second derivative test to the stationary points. We now generalise this to a method of classifying the stationary points of functions of several variables, using second partial derivatives.

The purpose of this subsection is to describe a method of doing this. But before going any further, we need definitions of 'local maximum' and 'local minimum' for functions of more than one variable. We will state such definitions for functions of two variables; it is not difficult to see how to generalise these to several variables.

Extrema

A function $f(x, y)$, defined on a domain D, has a **local minimum** at (a, b) in D if for all (x, y) in D sufficiently close to (a, b), we have $f(x, y) \geq f(a, b)$.

A function $f(x, y)$, defined on a domain D, has a **local maximum** at (a, b) in D if for all (x, y) in D sufficiently close to (a, b), we have $f(x, y) \leq f(a, b)$.

A point that is either a local maximum or a local minimum is an **extremum** (and vice versa).

If the function $f(x, y)$ has an extremum at (a, b), then the section function $z = f(x, b)$ (a function of x only) must also have an extremum at $x = a$, so assuming that $f(x, b)$ is sufficiently smooth, $(\partial f / \partial x)(a, b) = 0$. Similarly, $(\partial f / \partial y)(a, b) = 0$. It follows that every extremum of $f(x, y)$, assuming that the function is sufficiently smooth, is a stationary point of $f(x, y)$. However, not every stationary point is necessarily an extremum.

Saddle points

A stationary point of a function of two variables that is not an extremum is a **saddle point**.

The term saddle point originates from the shape of surfaces near some such points for functions of two variables. An example is provided by the shape of the hyperboloid shown in Figure 8(b) near a stationary point (in this case, the origin) – it looks like a rider's saddle. (A saddle drops *down* on either side of the rider, but rises *up* in front and behind.) For completeness, it is worth noting that there are more complicated possibilities for the shapes of surfaces near stationary points that are not extrema; all such points are referred to as saddle points, however.

Exercise 28

In Exercise 2 you found that the potential energy U of the mechanical system shown in Figure 5 can be written as $U(\theta, \phi) = -mga(\cos \theta + \cos \phi)$. Show that $U(\theta, \phi)$ has a stationary point at $(0, 0)$, and that this point is a local minimum.

If we are looking for the extrema of a given function, then we know that we should look among the stationary points. However, not all cases are as straightforward as Exercise 28, and we need some general means of classifying them (much as we have for functions of one variable). You will see next that we can use the second-order Taylor polynomial to construct a useful test that will often distinguish between local maxima, local minima and saddle points.

Let $f(x, y)$ have a stationary point at (a, b). To ensure that $f(x, y)$ has a local minimum at (a, b), it is not enough to stipulate that each of the section functions $f(x, b)$ and $f(a, y)$ through (a, b) has a local minimum at that point. There may still be directions through (a, b) along which the value of $f(x, y)$ decreases as we move away from (a, b).

For example, consider the function $f(x, y) = x^2 + 6xy + 7y^2$, which possesses a stationary point at $(0, 0)$. The section functions through $(0, 0)$ are $f(x, 0) = x^2$ and $f(0, y) = 7y^2$, each of which has a local minimum at $(0, 0)$. But let us move along the parametrised curve (actually a straight line) given by $x(t) = 2t$, $y(t) = -t$. Then

$$f(x(t), y(t)) = (2t)^2 + 6(2t)(-t) + 7(-t)^2 = -t^2.$$

$f_x = 2x + 6y$, so $f_x(0,0) = 0$.
$f_y = 6x + 14y$, so $f_y(0,0) = 0$.

As we move along this line from $(0, 0)$, the value of $f(x(t), y(t))$ becomes negative. As $f(0, 0) = 0$, it follows that $(0, 0)$ cannot be a local minimum of f.

One way to understand the reason for this behaviour is to express the function as a difference of two squares:

$$f(x, y) = x^2 + 6xy + 7y^2 = 2(x + 2y)^2 - (x + y)^2.$$

Strictly, as a difference of two squares this is
$$(\sqrt{2}x + 2\sqrt{2}y)^2 - (x + y)^2.$$

Then no matter how close to the origin we look, we see some points where the function is positive and some where it is negative. In particular, in the direction along which $x + 2y = 0$, the expression on the right-hand side reduces to $-(x + y)^2$, which is negative except when $(x, y) = (0, 0)$. However, in the direction $x + y = 0$, the expression is $2(x + 2y)^2$, which is positive except when $(x, y) = (0, 0)$. Therefore $(0, 0)$ is a saddle point of $f(x, y)$.

In general, $f(x, y)$ may not be a function that can be manipulated as easily as the polynomial above. Nevertheless, the quadratic approximation to $f(x, y)$ about (a, b) *is* a polynomial, and you will see in the next subsection that its second-order terms can usually be manipulated in such a way as to enable us to classify the stationary point at (a, b). The test that we will derive, based on expressing the quadratic approximation in terms of a matrix, is similar to the second derivative test for functions of one variable.

Before going on to derive this test, it is worth recalling the logic behind the second derivative test. The quadratic approximation to a function $f(x)$ of one variable about $x = a$ is given by

$$f(x) \simeq f(a) + f'(a)(x - a) + \tfrac{1}{2}f''(a)(x - a)^2.$$

If a is a stationary point, then $f'(a) = 0$ so $f(x) - f(a) \simeq \tfrac{1}{2}f''(a)(x - a)^2$.

Therefore (provided that $f''(a) \neq 0$) the quadratic approximation will have a minimum or a maximum, depending on the sign of $f''(a)$. Close enough to a, the approximation will behave like the function itself, thus allowing us to conclude that the function has a local minimum or maximum. Thus the second derivative test uses the second-order terms in the quadratic approximation to classify the stationary point.

3.2 Classifying stationary points using eigenvalues: functions of two variables

Consider a stationary point of $f(x,y)$ at (a,b) so that we have $f_x(a,b) = f_y(a,b) = 0$. It will prove convenient to introduce the variables p and q defined as displacements from the stationary point as $p = x - a$ and $q = y - b$. It will also be useful to write

$$A = f_{xx}(a,b), \quad B = f_{xy}(a,b)\,\big(= f_{yx}(a,b)\big), \quad C = f_{yy}(a,b). \tag{27}$$

As for functions of one variable, *close* to a point (a,b), the second-order Taylor polynomial for $f(x,y)$ about (a,b) behaves in the same way as $f(x,y)$ itself. This is a consequence of a theorem (similar to Taylor's theorem) that we do not include in this module.

The quadratic approximation to $f(x,y)$ is the second-order Taylor polynomial. Since we are assuming that the first derivatives are zero at (a,b), equation (26) gives

$$f(x,y) \simeq f(a,b) + \tfrac{1}{2}Q(x-a, y-b),$$

where

$$Q(p,q) = Ap^2 + 2Bpq + Cq^2.$$

Thus we will be able to classify the stationary point if we can determine the sign of $Q(p,q)$.

The first step in doing this is to define the real symmetric matrix

The polynomial $Q(p,q)$ is an example of a *quadratic form*, and it is always possible to express a quadratic form in terms of a symmetric matrix as in equation (29).

$$\mathbf{H} = \begin{pmatrix} A & B \\ B & C \end{pmatrix}, \tag{28}$$

which enables us to write

$$Q(p,q) = \begin{pmatrix} p & q \end{pmatrix} \mathbf{H} \begin{pmatrix} p \\ q \end{pmatrix}. \tag{29}$$

Exercise 29

Verify equation (29).

Let λ_1 and λ_2 be the eigenvalues of $\mathbf{H}$, with corresponding eigenvectors $\mathbf{v}_1$ and $\mathbf{v}_2$. Note that $\mathbf{H}$ is real and symmetric. We learned in Unit 5 that the eigenvalues of a real symmetric matrix are *real*, and that its eigenvectors are *real* and can be made *orthogonal*, that is, $\mathbf{v}_1^T \mathbf{v}_2 = 0$. (More specifically, for real symmetric matrices, if the eigenvalues are distinct, then the corresponding eigenvectors are orthogonal; otherwise, any two linearly independent vectors are eigenvectors and we are free to select any two that are mutually orthogonal.)

Furthermore, recall that an eigenvector is specified up to a constant scalar multiple. Thus, for later convenience, we are free to select the scalar multiple so that the eigenvectors have magnitude 1, that is, they are chosen to be *unit* vectors, so that $|\mathbf{v}_1|^2 = \mathbf{v}_1^T\mathbf{v}_1 = 1$ and similarly for $\mathbf{v}_2$. Eigenvectors with this property are said to be *normalised*. So, to summarise, we choose $\mathbf{v}_1$ and $\mathbf{v}_2$ to have the following properties:

$$\mathbf{v}_1^T\mathbf{v}_1 = \mathbf{v}_2^T\mathbf{v}_2 = 1, \quad \mathbf{v}_1^T\mathbf{v}_2 = \mathbf{v}_2^T\mathbf{v}_1 = 0. \tag{30}$$

Now, the vector $(p \quad q)^T$ can be expressed as a linear combination of $\mathbf{v}_1$ and $\mathbf{v}_2$:

$$\begin{pmatrix} p \\ q \end{pmatrix} = c_1\mathbf{v}_1 + c_2\mathbf{v}_2,$$

where c_1 and c_2 are real and depend on x and y, which are kept close to the stationary-point values. In fact, the values of c_1 and c_2 indicate the direction of (x, y) relative to the stationary point (a, b). Hence

For example, if $c_1 \neq 0$ and $c_2 = 0$, then $(p \quad q)^T$ points in the direction of $\mathbf{v}_1$, whereas it points in the direction of $\mathbf{v}_2$ if $c_1 = 0$ and $c_2 \neq 0$.

$$\mathbf{H}\begin{pmatrix} p \\ q \end{pmatrix} = c_1\mathbf{H}\mathbf{v}_1 + c_2\mathbf{H}\mathbf{v}_2$$

$$= c_1\lambda_1\mathbf{v}_1 + c_2\lambda_2\mathbf{v}_2,$$

and therefore

$$Q(p, q) = \begin{pmatrix} p & q \end{pmatrix}\mathbf{H}\begin{pmatrix} p \\ q \end{pmatrix}$$

$$= (c_1\mathbf{v}_1^T + c_2\mathbf{v}_2^T)(c_1\lambda_1\mathbf{v}_1 + c_2\lambda_2\mathbf{v}_2)$$

$$= \lambda_1 c_1^2 \mathbf{v}_1^T\mathbf{v}_1 + \lambda_2 c_1 c_2 \mathbf{v}_1^T\mathbf{v}_2 + \lambda_1 c_2 c_1 \mathbf{v}_2^T\mathbf{v}_1 + \lambda_2 c_2^2 \mathbf{v}_2^T\mathbf{v}_2.$$

Finally, applying the normalisation and orthogonality properties of the eigenvectors, as given in equations (30), leads to the expression

$$Q(p, q) = \lambda_1 c_1^2 + \lambda_2 c_2^2. \tag{31}$$

Since c_1 and c_2 are real, the sign of $Q(p, q)$ is wholly dependent on the signs of λ_1 and λ_2, the eigenvalues of $\mathbf{H}$. If both eigenvalues are positive, then $Q(p, q)$ is always positive, so the stationary point must be a local minimum. If both eigenvalues are negative, then $Q(p, q)$ is always negative, so the stationary point is a local maximum. However, if one eigenvalue is positive and the other is negative, then the sign of $Q(p, q)$ will depend on the direction of travel, which indicates that the stationary point is a saddle point. Finally, if one or both of the eigenvalues is zero, then the nature of the stationary point cannot be determined using this method – we need to consider higher-order terms in the Taylor expansion. For, clearly, if $\lambda_1 = \lambda_2 = 0$, then $Q(p, q) = 0$ along all directions, so the test is inconclusive. And if just one of the eigenvalues is zero, then $Q(p, q) = 0$ along the direction corresponding to the eigenvector with zero eigenvalue, so the test is still inconclusive.

Thus this so-called *eigenvalue test* can be summarised as follows.

> **Eigenvalue test for classifying a stationary point**
>
> Given that the (sufficiently smooth) function $f(x, y)$ has a stationary point at (a, b), let
>
> $$A = f_{xx}(a, b), \quad B = f_{xy}(a, b) \left(= f_{yx}(a, b)\right), \quad C = f_{yy}(a, b)$$
>
> and
>
> $$\mathbf{H} = \begin{pmatrix} A & B \\ B & C \end{pmatrix},$$
>
> and let λ_1 and λ_2 (which must be real) be the eigenvalues of $\mathbf{H}$.
>
> - If λ_1 and λ_2 are both positive, then there is a local minimum at (a, b).
> - If λ_1 and λ_2 are both negative, then there is a local maximum at (a, b).
> - If λ_1 and λ_2 are non-zero and opposite in sign, then there is a saddle point at (a, b).
> - If either, or both, of λ_1 or λ_2 is zero, then the test is inconclusive.

Example 13

Locate and classify the stationary point of the function

$$f(x, y) = 2x^2 - xy - 3y^2 - 3x + 7y.$$

Solution

Start by determining the first partial derivatives:

$$f_x = 4x - y - 3, \quad f_y = -x - 6y + 7.$$

The stationary point is determined by $f_x = f_y = 0$. From $f_x = 0$, $y = 4x - 3$, and substituting this into $f_y = 0$ gives $7 = x + 6y = 25x - 18$, so there is a stationary point at $(1, 1)$. The second partial derivatives are

$$f_{xx} = 4, \quad f_{xy} = f_{yx} = -1, \quad f_{yy} = -6.$$

It follows that $\mathbf{H} = \begin{pmatrix} 4 & -1 \\ -1 & -6 \end{pmatrix}$, and the characteristic equation is

$\lambda^2 + 2\lambda - 25 = 0$. The eigenvalues are therefore $\sqrt{26} - 1$ and $-\sqrt{26} - 1$. The eigenvalues are non-zero and of opposite sign, so the stationary point is a saddle point.

3.3 $AC - B^2$ criterion

The eigenvalue test can be extended to functions of more than two variables, as will be explained in the next subsection. In this subsection we continue to confine ourselves to functions of just two variables and show that it is possible to gain knowledge of the signs of the eigenvalues of $\mathbf{H}$ without explicitly evaluating them, in such a way that the nature of the stationary point can be deduced. It will turn out that this can be done solely from the sign of $AC - B^2$ and the sign of A if the former is positive, where A, B and C are given by equations (27). This leads to the somewhat simpler $AC - B^2$ test for classifying a fixed point.

To arrive at this test, recall from Unit 5 the following results for the sum and product of the eigenvalues λ_1 and λ_2 of the matrix $\mathbf{H} = \begin{pmatrix} A & B \\ B & C \end{pmatrix}$ in equation (28):

We showed in Unit 5 that the sum and product of the eigenvalues of any matrix $\mathbf{M}$ are $\operatorname{tr} \mathbf{M}$ and $\det \mathbf{M}$, respectively.

$$\lambda_1 + \lambda_2 = \operatorname{tr} \mathbf{H} = A + C, \tag{32}$$
$$\lambda_1 \lambda_2 = \det \mathbf{H} = AC - B^2. \tag{33}$$

We now consider three cases for $AC - B^2$.

- $AC - B^2 > 0$: It follows from equation (33) that $\lambda_1 \lambda_2 > 0$, so λ_1 and λ_2 have the same sign. Moreover, $AC > B^2 \geq 0$, so A and C have the same sign. Thus from equation (32), the sign of λ_1 and λ_2 is given by the sign of A. Hence if $A > 0$, λ_1 and λ_2 are both positive, so the stationary point is a minimum. Conversely, if $A < 0$, λ_1 and λ_2 are both negative, so the stationary point is a maximum.

- $AC - B^2 < 0$: It follows from equation (33) that $\lambda_1 \lambda_2 < 0$, so λ_1 and λ_2 are non-zero but have opposite signs. Hence the stationary point is a saddle point.

- $AC - B^2 = 0$: It follows from equation (33) that $\lambda_1 \lambda_2 = 0$, so either one or both of the eigenvalues is zero. Therefore the nature of the stationary point cannot be determined using this method.

Hence the resulting test can be summarised as follows.

$AC - B^2$ test for classifying a stationary point

Given that the (sufficiently smooth) function $f(x, y)$ has a stationary point at (a, b), let

$$A = f_{xx}(a, b), \quad B = f_{xy}(a, b) \left(= f_{yx}(a, b)\right), \quad C = f_{yy}(a, b).$$

- If $AC - B^2 > 0$, there is:

  - a local minimum at (a, b) if $A > 0$

  - a local maximum at (a, b) if $A < 0$.

- If $AC - B^2 < 0$, there is a saddle point at (a, b).

- If $AC - B^2 = 0$, the test is unable to classify the stationary point.

Note that this test is significantly simpler than the previous eigenvalue test for classifying a stationary point, in that it just requires the calculation of A, B and C, and the evaluation of $AC - B^2$, without having to explicitly solve the characteristic equation to determine the eigenvalues.

Example 14

Locate and classify the stationary point of the function
$$f(x, y) = e^{-(x^2+y^2)}.$$

Solution

Partially differentiating gives $f_x = -2xe^{-(x^2+y^2)}$ and $f_y = -2ye^{-(x^2+y^2)}$. Since $f_x = 0$ only when $x = 0$, and $f_y = 0$ only when $y = 0$, the stationary point is at $(0, 0)$.

Since $f_{xx} = -2e^{-(x^2+y^2)} + 4x^2 e^{-(x^2+y^2)}$, we have $A = f_{xx}(0, 0) = -2$. Also, $f_{yy} = -2e^{-(x^2+y^2)} + 4y^2 e^{-(x^2+y^2)}$, therefore $C = f_{yy}(0, 0) = -2$. Finally, $f_{xy} = 4xye^{-(x^2+y^2)}$, therefore $B = f_{xy}(0, 0) = 0$.

So we see that $AC - B^2 = 4 > 0$, and since $A = -2 < 0$, the stationary point is a local maximum.

Use the $AC - B^2$ test to do the following four exercises.

Exercise 30

Locate and classify the stationary point of the function
$$f(x, y) = 2x^2 - xy - 3y^2 - 3x + 7y.$$

Exercise 31

Locate and classify the four stationary points of the function
$$f(x, y) = x^3 - 12x - y^3 + 3y.$$

Exercise 32

Locate and classify the stationary points of the following functions.

(a) $f(x, y) = \sqrt{1 - x^2 + y^2}$

(b) $T(x, y) = \cos x + \cos y$

Exercise 33

Locate and classify the four stationary points of the function
$$f(x, y) = 3x^2 y^3 - 9x^2 y + x^3 - 15x - 50.$$

(The function has two extrema and two saddle points.)

3.4 Classifying stationary points using eigenvalues: functions of n variables

The eigenvalue test can be extended to functions of three or more variables. If f is a sufficiently smooth function of n variables, then a stationary point of f is a point $(a_1, a_2, \ldots, a_n)$ at which all the n first partial derivatives are zero. There will be n^2 second partial derivatives, and their values at $(a_1, a_2, \ldots, a_n)$ can be written in the form of an $n \times n$ matrix $\mathbf{H}$, the entry in the ith row and jth column being the value $\dfrac{\partial^2 f}{\partial x_i \, \partial x_j}(a_1, \ldots, a_n)$. This is called the **Hessian matrix** of f at the point $(a_1, \ldots, a_n)$.

Note that $\mathbf{H}$ in equation (28) is a two-dimensional version of the Hessian matrix.

It turns out that, as with the two-variable case, in the vicinity of the stationary point, f is well approximated by the quadratic approximation

$$f(x_1, \ldots, x_n) \simeq f(a_1, \ldots, a_n) + \tfrac{1}{2}\mathbf{p}^T \mathbf{H}\mathbf{p},$$

where

$$\mathbf{p}^T = (x_1 - a_1, \ldots, x_n - a_n).$$

Recall that $\frac{\partial f}{\partial x_i}(a_1, \ldots, a_n) = 0$, $i = 1, \ldots, n$, for a stationary point.

Our assumption that f is sufficiently smooth implies that $\mathbf{H}$ will be a *symmetric matrix*, since the mixed derivative theorem extends from the two-variable case to the several-variable case, so that $\mathbf{p}^T \mathbf{H}\mathbf{p}$ is a quadratic form whose sign determines the nature of the stationary point. Moreover, since $\mathbf{H}$ is a real symmetric matrix, its eigenvalues $\lambda_1, \ldots, \lambda_n$ are real, and its eigenvectors are real and can be made orthogonal. Hence, as with the two-variable case, we have

$$\mathbf{p}^T \mathbf{H}\mathbf{p} = \lambda_1 c_1^2 + \cdots + \lambda_n c_n^2, \tag{34}$$

where $c_1, \ldots, c_n$ are real. Equation (34) is just the n-variable generalisation of equation (31), and its derivation follows similarly, where now $\mathbf{H}$ has n orthogonal normalised eigenvectors $\mathbf{v}_1, \ldots, \mathbf{v}_n$, and we write $\mathbf{p} = c_1 \mathbf{v}_1 + \cdots + c_n \mathbf{v}_n$. Equation (34) now leads to the following classification.

We have
$$\mathbf{v}_i^T \mathbf{v}_j = \begin{cases} 1 & \text{for } i = j, \\ 0 & \text{for } i \neq j. \end{cases}$$

- If all the eigenvalues are positive, then there is a local minimum at $(a_1, \ldots, a_n)$.

- If all the eigenvalues are negative, then there is a local maximum at $(a_1, \ldots, a_n)$.

- If all the eigenvalues are non-zero but they are not all of the same sign, then there is a saddle point at $(a_1, \ldots, a_n)$.

- If one or more of the eigenvalues is zero, then the test is inconclusive.

In the case of more than two variables, the analogy of a saddle is not very helpful in visualising a saddle point. However, it remains true that there are sections through a saddle point giving a section function with a local minimum, and others giving a section function with a local maximum.

Example 15

Locate and classify the stationary point of the function

$$w(x, y, z) = 3y^2 + 3z^2 - 4xy - 2yz - 4zx.$$

Solution

We find the stationary point by solving the simultaneous equations

$$\begin{aligned} w_x &= -4y - 4z = 0, \\ w_y &= 6y - 4x - 2z = 0, \\ w_z &= 6z - 2y - 4x = 0. \end{aligned}$$

The only solution is $x = y = z = 0$.

The second partial derivatives of $w(x, y, z)$ are constants:

$$w_{xx} = 0, \quad w_{yy} = 6, \quad w_{zz} = 6,$$

$$w_{xy} = w_{yx} = -4, \quad w_{yz} = w_{zy} = -2, \quad w_{zx} = w_{xz} = -4.$$

Thus the required 3×3 Hessian matrix is

$$\mathbf{H} = \begin{pmatrix} w_{xx} & w_{xy} & w_{xz} \\ w_{yx} & w_{yy} & w_{yz} \\ w_{zx} & w_{zy} & w_{zz} \end{pmatrix} = \begin{pmatrix} 0 & -4 & -4 \\ -4 & 6 & -2 \\ -4 & -2 & 6 \end{pmatrix}.$$

To find the eigenvalues of $\mathbf{H}$, we find the values of λ that satisfy the characteristic equation $\det(\mathbf{H} - \lambda\mathbf{I}) = 0$. The solutions of the equation $\det(\mathbf{H} - \lambda\mathbf{I}) = -(\lambda - 8)^2(\lambda + 4) = 0$ are $\lambda_1 = -4$, $\lambda_2 = 8$ and $\lambda_3 = 8$. Our test then tells us immediately that there is a saddle point at the origin.

Exercise 34

Locate and classify the stationary point of the function

$$w(x, y, z) = 3x^2 + 3y^2 + 4z^2 - 2xy - 2yz - 2xz,$$

given that the characteristic equation of the matrix

$$\begin{pmatrix} 6 & -2 & -2 \\ -2 & 6 & -2 \\ -2 & -2 & 8 \end{pmatrix}$$

is $(8 - \lambda)\left((6 - \lambda)^2 - 12\right) = 0$.

Exercise 35

Classify the stationary point at the origin of the function

$$w(x, y, z) = x^2 + 2y^2 + z^2 + 2\sqrt{3}xz.$$

Learning outcomes

After studying this unit, you should be able to:

- calculate first and second partial derivatives of a function of several variables
- understand the use of a surface to represent a function of two variables
- construct the equation of the tangent plane at a given point on a surface
- calculate the Taylor polynomials of degree n for a function of one variable
- calculate the first-order and second-order Taylor polynomials for a function of two variables
- locate the stationary points of a function of two (or more) variables by solving a system of two (or more) simultaneous equations
- classify the stationary points of a function of two variables by using the $AC - B^2$ test
- classify the stationary points of a function of two (or more) variables by examining the signs of the eigenvalues of an appropriate matrix.

Solutions to exercises

Solution to Exercise 1

(a) $f(2,3) = 12 - 54 = -42$.

(b) $f(3,2) = 27 - 16 = 11$.

(c) $f(a,b) = 3a^2 - 2b^3$.

(d) $f(b,a) = 3b^2 - 2a^3$.

(e) $f(2a,b) = 3(2a)^2 - 2b^3 = 12a^2 - 2b^3$.

(f) $f(a-b,0) = 3(a-b)^2$.

(g) $f(x,2) = 3x^2 - 16$.

(h) $f(y,x) = 3y^2 - 2x^3$.

Solution to Exercise 2

The potential energy U of a particle of mass m placed at height h (relative to O) is given by $U(h) = mgh$. We can see that A is $a\cos\theta$ below O, and B is $a\cos\phi$ below A; so B is $a(\cos\theta + \cos\phi)$ below O. Thus in this case we have

$$U(\theta,\phi) = -mga(\cos\theta + \cos\phi).$$

The least possible value of U occurs when $\cos\theta$ and $\cos\phi$ take their greatest values, and this happens when $\theta = \phi = 0$. So the least value of U is $U(0,0) = -2mga$, and it occurs when the system is hanging vertically.

Solution to Exercise 3

The section function of $F(x,y) = 100e^{-(x^2+y^2)}$ with y fixed at 0 is $F(x,0) = 100e^{-x^2}$. So

$$\frac{d}{dx}(F(x,0)) = -200xe^{-x^2}.$$

This derivative is zero when $x = 0$, so $F(x,0)$ has a stationary point at $x = 0$.

Differentiating again with respect to x, we obtain

$$\frac{d^2}{dx^2}(F(x,0)) = -200\frac{d}{dx}(xe^{-x^2}) = -200(1 - 2x^2)e^{-x^2}.$$

This derivative equals -200 when $x = 0$. It follows that the section function has a local maximum at $x = 0$.

Solution to Exercise 4

The contours are given by $f(x,y) = x^2 + y = c$ or $y = c - x^2$ for various constant values of c. These are shown in the following figure, with red contours for $c > 0$, blue for $c < 0$, and green for $c = 0$.

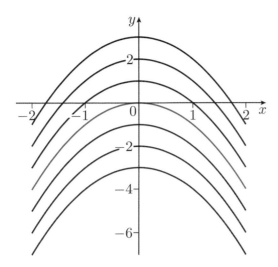

Some additional insight can be gained from viewing the contours superimposed on the surface $z = f(x, y) = x^2 + y$ in a three-dimensional plot (although this was not requested), as in the following figure.

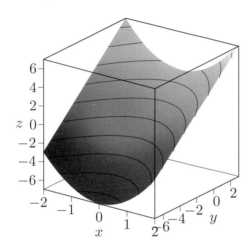

Solution to Exercise 5

$$\frac{\partial f}{\partial x} = 3x^2 \cos y + y^2 \cos x,$$

$$\frac{\partial f}{\partial y} = -x^3 \sin y + 2y \sin x.$$

Solution to Exercise 6

$$\frac{\partial f}{\partial x} = 2x \sin(xy) + (x^2 + y^3)y \cos(xy),$$

$$\frac{\partial f}{\partial y} = 3y^2 \sin(xy) + (x^2 + y^3)x \cos(xy).$$

Solution to Exercise 7

$u_\theta = \cos\theta + \phi \sec^2\theta$ and $u_\phi = \tan\theta$. Hence, on recalling that $\cos\frac{\pi}{4} = \frac{1}{\sqrt{2}}$, $\sec\frac{\pi}{4} = \sqrt{2}$ and $\tan\frac{\pi}{4} = 1$, we have

$$u_\theta\left(\tfrac{\pi}{4}, \tfrac{\pi}{2}\right) = \tfrac{1}{\sqrt{2}} + \tfrac{\pi}{2} \times 2 = \tfrac{1}{\sqrt{2}} + \pi$$

and

$$u_\phi\left(\tfrac{\pi}{4}, \tfrac{\pi}{2}\right) = 1.$$

Solution to Exercise 8

(a) Treating y and t as constants, and differentiating with respect to x,

$$f_x = 2xy^3t^4 + 2y + 8t^2x.$$

Treating x and t as constants, and differentiating with respect to y,

$$f_y = 3x^2y^2t^4 + 2x + 1.$$

Treating x and y as constants, and differentiating with respect to t,

$$f_t = 4x^2y^3t^3 + 8tx^2.$$

(b) We have $\dfrac{\partial z}{\partial x} = 2(1+x)$ and $\dfrac{\partial z}{\partial y} = 3(1+y)^2$.

Sketches of the section functions $z(x,0) = (1+x)^2 + 1$ and $z(0,y) = 1 + (1+y)^3$ are shown below.

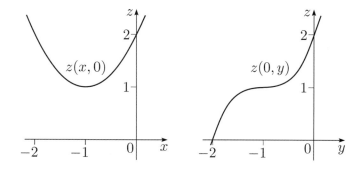

We obtain $(\partial z/\partial x)(0,0) = 2$, which represents the slope of the left-hand graph where $x = 0$. Also, we obtain $(\partial z/\partial y)(0,0) = 3$, which represents the slope of the right-hand graph where $y = 0$.

Solution to Exercise 9

From Exercise 8(b),

$$\frac{\partial z}{\partial x} = 2(1+x), \quad \frac{\partial z}{\partial y} = 3(1+y)^2.$$

So we have

$$\frac{\partial z}{\partial x}(0,2) = 2, \quad \frac{\partial z}{\partial y}(0,2) = 27.$$

Hence

$$\delta z \simeq 2\,\delta x + 27\,\delta y.$$

Solution to Exercise 10

We have

$$\frac{\partial z}{\partial x} = y\cos x, \quad \frac{\partial z}{\partial y} = \sin x, \quad \frac{dx}{dt} = e^t, \quad \frac{dy}{dt} = 2t,$$

so

$$\frac{dz}{dt} = \frac{\partial z}{\partial x}\frac{dx}{dt} + \frac{\partial z}{\partial y}\frac{dy}{dt} = (y\cos x)e^t + (\sin x)2t$$
$$= t^2\cos(e^t)e^t + \sin(e^t)2t$$
$$= t\left(te^t\cos(e^t) + 2\sin(e^t)\right).$$

Thus

$$\frac{dz}{dt}(0) = 0.$$

Solution to Exercise 11

(a) We have

$$\nabla f(x,y) = (4xy + 3y^3)\mathbf{i} + (2x^2 + 9xy^2)\mathbf{j}.$$

(b) $\nabla f(2,1) = 11\mathbf{i} + 26\mathbf{j}$, so the slope at $(2,1,14)$ in the direction $\frac{3}{5}\mathbf{i} + \frac{4}{5}\mathbf{j}$ is

$$(11\mathbf{i} + 26\mathbf{j}) \cdot \left(\tfrac{3}{5}\mathbf{i} + \tfrac{4}{5}\mathbf{j}\right) = \tfrac{137}{5}.$$

Solution to Exercise 12

We need to evaluate the partial derivatives at $x = 2$ and $y = 1$. Since $\partial z/\partial x = x$ and $\partial z/\partial y = 2\sqrt{3}y$, equation (15) becomes $dz/dt = 2\cos\alpha + 2\sqrt{3}\sin\alpha$. We see that the slope dz/dt is a function of α only, but to make the argument clear, we replace the slope dz/dt by $s(\alpha)$, so

$$s(\alpha) = 2\cos\alpha + 2\sqrt{3}\sin\alpha.$$

We are required to find the maximum value of $s(\alpha)$ for varying values of α.

The stationary points of $s(\alpha)$ occur when

$$\frac{ds}{d\alpha} = -2\sin\alpha + 2\sqrt{3}\cos\alpha = 0,$$

which gives $\tan\alpha = \sqrt{3}$. This equation has two solutions in the interval $0 \le \alpha < 2\pi$, at $\alpha = \frac{\pi}{3}$ and $\alpha = \frac{4\pi}{3}$. Using the second derivative test, we see that $\alpha = \frac{\pi}{3}$ corresponds to a maximum value of $s(\alpha)$ (while $\alpha = \frac{4\pi}{3}$ gives a minimum value). It follows that the greatest slope at the point $(2, 1, 2 + \sqrt{3})$ is

$$2\cos\tfrac{\pi}{3} + 2\sqrt{3}\sin\tfrac{\pi}{3} = 1 + (2\sqrt{3})\tfrac{\sqrt{3}}{2} = 4.$$

The direction of the greatest slope of $z = f(x,y)$ at $(2, 1, 2 + \sqrt{3})$ is at an angle of $\frac{\pi}{3}$ measured anticlockwise from the positive x-axis.

Now $\nabla f(2,1) = 2\mathbf{i} + 2\sqrt{3}\mathbf{j}$, so the angle θ between $\nabla f(2,1)$ and the positive x-axis (measured anticlockwise) is also given by $\tan\theta = \sqrt{3}$. So since both components of $\nabla f(2,1)$ are positive, $\theta = \frac{\pi}{3}$. Thus the direction of greatest slope is the same as the direction of $\nabla f(2,1)$.

Solution to Exercise 13

(a) We have
$$f_x = 3(x+2y)^2 - 4(2x - y) \quad \text{and} \quad f_y = 6(x+2y)^2 + 2(2x - y),$$
so
$$\nabla f(x,y) = \left(3(x+2y)^2 - 4(2x-y)\right)\mathbf{i} + \left(6(x+2y)^2 + 2(2x-y)\right)\mathbf{j}.$$

(b) Note that
$$\nabla f(1,0) = -5\mathbf{i} + 10\mathbf{j}.$$

The vector $\mathbf{i}+\mathbf{j}$ has length $\sqrt{2}$, so $\widehat{\mathbf{d}} = \frac{1}{\sqrt{2}}(\mathbf{i}+\mathbf{j})$ is a unit vector in the required direction. At the point $(1,0,-3)$, we have
$$\nabla f \cdot \widehat{\mathbf{d}} = (-5\mathbf{i}+10\mathbf{j}) \cdot \tfrac{1}{\sqrt{2}}(\mathbf{i}+\mathbf{j}) = \tfrac{5}{\sqrt{2}}.$$

(c) Note that from equation (18), the greatest slope of the surface at $(1,0,-3)$ is given by $|\nabla f(1,0)|$, and that the vector $\nabla f(1,0)$ points along the direction of greatest slope. Hence the greatest slope is given by
$$|\nabla f(1,0)| = |-5\mathbf{i}+10\mathbf{j}| = \sqrt{5^2 + 10^2} = 5\sqrt{5},$$

and the unit vector $\widehat{\mathbf{n}}$ in the direction of $\nabla f(1,0)$ (direction of greatest slope) is given by
$$\widehat{\mathbf{n}} = \frac{\nabla f(1,0)}{|\nabla f(1,0)|} = \frac{1}{5\sqrt{5}}(-5\mathbf{i}+10\mathbf{j}) = \frac{1}{\sqrt{5}}(-\mathbf{i}+2\mathbf{j}).$$

(d) We know from the previous discussion that $\nabla f(1,0)$ points in the direction normal to the contour curve through the point $(1,0,-3)$ and is therefore perpendicular to a vector tangential to the contour at this point. If $\widehat{\mathbf{t}}$ denotes a tangential unit vector and $\widehat{\mathbf{n}}$ the unit vector along $\nabla f(1,0)$ as found in part (c), then we must have that $\widehat{\mathbf{n}} \cdot \widehat{\mathbf{t}} = 0$. Writing $\widehat{\mathbf{t}} = t_1\mathbf{i} + t_2\mathbf{j}$, the condition $\widehat{\mathbf{n}} \cdot \widehat{\mathbf{t}} = 0$ becomes
$$\frac{1}{\sqrt{5}}(-\mathbf{i}+2\mathbf{j}) \cdot (t_1\mathbf{i}+t_2\mathbf{j}) = 0,$$

thus $-t_1 + 2t_2 = 0$, so $t_1 = 2t_2$, therefore $\widehat{\mathbf{t}} = t_2(2\mathbf{i}+\mathbf{j})$. But $|\widehat{\mathbf{t}}| = 1$, therefore $t_2\sqrt{1+2^2} = 1$, so finally we have
$$\widehat{\mathbf{t}} = \frac{1}{\sqrt{5}}(2\mathbf{i}+\mathbf{j}).$$

Note that $-\widehat{\mathbf{t}}$ is also tangential to the contour through $(1,0,-3)$, so in this sense the tangential vector is not unique.

Solution to Exercise 14

$p_1(0) = 0$ and $f(0) = \sin 0 = 0$, thus $p_1(0) = f(0)$.

$p_1'(x) = 1$, so $p_1'(0) = 1$, and $f'(x) = \cos x$, so $f'(0) = 1$.
Thus $p_1'(0) = f'(0)$.

$p_1''(x) = 0$, so $p_1''(0) = 0$, and $f''(x) = -\sin x$, so $f''(0) = 0$.
Thus $p_1''(0) = f''(0)$.

$p_2(0) = 1 - 0 = 1$ and $g(0) = \cos 0 = 1$, thus $p_2(0) = g(0)$.

$p_2'(x) = -x$, so $p_2'(0) = 0$, and $g'(x) = -\sin x$, so $g'(0) = 0$.
Thus $p_2'(0) = g'(0)$.

$p_2''(x) = -1$, so $p_2''(0) = -1$, and $g''(x) = -\cos x$, so $g''(0) = -1$.
Thus $p_2''(0) = g''(0)$.

$p_2'''(x) = 0$, so $p_2'''(0) = 0$, and $g'''(x) = \sin x$, so $g'''(0) = 0$.
Thus $p_2'''(0) = g'''(0)$.

Solution to Exercise 15

From Example 7, we have
$$p_0(x) = 1, \quad p_1(x) = 1 + 2x, \quad p_2(x) = 1 + 2x + 2x^2.$$
Thus
$$p_0(0.1) = 1, \quad p_1(0.1) = 1.2, \quad p_2(0.1) = 1.22.$$
Also, $f(0.1) = e^{0.2} = 1.221\,40$, to five decimal places.

Thus
$$p_0(0.1) = f(0.1) \text{ to the nearest integer,}$$
$$p_1(0.1) = f(0.1) \text{ to 1 d.p.,}$$
$$p_2(0.1) = f(0.1) \text{ to 2 d.p..}$$

Solution to Exercise 16

$f_x = \sin(xy) + xy\cos(xy)$ and $f_y = x^2\cos(xy)$, so
$$f_{xx} = y\cos(xy) + y\cos(xy) - xy^2\sin(xy) = 2y\cos(xy) - xy^2\sin(xy),$$
$$f_{yy} = -x^3\sin(xy),$$
$$f_{xy} = 2x\cos(xy) - x^2y\sin(xy),$$
$$f_{yx} = x\cos(xy) + x\cos(xy) - x^2y\sin(xy) = 2x\cos(xy) - x^2y\sin(xy).$$

Solution to Exercise 17

$f_x = 2e^{2x+3y}$ and $f_y = 3e^{2x+3y}$, so
$$f_{xx} = 4e^{2x+3y}, \quad f_{xy} = f_{yx} = 6e^{2x+3y}, \quad f_{yy} = 9e^{2x+3y}.$$
Then
$$f_x(0,0) = 2, \quad f_y(0,0) = 3,$$
$$f_{xx}(0,0) = 4, \quad f_{yy}(0,0) = 9, \quad f_{xy}(0,0) = f_{yx}(0,0) = 6.$$

Solution to Exercise 18

$f_x(x,y) = 3(x^2 + 2y^2 - 3xy)^2(2x - 3y)$ and
$f_y(x,y) = 3(x^2 + 2y^2 - 3xy)^2(4y - 3x)$, so

$$f_{xx}(x,y) = 6(x^2 + 2y^2 - 3xy)(2x - 3y)^2 + 6(x^2 + 2y^2 - 3xy)^2,$$
$$f_{xy}(x,y) = 6(x^2 + 2y^2 - 3xy)(2x - 3y)(4y - 3x) - 9(x^2 + 2y^2 - 3xy)^2,$$
$$f_{yy}(x,y) = 6(x^2 + 2y^2 - 3xy)(4y - 3x)^2 + 12(x^2 + 2y^2 - 3xy)^2.$$

Then

$$f_{xx}(1,-1) = 6(1 + 2 + 3)(2 + 3)^2 + 6(1 + 2 + 3)^2 = 1116,$$
$$f_{xy}(1,-1) = 6(1 + 2 + 3)(2 + 3)(-4 - 3) - 9(1 + 2 + 3)^2 = -1584,$$
$$f_{yy}(1,-1) = 6(1 + 2 + 3)(-4 - 3)^2 + 12(1 + 2 + 3)^2 = 2196.$$

Solution to Exercise 19

$f_x = 3e^{3x-y}$ and $f_y = -e^{3x-y}$, so

$$f(0,0) = 1, \quad f_x(0,0) = 3, \quad f_y(0,0) = -1.$$

Thus the tangent approximation near $(0,0)$ is

$$p_1(x,y) = f(0,0) + f_x(0,0)x + f_y(0,0)y$$
$$= 1 + 3x - y.$$

Solution to Exercise 20

(a) $q_x = \beta + 2Ax + By, \quad q_y = \gamma + Bx + 2Cy,$

$\quad q_{xx} = 2A, \quad q_{xy} = B, \quad q_{yy} = 2C.$

(b) $q(0,0) = \alpha, \quad q_x(0,0) = \beta, \quad q_y(0,0) = \gamma,$

$\quad q_{xx}(0,0) = 2A, \quad q_{xy}(0,0) = B, \quad q_{yy}(0,0) = 2C.$

Solution to Exercise 21

$f(0,0)$, $f_x(0,0)$ and $f_y(0,0)$ are constants, so the equation is that of a plane. Since $g(0,0) = f(0,0)$, the plane goes through $(0,0,f(0,0))$.

Now $g_x(x,y) = f_x(0,0)$ and $g_y(x,y) = f_y(0,0)$, so $g_x(0,0) = f_x(0,0)$ and $g_y(0,0) = f_y(0,0)$.

Thus at $(0,0)$, the plane has gradient

$$\nabla g(0,0) = g_x(0,0)\,\mathbf{i} + g_y(0,0)\,\mathbf{j}$$
$$= f_x(0,0)\,\mathbf{i} + f_y(0,0)\,\mathbf{j}$$
$$= \nabla f(0,0),$$

which is the gradient of $z = f(x,y)$ at $(0,0)$.

Solution to Exercise 22

We have

$$f(0,0) = 1, \quad f_x(0,0) = 2, \quad f_y(0,0) = 3,$$
$$f_{xx}(0,0) = 4, \quad f_{yy}(0,0) = 9, \quad f_{xy}(0,0) = 6.$$

Substituting these values into equation (25), we obtain

$$p_2(x,y) = 1 + 2x + 3y + \tfrac{1}{2}(4x^2 + 12xy + 9y^2)$$
$$= 1 + 2x + 3y + 2x^2 + 6xy + \tfrac{9}{2}y^2.$$

Solution to Exercise 23

We have $U(0,0) = -2mga$, and

$$\frac{\partial U}{\partial \theta} = mga\sin\theta, \quad \frac{\partial U}{\partial \phi} = mga\sin\phi,$$

so

$$\frac{\partial U}{\partial \theta}(0,0) = \frac{\partial U}{\partial \phi}(0,0) = 0.$$

We also see that

$$\frac{\partial^2 U}{\partial \theta^2} = mga\cos\theta, \quad \frac{\partial^2 U}{\partial \phi^2} = mga\cos\phi, \quad \frac{\partial^2 U}{\partial \theta\,\partial \phi} = 0,$$

so

$$\frac{\partial^2 U}{\partial \theta^2}(0,0) = \frac{\partial^2 U}{\partial \phi^2}(0,0) = mga, \quad \frac{\partial^2 U}{\partial \theta\,\partial \phi}(0,0) = 0.$$

It follows from equation (25) that the second-order Taylor polynomial about $(0,0)$ is

$$p_2(\theta,\phi) = -2mga + \tfrac{1}{2}mga(\theta^2 + \phi^2).$$

Solution to Exercise 24

$f_x = ye^{xy} + 2(x+y)$ and $f_y = xe^{xy} + 2(x+y)$, so

$$f_{xx} = y^2 e^{xy} + 2, \quad f_{xy} = e^{xy} + xye^{xy} + 2, \quad f_{yy} = x^2 e^{xy} + 2.$$

Therefore

$$f(0,0) = 1, \quad f_x(0,0) = f_y(0,0) = 0,$$
$$f_{xx}(0,0) = 2, \quad f_{xy}(0,0) = 3, \quad f_{yy}(0,0) = 2.$$

Thus, from equation (25), the second-order Taylor polynomial about $(0,0)$ is

$$p_2(x,y) = 1 + \tfrac{1}{2}\left(2x^2 + 2(3xy) + 2y^2\right)$$
$$= 1 + x^2 + 3xy + y^2.$$

Solution to Exercise 25

(a) $f_x = 3(2 + x + 2y)^2$ and $f_y = 6(2 + x + 2y)^2$, so

$$f_{xx} = 6(2 + x + 2y), \quad f_{xy} = 12(2 + x + 2y),$$
$$f_{yy} = 24(2 + x + 2y).$$

It follows that

$$f(0,0) = 8, \quad f_x(0,0) = 12, \quad f_y(0,0) = 24,$$
$$f_{xx}(0,0) = 12, \quad f_{xy}(0,0) = 24, \quad f_{yy}(0,0) = 48.$$

Therefore

$$p_1(x, y) = f(0,0) + f_x(0,0)x + f_y(0,0)y$$
$$= 8 + 12x + 24y$$

and

$$p_2(x, y) = f(0,0) + f_x(0,0)x + f_y(0,0)y$$
$$+ \tfrac{1}{2}\left(f_{xx}(0,0)x^2 + 2f_{xy}(0,0)xy + f_{yy}(0,0)y^2\right)$$
$$= 8 + 12x + 24y + 6x^2 + 24xy + 24y^2.$$

Expanding the bracket in the expression for f, we obtain

$$f(x, y) = 8 + 12x + 24y + 6x^2 + 24xy + 24y^2 + x^3$$
$$+ 6x^2y + 12xy^2 + 8y^3.$$

Notice that the function $f(x, y)$ is itself a polynomial of degree 3, and that the Taylor polynomial of degree 2 about $(0,0)$ consists of the terms of f of degree less than 3.

(b) $f(1, -1) = 1, \quad f_x(1, -1) = 3, \quad f_y(1, -1) = 6,$

$$f_{xx}(1, -1) = 6, \quad f_{xy}(1, -1) = 12, \quad f_{yy}(1, -1) = 24.$$

It follows that

$$p_1(x, y) = f(1, -1) + f_x(1, -1)(x - 1) + f_y(1, -1)(y + 1)$$
$$= 1 + 3(x - 1) + 6(y + 1)$$

and

$$p_2(x, y) = f(1, -1) + f_x(1, -1)(x - 1) + f_y(1, -1)(y + 1)$$
$$+ \tfrac{1}{2}\left(f_{xx}(1, -1)(x - 1)^2 + 2f_{xy}(1, -1)(x - 1)(y + 1)\right.$$
$$\left. + f_{yy}(1, -1)(y + 1)^2\right)$$
$$= 1 + 3(x - 1) + 6(y + 1) + 3(x - 1)^2$$
$$+ 12(x - 1)(y + 1) + 12(y + 1)^2.$$

(c) $F_X = 3(1 + X + 2Y)^2$ and $F_Y = 6(1 + X + 2Y)^2$, so

$$F_{XX} = 6(1 + X + 2Y), \quad F_{XY} = 12(1 + X + 2Y),$$
$$F_{YY} = 24(1 + X + 2Y).$$

It follows that

$$F(0,0) = 1, \quad F_X(0,0) = 3, \quad F_Y(0,0) = 6,$$
$$F_{XX}(0,0) = 6, \quad F_{XY}(0,0) = 12, \quad F_{YY}(0,0) = 24.$$

Therefore

$$p_1(X,Y) = 1 + 3X + 6Y$$

and

$$p_2(X,Y) = 1 + 3X + 6Y + 3X^2 + 12XY + 12Y^2.$$

(By substituting $X = x - 1$ and $Y = y + 1$, these polynomials are the same as those that you obtained in part (b). Finding the Taylor polynomials for f near $(1, -1)$ is equivalent to making a suitable change of variables and then calculating the Taylor polynomials near $(0, 0)$. This may lead to simpler arithmetic, because evaluations of the partial derivatives at $(0, 0)$ are often particularly easy. You can then change variables back again to obtain the polynomial in terms of the original variables.)

Solution to Exercise 26

$f_x(x, y) = 6x - 4y + 4$ and $f_y(x, y) = -4x + 4y - 8$, so there is one stationary point, at the solution of the simultaneous equations

$$6x - 4y = -4,$$
$$-4x + 4y = 8,$$

which is $x = 2$, $y = 4$. Thus the only stationary point is $(2, 4)$.

Solution to Exercise 27

$f_x = 2xy + y^2 - 3y = y(2x + y - 3)$ and
$f_y = 2xy + x^2 - 3x = x(2y + x - 3)$, so to find the stationary points, we have to solve the simultaneous equations

$$y(2x + y - 3) = 0,$$
$$x(2y + x - 3) = 0.$$

From the first equation, we have two cases.

If $y = 0$, then the second equation becomes $x(x - 3) = 0$; thus $x = 0$ or $x = 3$, so we have found the two solutions $(0, 0)$ and $(3, 0)$.

If $2x + y - 3 = 0$, that is, $y = 3 - 2x$, then the second equation becomes $x(3 - 3x) = 0$, and we have $x = 0$ or $x = 1$. Substituting these values for x into $y = 3 - 2x$ gives $y = 3$ when $x = 0$ and $y = 1$ when $x = 1$. Thus we have two more solutions, $(0, 3)$ and $(1, 1)$.

So we have four stationary points: $(0, 0)$, $(3, 0)$, $(0, 3)$ and $(1, 1)$.

Solution to Exercise 28

We have $U_\theta = mga \sin\theta$ and $U_\phi = mga \sin\phi$, so $U_\theta(0, 0) = U_\phi(0, 0) = 0$, which shows that $(0, 0)$ is a stationary point. Also, $U(0, 0) = -2mga$, and near $(0, 0)$, $0 < \cos\theta \leq 1$ and $0 < \cos\phi \leq 1$, so $U(\theta, \phi) \geq -2mga$, and it follows that $(0, 0)$ is a local minimum.

Solution to Exercise 29

We have
$$\mathbf{H}\begin{pmatrix} p \\ q \end{pmatrix} = \begin{pmatrix} A & B \\ B & C \end{pmatrix}\begin{pmatrix} p \\ q \end{pmatrix} = \begin{pmatrix} Ap + Bq \\ Bp + Cq \end{pmatrix},$$
so
$$\begin{pmatrix} p & q \end{pmatrix}\mathbf{H}\begin{pmatrix} p \\ q \end{pmatrix} = \begin{pmatrix} p & q \end{pmatrix}\begin{pmatrix} Ap + Bq \\ Bp + Cq \end{pmatrix} = p(Ap + Bq) + q(Bp + Cq)$$
$$= Ap^2 + 2Bpq + Cq^2$$
$$= Q(p, q).$$

Solution to Exercise 30

$f_x = 4x - y - 3$ and $f_y = -x - 6y + 7$, so to find the stationary point, we need to solve the simultaneous equations
$$4x - y - 3 = 0,$$
$$-x - 6y + 7 = 0.$$

The solution is $x = 1$, $y = 1$, so the stationary point is at $(1, 1)$.

Also, $f_{xx} = 4$, $f_{xy} = -1$ and $f_{yy} = -6$, so $AC - B^2 = -25$; therefore the stationary point is a saddle point.

Note that this exercise is the same as Example 13, which was solved using the eigenvalue test.

Solution to Exercise 31

$f_x = 3x^2 - 12$ and $f_y = -3y^2 + 3$, so the stationary points are at the points (x, y) where $x^2 = 4$ and $y^2 = 1$, namely $(2, 1)$, $(2, -1)$, $(-2, 1)$, $(-2, -1)$.

Also, $f_{xx} = 6x$, $f_{xy} = 0$ and $f_{yy} = -6y$. Thus at $(2, 1)$ and $(-2, -1)$, we have $AC - B^2 = -36xy = -72$, and these are saddle points. At $(2, -1)$ and $(-2, 1)$, we have $AC - B^2 = -36xy = 72$. Since $A > 0$ at $(2, -1)$, this is a local minimum; since $A < 0$ at $(-2, 1)$, this is a local maximum.

Solution to Exercise 32

(a) Partially differentiating,
$$f_x = -x(1 - x^2 + y^2)^{-1/2}, \quad f_y = y(1 - x^2 + y^2)^{-1/2},$$
so the only stationary point is at $(0, 0)$. We also have
$$f_{xx} = -(1 - x^2 + y^2)^{-1/2} - x^2(1 - x^2 + y^2)^{-3/2},$$
so $A = f_{xx}(0, 0) = -1$. Since
$$f_{xy} = xy(1 - x^2 + y^2)^{-3/2},$$
we have $B = f_{xy}(0, 0) = 0$. Also,
$$f_{yy} = (1 - x^2 + y^2)^{-1/2} - y^2(1 - x^2 + y^2)^{-3/2},$$
so $C = f_{yy}(0, 0) = 1$.

So $AC - B^2 = -1 < 0$, and there is a saddle point at the origin.

(b) $T_x = -\sin x$ and $T_y = -\sin y$, so the stationary points occur when $\sin x = 0$ and $\sin y = 0$, that is, at the points $(n\pi, m\pi)$ where n and m are integers.

We also see that $T_{xx} = -\cos x$, $T_{xy} = 0$ and $T_{yy} = -\cos y$, so at the stationary point $(n\pi, m\pi)$ we have $A = -\cos n\pi$, $B = 0$ and $C = -\cos m\pi$. There are three cases to consider.

If m and n are both even, then $AC - B^2 = 1 > 0$ and $A = -1 < 0$, so there is a local maximum at $(n\pi, m\pi)$.

If m and n are both odd, then $AC - B^2 = 1 > 0$ and $A = 1 > 0$, so there is a local minimum at $(n\pi, m\pi)$.

Otherwise, $AC - B^2 = -1 < 0$ and there is a saddle point at $(n\pi, m\pi)$.

Solution to Exercise 33

Partially differentiating,

$$f_x = 6xy^3 - 18xy + 3x^2 - 15, \quad f_y = 9x^2y^2 - 9x^2 = 9x^2(y^2 - 1),$$

The stationary points must satisfy $f_y = 0$, which has solutions at $x = 0$ and $y = \pm 1$. They must also satisfy $f_x = 0$, but note that $x = 0$ can never solve $f_x = 0$. Substituting $y = 1$ into the equation $f_x = 0$ gives

$$3x^2 - 12x - 15 = 3(x^2 - 4x - 5) = 3(x + 1)(x - 5) = 0,$$

which has solutions $x = -1$ and $x = 5$. So there are stationary points at $(-1, 1)$ and $(5, 1)$. Substituting $y = -1$ into the equation $f_x = 0$ gives

$$3x^2 + 12x - 15 = 3(x^2 + 4x - 5) = 3(x - 1)(x + 5) = 0,$$

which has solutions $x = 1$ and $x = -5$. So there are two more stationary points at $(1, -1)$ and $(-5, -1)$.

To classify these stationary points, we need

$$f_{xx} = 6y^3 - 18y + 6x = 6y(y^2 - 3) + 6x,$$
$$f_{xy} = 18x(y^2 - 1),$$
$$f_{yy} = 18x^2y.$$

So for $(-1, 1)$ we have $A = f_{xx}(-1, 1) = -18$, $B = f_{xy}(-1, 1) = 0$ and $C = f_{yy}(-1, 1) = 18$. Since $AC - B^2 = -18^2 < 0$, there is a saddle point at $(-1, 1)$.

For $(5, 1)$ we have $A = f_{xx}(5, 1) = 18$, $B = f_{xy}(5, 1) = 0$ and $C = f_{yy}(5, 1) = 450$. Since $AC - B^2 = 18 \times 450 > 0$ and $A = 18 > 0$, there is a local minimum at $(5, 1)$.

For $(1, -1)$ we have $A = f_{xx}(1, -1) = 18$, $B = f_{xy}(1, -1) = 0$ and $C = f_{yy}(1, -1) = -18$. Since $AC - B^2 = -18^2 < 0$, there is a saddle point at $(1, -1)$.

Finally, for $(-5, -1)$ we have $A = f_{xx}(-5, -1) = -18$, $B = f_{xy}(-5, -1) = 0$ and $C = f_{yy}(-5, -1) = -450$. Since $AC - B^2 = 18 \times 450 > 0$ and $A = -18 < 0$, there is a local maximum at $(-5, -1)$.

Solution to Exercise 34

First we find the stationary point by solving the simultaneous equations

$$w_x = 6x - 2y - 2z = 0,$$
$$w_y = 6y - 2x - 2z = 0,$$
$$w_z = 8z - 2y - 2x = 0.$$

The only solution is $x = y = z = 0$, so the stationary point is at $(0, 0, 0)$.

Now $w_{xx} = 6$, $w_{yy} = 6$, $w_{zz} = 8$, $w_{xy} = -2$, $w_{xz} = -2$ and $w_{yz} = -2$, so the Hessian matrix is

$$\begin{pmatrix} w_{xx} & w_{xy} & w_{xz} \\ w_{yx} & w_{yy} & w_{yz} \\ w_{zx} & w_{zy} & w_{zz} \end{pmatrix} = \begin{pmatrix} 6 & -2 & -2 \\ -2 & 6 & -2 \\ -2 & -2 & 8 \end{pmatrix}.$$

The given characteristic equation of this matrix is

$$0 = (8 - \lambda)\left((6 - \lambda)^2 - 12\right)$$
$$= (8 - \lambda)(6 - \lambda + 2\sqrt{3})(6 - \lambda - 2\sqrt{3}),$$

so the eigenvalues are 8, $6 - 2\sqrt{3}$ and $6 + 2\sqrt{3}$. These are all positive, thus there is a local minimum at the origin.

Solution to Exercise 35

We have

$$w_x = 2x + 2\sqrt{3}z, \quad w_y = 4y, \quad w_z = 2z + 2\sqrt{3}x,$$
$$w_{xx} = 2, \quad w_{yy} = 4, \quad w_{zz} = 2,$$
$$w_{xy} = 0, \quad w_{xz} = 2\sqrt{3}, \quad w_{yz} = 0.$$

So the Hessian matrix is

$$\begin{pmatrix} 2 & 0 & 2\sqrt{3} \\ 0 & 4 & 0 \\ 2\sqrt{3} & 0 & 2 \end{pmatrix}.$$

The characteristic equation is $(4 - \lambda)(\lambda^2 - 4\lambda - 8) = 0$, obtained by expanding the relevant determinant by the middle row, giving the eigenvalues 4, $2 - 2\sqrt{3}$ and $2 + 2\sqrt{3}$. Two of these are positive and one is negative, thus the stationary point is a saddle point.

Index

Index